health

healing

AND *shalom*

Over the last century, healthcare professionals focused on technology and spiritual leaders concerned with church-building have alike often lost sight of shalom, the core of both physical and spiritual health. Various authors have wrestled with the interface between the good news, the church, health, and healing, but nowhere have I seen that done to the depth and breadth of this work. The authors have selected for discussion both foundational aspects of that topic and practical aspects rarely discussed but having great effect on millions of people in the church or treated by Christian health professionals. And they have picked the right persons to write each chapter—either world-class experts or experienced frontline practitioners with deeply biblical perspectives. Each chapter has fresh and challenging insights—the neglect of which has given rise all over the world to unnecessary suffering, ineffective helpers, wasteful systems, and distortion of the good news. This book should be required reading for all pastors and missions leaders and for all health professionals who want to serve God with their lives.

Carolyn Klaus, MD
author of *Prescription for Hope*
cofounder of Esperanza Health Center

Health, Healing, and Shalom is a must-read for healthcare ministers in training and practice. In working with medical students/graduates, urban health professionals, and congregational partners, this is a much-needed manual in answering key questions and providing equipping tools for the church to "preach the kingdom of God and heal the sick" (Luke 9:2). Praise the Lord for this enlightening perspective and powerful movement to integrate faith and health!

C. Channing Frykman, MD, FAAP
chair of the board of directors, Los Angeles Christian Health Centers
UCLA campus advisor, Christian Medical and Dental Associations

A feast for those engaged in or considering involvement with health-related missions awaits readers in the pages of *Health, Healing, and Shalom*. Those of us who knew, loved, and were inspired by the life of Dr. Dan Fountain find in the diverse chapters multiple treasures of careful reflection on the issues that have filled our conversations for so many years: the social, economic, and spiritual causes of disease; the value of community-based primary health care; and a probing of the theological foundations for our work. But we are also pressed forward to engage contemporary health concerns, from noncommunicable diseases such as rampant obesity to choosing roles as neighbors with the underserved urban poor. Troubling, enlightening, and motivating, this book is an important stimulus to reflection and assessment for Christians in health fields and beyond.

Evvy Hay Campbell, BSN, MS, CTCM&H (LSTM), PhD
associate professor of intercultural studies emerita, Wheaton College
board chair, World Hope International

Health, Healing, and Shalom provides a comprehensive and compelling resource for healthcare workers and professionals involved in mission work. The book covers an array of complex health, relational, and social issues typically encountered in working with vulnerable populations globally. Most significantly, a Christian theoretical framework is provided that reinforces the power of God's desire to heal the body, spirit, and emotions of both the healthcare worker and the sick in union with God's ultimate restoration of shalom.

Mary Wickman, RN, PhD
director of nursing, Vanguard University

I think this book would be a great resource for community health programs at Christian higher education institutions, health science majors of all types, community development courses, and those leading and guiding the many thousands of health-related short-term mission trips. Several times I have searched for resources for the faculty sponsors of Taylor's health-related mission projects and been disappointed. This would provide a helpful framework out of which to build such programs and projects.

Jenny Collins, MAR
associate professor of intercultural studies, Taylor University

health
healing
AND *shalom*

FRONTIERS AND CHALLENGES FOR CHRISTIAN HEALTH MISSIONS

BRYANT L.
MYERS

ERIN
DUFAULT-HUNTER

ISAAC B.
VOSS

WILLIAM CAREY
LIBRARY

Published by William Carey Library
1605 E. Elizabeth St.
Pasadena, CA 91104 | www.missionbooks.org

Aidan Lewis, editor
Susan Wood, copyeditor
Josie Leung, graphic design

William Carey Library is a ministry of
Frontier Ventures
Pasadena, CA 91104
www.frontierventures.org

Printed in the United States of America
19 18 17 16 15   5 4 3 2 1 BP300

Library of Congress Cataloging-in-Publication Data

Health, healing, and shalom : frontiers and challenges for Christian healthcare missions / edited by Bryant L. Myers, Erin Dufault-Hunter, Isaac Voss.

    pages cm

Includes bibliographical references and index.

    ISBN 978-0-87808-540-8 -- ISBN 0-87808-540-8 1. Missions, Medical. 2. World Council of Churches. Christian Medical Commission. 3. Medical care--Religious aspects--Christianity. 4. Religion and medicine. 5. Healing--Religious aspects--Christianity. 6. Health--Religious aspects--Christianity. I. Myers, Bryant L., editor. II. Dufault-Hunter, Erin Elizabeth, 1963- editor. III. Voss, Isaac, 1977- editor.

    RA975.C37H435 2015

    610--dc23

                         2014050158

CONTENTS

NEW FRONTIERS IN HEALTHCARE
MISSIONS PRACTICE

NEW APPROACHES IN HEALTHCARE MISSIONS

Figures and Tables

FOREWORD

Our church-based short-term medical mission trip to Kunming, China, was in grave danger of collapsing entirely. After arriving, my team coleader and I met in our hotel only to find that neither of us had brought the team money with us. Two days later, our dentists were notified of a family emergency and returned immediately to the United States, and as a result the dental hygienists and assistants were thinking about returning home. Nobody wants to go on a mission trip only to feel that they failed to make a difference.

As I walked back to the hotel in the midst of the turmoil, I was impressed by the truth that God is sufficient and worthy of my trust. Though I had little to offer as a leader, I remembered that God would answer the questions, meet the needs, and provide relevance and value for the team members. By God's grace, the team held together, and we eventually headed off to a remote village. There we went about doing what we were trained to do: teeth were extracted, wounds were cleaned, and medications were distributed for minor conditions. In the middle of all of the activity, one of our nurses sat quietly with a middle-aged woman who was missing fingers and her nose due to the devastating effects of leprosy. Without speaking a word, she conveyed the love of Christ by hugging the woman and touching her face. It struck me that our nurse had chosen the best way to attend to the woman's health and healing.

Most who have been engaged in health missions contemplate tough questions: What makes Christian medical missions "Christian"? How do we prepare Christian healthcare missionaries so that they embrace a kingdom mindset? What is health really supposed to mean to the church, and what should it look like for the church to be fully engaged in ministries of health, healing, and wholeness? One physician who grappled with these questions was Dr. Dan Fountain, who served as a medical missionary for thirty-five years at Vanga Evangelical Hospital in the Democratic Republic of Congo. He first published his insights in *Health, the Bible and the Church* in 1989. Upon his return to the United States in 1996, he served as a mentor to many in healthcare missions.

Dr. Mike Soderling offers a telling anecdote, one that highlights the reason for Fountain's passion for change. Fountain sat at his kitchen table in Guatemala several years ago, head in his hands and near tears. A pastor friend had told him that a young woman attending nursing school at the Vanga Hospital had become ill; despite their efforts, she died. In response, her friends became enraged, went to her village, and attempted to destroy it. Why? Because they assumed someone there had put a curse on her, rendering all medical efforts ineffective.

While many others in Western medicine have only recently done so, Fountain recognized many years ago the importance of the biblical worldview and values for understanding medicine's role. He underscored Scripture's vision for holistic health—that is, God's desire to heal the body, spirit, and emotions. Frustrated at times by the inability of both seminaries and Christian healthcare science schools to effectively train people for this ministry, Fountain delivered addresses and conducted workshops around the world. Before his death in 2013, he committed to help develop a Christ-centered medical school. Fountain never gave up on the church as a means of God's work, and he sought to deepen the understanding of health as shalom, extending our calling to bring healing and wholeness to all peoples and, indeed, all of creation. For many in healthcare missions, Fountain continues to provide guidance and inspiration.

I met Fountain at the Global Missions Health Conference in Louisville in 2002, where he was a keynote speaker. I realized then that practitioners on the West Coast also needed these resources. With much help, I began the West Coast Healthcare Missions and Ministry Conference. Fountain was one of our first-year plenary speakers. The conference was designed from the beginning to be multidisciplinary, focusing on a biblical understanding of health, largely as outlined by Fountain. We purposefully embrace health disciplines as well as Christian theology. He encouraged us to address the educational, empowerment, and networking needs of those in healthcare ministry, from Christian nurses, physicians, and dentists to psychologists, chiropractors, public health workers, and physical therapists. The conference represents one of the myriad ways Fountain shaped healthcare missions.

One of the most enduring results of the conference is the network of people interested in identifying the best practices for short-term health missions—"God's work done God's way." The group subsequently created a series or guidelines found on their website (http://www.csthmbestpractices.org/), which point to the best practices in Christian health missions and ministry. Much of what follow reflects "best practices" thought and passion from the West Coast Healthcare Missions Conference that took place at Fuller Theological Seminary in 2012. While I cannot acknowledge here the many volunteers, presenters, and friends who make such gatherings and continued networking possible, I do want to thank Doris and Bob Arrington for their partnership over the years, as well as my family. Such good work is only possible and sustained by such friends and family.

We pray that such conferences, workshops, and training will be an inspiration to future Christian health professionals who sacrifice their time, money, reputations, and even lives to spread the gospel message and witness to God's healing of individuals and communities. We trust that such gatherings as well as this book continue the legacy of Daniel Fountain and all those who seek the healing of the world because of the hope we have in Christ.

Peter Yorgin, MD
Clinical Director of Pediatric Nephrology
University of California, San Diego / Rady Children's Hospital

*The Continuing Contribution
of the Church to Health,
Healing, and Shalom*

Bryant L. Myers, PhD

In the Beginning

It all began in the beginning. God created male and female in God's image and by so doing made them cocreators after God. We were made to be healthy and whole, to flourish in the world God had made, to work for the well-being of all humankind and God's creation. Our disobedience changed all that, and things began to get hard and we began to serve ourselves. With sin, disease in all its forms—medical, psychological, relational—became the norm. But this was not the end of the story.

God as a God of grace did two things. The big thing was a plan to redeem and restore God's creation and the sinful human beings therein. This is the story of the incarnation, life, death, and resurrection of Jesus Christ. The small thing God did was allowing some of the original good in human beings to continue to find expression for health, healing, and justice in God's world.

We cannot create from nothing; only God can do that. But we can figure out how God's world works and we can create from what God has made. And so we did. Over a long period of time, we figured out how to domesticate crops and then animals. We figured out agriculture in slow and halting steps. We became larger, stronger, and a little less susceptible to disease. In time our understanding of how God's world works grew deeper and came faster. As we learned, we created new things, new institutions, and eventually new science.

The role of Christianity in the care and improvement of human health is part of this story of God's grace and our faithfulness to God's command that we make God's world fruitful and productive. This vocation, given by God, was far more than simply having lots of children, although that was a good thing in the midst of scarcity and the struggle for God's creatures to survive. This vocation extended to using the gifts that God gave to human beings—curiosity, rationality, perception of patterns and a desire to order and to make things more productive—to enable each other at first to survive and then to flourish. This is the vocation of humankind.

The Church and Caring for the Health of People

The Christian church has been in the health business from the beginning. Between the incarnation and the resurrection, Jesus healed those whose image had been reduced or marred by loss of sight and failure of limb. He healed those excluded from society—the lepers, the demon possessed, even the dead. Healing was even Sabbath business. This was not a distraction; Jesus was not succumbing to mission drift. As we will learn from the first chapter, "Health, Healing, and Wholeness," healing and salvation are deeply intertwined theologically.

And so the church has been emulating its Master. Following Christ's command to go to the ends of the earth witnessing to what they saw and heard, the Christian community continued to seek out the least of these; the church in mission took care of the orphans and widows, the slaves and the excluded.

While this book is not a history of the church in mission and its contribution to health, an outline of the church and healthcare missions may be helpful in reminding us that health and salvation were always seen as intertwined (Schmidt 2004, 151–69).

- The early Christian church introduced the first asylums for
  the mentally impaired in 321.

- The first ecumenical council (Nicaea 325) called for a hospice—a place for the poor, the sick, and pilgrims—in every city with a cathedral.
- The first institution for the blind was established in Jerusalem in 630.
- A group of devout nuns volunteered to take care of the sick at the Hotel Dieu in Paris in 650, establishing a model of nursing that continues to this day.
- Hospitals—the world's first voluntary charitable institutions—were widely established by Eastern and Western churches by the sixth century.
- By the eighth century, Christian hospitals had spread to continental Europe and England.
- The *Hospitalers* of St. Lazarus extended health care to lepers in the twelfth century.
- The Foundling Hospital for abandoned children, the Magdalen Hospital for reforming prostitutes, and the London Lock Hospital for treating venereal disease in England were established in the eighteenth century. (Sirota 2014)

These ministries providing palliative care and good news to the sick and dying represented the *first major contribution* of the church to health and healing in the world. It continued with the work of Pinel and Dix, who reintroduced and upgraded the treatment of the mentally ill in the nineteenth century. Rebecca Gagne Henderson is calling us back to this tradition in her chapter on hospice and end-of-life issues in chapter 10.

The *second major contribution* of the church to health and health care came with the emergence of modern medicine. In the seventeenth century, Christians like Bacon, Grosseteste, and Boyle encouraged understanding how God's world works through observation and experiment, not tradition. This profound shift contributed to the emergence of modern medicine in the West. Of particular interest to healthcare missions, the Christian hospital movement reemerged in the eighteenth century during the Wesleyan Revival, after the suppression of the monasteries (and the destruction of their capacity for health provision) in England by Henry XVIII.

Consistent with the history of the church in mission as a church of healing for those on the margins of society, building hospitals and sharing the new health interventions of Europe with the rest of the world became one of the centerpieces of the Protestant mission movement. People like John Scudder, a medical doctor, went to Ceylon in 1819. Hudson Taylor, Ida Scudder, David Livingstone, Albert Schweitzer, Paul Brand—these and many others spread the gospel and Western medicine to Africa and Asia. Denominational hospitals, hospices, and clinics delivered medical care to the ends of the earth. This was *the third major contribution* of the church to the health and salvation of the world. By the mid-1900s, however, this "age of hospitals" was waning. Hospitals were becoming too costly, and newly independent countries were suspicious of anything "foreign," yet they lacked the funding to take them over.

Among other things, this led to the formation of the Christian Medical Commission (CMC) by the World Council of Churches in 1968. The CMC had two tasks. Its theological task was "to help the churches in their search for a Christian understanding of health and healing," and its medical task was "to promote innovative approaches to health care" (Oslo 2010, 3). The CMC theological work combined with reports from church-related programs around the world led to a strong reaction against hospitals (factories of repair) in contrast to healing Christian communities (sources of health and wholeness) (McGilvray 1981).

The field investigations of the CMC brought to light new models of community-based primary health care at a time when the World Health Organization (WHO) was searching for alternative concepts for health care, as it had become clear that the historical Western commitment to largely curative health care was not providing a global solution to the problems of global health.

Based on their medical missions experience around the world, the CMC argued that health is not just the absence of disease and therefore provision of treatment alone was not enough. Further, based on their theology, they argued that the lack of health services was an issue of economic inequality, social justice, and a failure in solidarity. Finally, from their understanding of a Christian anthropology, they argued that people need to take responsibility and be equipped to take care of their own health and that of their community to the extent possible.

The conversation between WHO and the Christian Medical Commission culminated in the 1978 Alma-Ata Declaration calling for "health for all by the year 2000." Resisting pressure from national associations of doctors for more doctors and pharmaceutical companies for more drugs, the Alma-Ata Declaration was the first international call underlining the importance of primary health care.

The first section defined health as "a state of complete physical, mental and social well-being and not merely the absence of disease or infirmity." The definition seeks to include social and economic sectors within the scope of attaining health, and it reaffirms health as a human right. Listen to the echoes of the CMC definition of health: "Health is not primarily medical. . . . The churches are called to recognize that the causes of disease in the world are social, economic and spiritual, as well as bio-medical. Health is most often an issue of justice, of peace, of integrity of creation, and of spirituality" (Oslo 2010, 3).

In affirmation of the Christian principle of solidarity, people were put at the center of health care, not doctors, hospitals, or pharmaceutical companies (Oslo 2010, 4). The traditional top-down, money-and-technology approach to health care was replaced by community-based, multidisciplinary approaches to health that built on participation of the people involved.

Sadly, in time, the WHO commitment to primary health care began to erode. As Oslo reports, "The tension between high-technology-based medicine on the one hand and primary health care on the other has been detrimental to the struggle for a better and healthier world" (2010, 4).

Then in the 1990s the Christian Medical Commission faded from the global scene and was decommissioned.

The Good News about Global Health Today

The global health situation is improving. The world has made significant progress in reducing child deaths by 40 percent from nearly 12 million deaths in 1990 to less than 7 million in 2011 as immunizations, clean water and better sanitation, and training in maternal child health have had their impact. Almost 1.9 billion people have gained access to improved sanitation facilities since 1990. Between 1990 and 2011, the proportion of stunted children under five years in low-income countries decreased from 59 to 38 percent. Fewer people are dying from HIV as antiretrovirals save lives. The HIV infection rate is declining, albeit slowly. (Statistics taken from WHO 2013a.)

Christians and mission organizations continue to be on the health front lines, especially in the Global South. The Roman Catholic Church provides more than a quarter of the hospitals and clinics in the world (Catholic News Service 2010). In Uganda, faith-based organizations (FBOs), mostly Christian, account for the provision of over 30 percent of the country's health care (Marshall and Bronwyn 2007, 38). According to a Tear Fund Report, one third of Zambia's health care comes from Zambian Christian Health Services (Boyd 2009), while the Christian Health Association provides 40 percent of Lesotho's health services through its 8 hospitals and 70 health centers (Boyd 2009; cf. Marshall and Bronwyn 2007, 42). In India, the Catholic Church is the single largest organizational network providing care for people affected by HIV (Boyd 2009). In a study on orphans and vulnerable children in Africa, local FBOs were judged to be more active than and as professional as larger NGOs and the government (Foster 2003).

There is also good news in terms of how those involved in healthcare missions are sharing and learning from each other. There are four health-related mission conferences each year in the United States:

Global Missions Health Conference, Urbana–Health Track, Christian Community Health Fellowship, West Coast Healthcare Missions Conference, and the Christian Medical and Dental Associations Conference. There are Christian health and development programs at Azusa Pacific University, Biola, Cal Baptist, Trinity Evangelical Divinity School, and Taylor University.

The Not-So-Good News about Global Health Today

Sadly, there is still plenty of not-so-good news about health, especially for those living in the Global South. According to the WHO Global Health Statistics report for 2013:

- Over 7 million children under five are still dying each year, with 75 percent of these deaths caused by neonatal causes (preterm birth, birth asphyxia, and infections), pneumonia, diarrhea, malaria, HIV/AIDS, and measles.
- About 34 million people are living with HIV worldwide, of which 75 percent live in sub-Saharan Africa.
- The world is facing a double burden of malnutrition, with undernutrition and overweight impeding survival and causing serious health problems.
- Preterm birth is the world's leading killer of newborn babies, causing one million deaths each year.
- Almost 10 percent of the world's adult population has diabetes.
- More than one third of the global population (2.5 billion people) is still without access to improved sanitation facilities.
- Almost half of all countries surveyed have access to less than half the essential medicines they need for basic health care in the public sector.
- In some countries, women from the wealthiest 20 percent of households are 10 times more likely than the poorest 20 percent to receive care from a skilled birth attendant during childbirth.

- About 104 million children worldwide (2010 data) are underweight, while about 1.5 billion people are overweight worldwide (2008 data), of whom 500 million are obese. (WHO 2013b)

The Future Challenges for Healthcare Missions

The important question today is what will be the fifth major contribution of the church and churches to health, healing, and wholeness in the future. This book is not written by prophets, and the future next major movement is not yet clear. But this book does try to alert us to the kinds of continuing issues that require our attention in the future as Christian health professionals.

First, there is a need for continuing commitment to extending health systems, services, and new health practices to the poor wherever they are. A biblically based and theologically sound approach to health, healing, and wholeness is still urgently needed. Secular and profit-seeking models alone are simply not up to the task as we understand it as Christians. There is a need to reawaken the church to the centrality of health, healing, and wholeness to the mission that Christ gave us and calls us to. Who else will provide the prophetic call to the injustice and disparity in health provision around the world today? Who else will reissue the CMC's historic call for "equity, community, sacrifice and accountability?" It is not clear that the health missions networks in the United States have such a global agenda.

Second, the Christian healthcare missions community needs to find a way to reengage WHO again for two reasons. First, as Arnold Gorske has been calling us to do, we need to meet contemporary WHO medical standards and legal standards to ensure that our health work is among the best in the world as part of our witness to Christ. Second, in the absence of the CMC today, we need to be sure that what health missions professionals and lay people are learning by working on the front lines in the Global South, and what our deepening theology tells us about human beings and their health and well-being, is being heard. The time for this is now. There is a resurgence of interest in WHO in the Alma-Ata Declaration and community-based primary health care. Will we join our secular friends in their call to revisit this important idea?

> The revolutionary principles—equity, social justice, and health for all; community participation; health promotion; appropriate use of resources; and intersectoral action—raised by the 1978 Alma-Ata Declaration, [marked] a historic event for health and primary health care. . . . Revitalizing Alma-Ata and learning from three decades of experience is crucial to reach the ambitious goal of health for all in all countries, both rich and poor. (Lawn et al. 2008)

Third, we need to pay attention to the newly emerging frontiers in global health. We need to be sure that our healthcare practice, theory, and theology reflect our best thinking and practice. Do our efforts reflect a firm and substantial theological foundation or are we just baptizing modern Western medicine with some Bible verses and prayers, as Dan Fountain wonders in this volume? Does our work reflect what we now understand to be best practices in global healthcare missions?

Finally, we need to wonder what we might be overlooking in our rapidly changing world. Are there subgroups such as children at risk or the urban poor who need special and specialized attention? Are there new learnings in health care such as the importance of recognizing and treating trauma, caring for people at the end of life, and the like that are not now finding expression in the Global South? Do we have the training and relational skills to help? What might our weaknesses or blind spots be?

The Purpose and Outline of this Book

Examining these questions and suggesting answers is the purpose of this book. Written by practitioners with long experience, new frontiers are named, challenges are articulated, and some new models of practice are described. This book is intended for healthcare missions practitioners, for pastors and missions committees, and for students seeking Christian health-related degrees and service opportunities.

The conversation that culminated in this book emerged through a collaborative project at the West Coast Healthcare Missions Conference organized by Dr. Peter Yorgin and his team. The theological lens of shalom—right relationships with God, self, one's community, others, and the environment—was chosen by the editors as the most useful way to start an interdisciplinary conversation that draws on insights from such fields as psychology, public health, medicine, nursing, theology, and international development. Papers were solicited as conference papers, and hard choices were made as to which ones should become chapters of this book. We hope that this book will serve as a constructive contribution to the ongoing conversation within the health missions movement and enhance the health-related ministries of the worldwide church and of local churches.

The book begins with a chapter by Dan Fountain, one of the last things he wrote before his going home last year. Fountain retraces the importance of his African experience as part of his pilgrimage away from a reductionist Western biomedical model of disconnected body, mind, soul, and social relationships in favor of a more biblical anthropology. Western medicine cures diseases; Jesus healed sick people, he reminds us. Fountain makes two major contributions to our conversation. First, there are new questions and answers from those you go to serve if only you have eyes to see and ears to hear from the people of the Global South. Second, a biblical understanding of the body, mind, and soul as inseparably related and connected may be a significant point of recovery for us in the West. We need to be sure we have recovered and are not part of the problem, something Soderling also calls our attention to in chapter 9, which is on short-term healthcare missions.

PART 1: NEW FRONTIERS IN THEOLOGY AND HEALTHCARE MISSIONS

The book moves to three chapters that explore the contribution that
theological reflection can make to enhance our theory and practice of
healthcare missions. Chapter 2 builds on the conversation that Dan
Fountain and others began on the biblical idea of shalom. In a piece of
practical theology, I argue that the theological themes of creation, the
image of God, shalom, and salvation may call into question some of our
modern healthcare thinking and practices. Is our view of the human being holistic (an integrated body/mind/soul) and relational? What is the
relationship between shalom and salvation, and where do health, healing, and wholeness fit in? This foundational chapter was sent to all the
authors of this volume with an invitation to use its theological material
as they saw fit in their reflections on their work and thinking.

Chapter 3 examines the important question of how evangelism and
Christian witness can find a seamless and integrated home in Christian
healthcare missions. What makes medical missions genuinely Christian
at the end of the day? Drawing on my work with transformational development, I argue that this is fundamentally a worldview issue in which
the modern worldview's separation of the material and the spiritual
encourages separating medicine and psychology from evangelism and
spiritual things. How does the modern healthcare professional avoid the
segmentation of being a good, witnessing Christian on the weekends and
then acting like any secular health practitioner from Monday to Friday?
Since Western medicine no longer requires God as part of the explanation for why immunizations, surgeries, and other health interventions
work, we have to provide a better answer for why children do not die,
or pharmaceuticals work, or surgeries heal. If we do not, the credit for
healing goes to the provider—the doctor, midwife, or nurse. This is a
Christian witness challenge of the first order.

In chapter 4, David Scott, a professor of children at risk, describes
a very practical and flexible theological framework that emerged from a
series of meetings between children-at-risk practitioners and theologians

concerned for children's well-being. The purpose was to help practitioners act theologically as well as professionally. "Understanding God's Heart for Children" is a framework for theology of children and child well-being that may be helpful to healthcare missions professionals who work with children of all kinds around the world. Scott then concludes with a clarion call to those working in missions focused on children not to overlook the urgent need of children living on the margins of society without parents—children who have disabilities and are exposed to chronic trauma in the form of poverty, violence, abuse, and misuse. Keep this chapter in mind when you read chapters 6 (White and Henry) and 7 (Wong-McDonald).

PART 2: NEW FRONTIERS IN HEALTHCARE MISSIONS PRACTICE

The eight chapters that follow part 1 focus on new frontiers that may expand the reach or improve the impact of healthcare missions. We do not presume that this list is either exhaustive or complete. But the editors did agree that these chapters describe important ideas of which the larger community needs to be aware.

In chapter 5, Arnold Gorske, editor of content for the "Health Education Program for Developing Countries" and specialty advisor for community health and primary care for Global Health Outreach, and myself call attention to the "slow-motion disaster" that is threatening global health. Noncommunicable diseases related to obesity and smoking pose an urgent global challenge. Gorske and I make a passionate call to local churches to recover their historic call and commitment to be healers and seekers of shalom in their communities once again. We then describe the Community-Based (church-based) Health Screening and Education approach, developed by the Christian Medical Commission forty years ago, as being ideally suited to churches that are prepared to take up the challenge.

In chapter 6, Katy White and Kathleen Henry, both of whom work in federally qualified health centers, reflect on their experience working with the urban poor and what seems to be the limitless number of barriers and problems facing the urban poor and their access to even the few health services available to them. Forms, permissions, technical instructions, access only during working hours, and the like are a bewildering maze. White and Henry add accompaniment to the list of requirements for those who work for health and healing among the urban poor, and by so doing they connect a theology of incarnation to the theology of shalom. With sympathy and humility, White and Henry sound a prophetic call to the health missions world: send us professional healthcare missionaries who "will move into the neighborhood, enter the pain of the people, and form communities of shalom." At the end of the day, the urban poor need an incarnational, walking-alongside approach to health and wholeness.

Recent research on the impact of trauma on health in the United States and around the world is addressed by Ana Wong-McDonald of the Salvation Army in chapter 7. She calls our attention to the fact that trauma resulting from chronic poverty, violence, and social unrest is part of everyday life in the Global South, a part of the world where trauma is least understood and too often untreated. Wong-McDonald's concern is that the healthcare missions community is not prepared, equipped, or even as alert as it needs to be to this critical health issue. Too often, she argues, the lack of awareness and professional equipping on the part of healthcare missions people means that trauma goes ignored, misdiagnosed, or untreated. Wong-McDonald then introduces a relational model of human beings to describe both the impact of trauma and a Christian response.

Debbie Dortzbach, of World Relief, and Meredith Long, of World Concern, call us to reimagine our response to HIV and AIDS in chapter 8. While improved access to treatment worldwide has resulted in greater hope for millions of those infected, long-term suffering and deep inequities are still a reality for many. Dortzbach and Long alert us to the need to change our mental model from an understanding of HIV and

AIDS as a problem to be solved to a process model of walking with those impacted by HIV and AIDS in their hard and long journey. We need to understand and address HIV and AIDS in the context of relationships—broken, restored, and redeemed. This is the seeking of shalom. Michael Soderling, currently developing an intercultural health program at Campbell University College of Medicine and active in the Center for Health in Missions, addresses in chapter 9 some critical shortcomings in short-term medical missions today. He briefly explores how the modern dualistic (material/spiritual) worldview is affecting health missions and short-term missions in particular. He then proposes some antidotes that may help alter this modern framework. Whole-person care (see Daniel Fountain's chapter) means seeking shalom in its fullness. Cross-cultural partnerships are critical to effectiveness and sustainability. Finally, excellence in care is a kingdom value and thus must be our goal in short-term missions. (Chapter 5 also addresses a significant weakness in short-term missions, as it has become increasingly drug centered.)

In chapter 10, Rebecca Gagne Henderson raises the awkward issue that many Christian healthcare providers act as if it were God's plan that they watch helplessly as their patients die. Christians affirm that God is involved in every birth and has a design for every life, yet they act as if God has no plan or involvement when people face death. She then examines what is known about the physiology of death, dehydration, and starvation and, looking to the Bible, concludes that the physiology of human dying is in fact a demonstration of God's mercy toward the dying, not God's disinterest or abandonment. The chapter goes on to suggest that this knowledge creates an opportunity to witness to and be a source of shalom to dying patients and their families, while giving the glory to God.

Erin Dufault-Hunter, a professor of ethics, underscores the need for all Christian health practitioners to add the ancient practice of lament to their healthcare spirituality in chapter 11. While healthcare providers must live out Christian hope as they work and care for others, they must also lament the brokenness and pain they regularly experience when interventions fail. Professional detachment is not a healthy practice if overdone. Mourning can be a hopeful practice for the Christian, Dufault-Hunter argues. It is through the embodied practice of these two aspects of hope—compassionate action and active lament—that all of us proclaim the gospel, by "imitat[ing] the one who was full of mercy and truth, the Great Physician who entrusts to us his ministry of healing and hope, until his kingdom of shalom comes fully, and every tear is finally wiped away by his hand (Rev 7:17 and 21:4)."

In chapter 12, psychologists Cynthia Eriksson and Ashley Wilkins, along with missionary self-care specialist Judith Tiersma Watson, examine the issue of caring for and supporting healthcare practitioners. Participation in health missions seeking shalom must demonstrate the reciprocal relationship between redemption and restoration; we are restored as we participate in the restoration of others. But, the authors point out, too often practitioners of Christian ministries of health care or psychotherapy find themselves exhausted, disillusioned, and in despair. Practices of seeking the shalom of practitioners are then explored.

PART 3: NEW APPROACHES IN HEALTHCARE MISSIONS

In chapter 13, Anntippia Short and Isaac Voss of World Impact reflect on their experience using spiritual practices in a primary healthcare clinic serving an underserved neighborhood in South Los Angeles. The practices of hospitality, encounter, compassion, Christian witness, and justice contributed to transformed relationships of shalom within the complex context of the city.

Grace Tazelaar of InterVarsity's Nurses Christian Fellowship and Carolyn Newhof, developer of the Parent Child Ministry in Cary, Mississippi, persuasively argue in chapter 14 that, while there is an important role for physicians, nurses, and other healthcare specialists in the future of health care, they also see a place for health workers without professional training. The authors describe the effective deployment of lay health workers among marginalized patient populations in both international and domestic settings. Given proper training and supervision—as was the case with their Ugandan coworker John Kiyimba—local people without formal education can perform many crucial health- and ministry-related functions.

Finally, Terry Dalrymple, coordinator of the Global CHE Network, and Jody Collinge describe Stan Rowland's holistic Community Health Evangelism model. Community Health Evangelism (CHE) is a strategy to empower communities to address issues that are of importance to them. The authors place a particular emphasis on the role of the local church as a key agent of change, thus reinforcing the important message in Arnold Gorske's chapter. They present a basic overview of Community Health Evangelism and its key principles, including its outcomes and indicators of effectiveness. This is a useful guide for local churches who wish to start a CHE ministry.

References Cited

Boyd, Seren. 2009. *In the Thick of It: Why the Church Is an Essential Partner for Sustainable Development in the World's Poorest Countries*. UK: Tearfund.

Catholic News Agency. 2010. "Catholic Hospitals Comprise One Quarter of World's Healthcare." February 10. Available at http://www. catholicnewsagency.com/news/catholic_hospitals_represent_26_percent_of_worlds_health_facilities_reports_pontifical_council/ (accessed December 30, 2013).

Foster, Geoff, ed. 2003. "Study of the Response of Faith-Based Organizations to Orphans and Vulnerable Children." Geneva: UNICEF and WCRP.

Lawn, J. E., J. Rohde, S. Rifkin, M. Were, V. K. Paul, and M. Chopra. 2008. "Alma-Ata 30 Years On: Revolutionary, Relevant, and Time to Revitalise." Lancet 372 (9642): 917–27.

Marshall, Katherine, and Marissa Van Saanen Bronwyn. 2007. *Development and Faith: Where Mind, Heart, and Soul Work Together*. Washington, DC: World Bank.

McGilvray, J. C. 1981. *The Quest for Health and Wholeness*. Tübingen: German Institute for Medical Mission.

Oslo, Jacob. 2010. "'Health Is Not Primarily Medical': History and Impact of
    the WCC's Christian Medical Commission." August 26. Anglican
    Health Organization presentation. Available at http://www.google.
    com/url?sa=t&rct=j&q=&esrc=s&source=web&cd=2&ved=0CDEQ
    FjAB&url=http%3A%2F%2Fwww.anglicanhealth.org%2FResourc
    es%2FPDF%2FAHN%2520resources%2FFaith%2520and%2520h
    ealth%2520care%2F2010-08-26%2520Jakob%2520Oslo%2520pre
    sentation.doc&ei=FxPCUtXnCOTn2QXa4YHADw&usg=AFQjC
    NEEDEJmde1vx0bsLD1IahQe9gkVGQ&bvm=bv.58187178,d.b2I
    (accessed December 30, 2013).
Schmidt, Alvin J. 2004. *How Christianity Changed the World*. Grand Rapids,
    MI: Zondervan.
Sirota, Brent. 2014. "The First Big Society: Eighteenth Century Britain's Age of
    Benevolence." ABC Religion and Ethics website. January 9. Available
    at http://www.abc.net.au/religion/articles/2014/01/09/3922667.htm.
WHO. 2013a. "Global Health Statistics." Available at http://apps.who.int/iris/
    bitstream/10665/82058/1/WHO_HIS_HSI_13.1_eng.pdf (accessed
    December 29, 2013).
———. 2013b. "Obesity and Overweight." Factsheet no. 311. Available
    at http://www.who.int/mediacentre/factsheets/fs311/en/ (accessed
    October 25, 2014).

Putting the Whole
Person Back Together
Lessons from Africa

Daniel E. Fountain, MD, MPH

God gave my wife, Miriam, and me the wonderful privilege of serving him for thirty-five years in the Democratic Republic of the Congo. We helped build the Vanga Evangelical Hospital in the Bandundu Region in western Congo, 250 kilometers east of Kinshasa, into a comprehensive Christian and sustainable health service. As we worked with the Congolese church and health colleagues, we learned many lessons about life and about healing. A key one among them was how to restore wholeness to medicine, to sick persons, and to ourselves as health professionals. In our busy medical ambiance, how can we care for people as whole persons? That is what this chapter is about.

A Serious Problem without an Answer

I stood by the bed of Baledi feeling frustrated and confused. For weeks he had grown worse with rapidly advancing cirrhosis, and he was now almost comatose. His cousin told me a story I could not process. An older brother of Baledi, a rich merchant in Kinshasa, had gone to a shaman years ago to get a powerful charm to make him rich. The price for the charm was the lives of five members of his family, and the older brother had designated five siblings to the shaman to destroy. The other four had all died, and Baledi was the last of them. Within a few days, Baledi died. The "debt" had been paid.

Is such a thing possible? How can the curse of a shaman kill someone by cirrhosis or any other disease? Had I known about this earlier,
could I have done something?

People from Mukilu Mbemi brought Papa Abraham Kilesa to the
Vanga Hospital on a stretcher. He had convulsed and was now in coma.
His blood pressure was 240/160 and he had suffered a cerebral vascular
accident. The family explained that a nephew of Abraham had recently
been killed in the forest when a limb of a tree fell on him. In Africa, accidents do not occur; they are caused. Any such death must not only be
explained but avenged. A village inquest had taken place, and a shaman
had been consulted. Papa Abraham was accused of having cursed the
nephew and caused his death. Shortly thereafter, this cerebral vascular
accident occurred.

I could understand this one. Acute stress, anger, fear, and grief provoke the secretion of high levels of adrenaline, with the blood pressure
often rising to dangerous levels. Once we were able to control his blood
pressure with IV antihypertensives, Abraham regained consciousness
and we were able to talk and pray with him. He claimed total innocence
in this affair and seemed as grieved over the nephew's death as anyone
else. But pleas of innocence do not negate the accusations of sorcery, for
in the traditional tribal belief system, one can curse someone else even
unconsciously. Because of the word of the shaman, the whole family believed Abraham was guilty. Much counsel and prayer ensued, with some
benefits, but Abraham succumbed to hypertension within a few weeks.

How can feelings and emotions affect us physiologically? How do
high levels of stress over time damage organ systems? What can health
professionals do about it? These questions disturbed me during my years
of training in the 1950s. I frequently asked my professors about a relationship between stress from life events and conditions such as asthma,
allergies, rheumatoid arthritis, and others. The answer was always the
same: there is no demonstrable relationship between these conditions and
the psychological state of the person. I was not satisfied with that answer.

During twenty years of service in the Congo I struggled with the essential conundrum that separates Western medicine and my experience as a missionary: Medicine cures diseases; Jesus healed sick people.

Reductionism in Medicine

The biomedical model of medicine operates on the assumptions that every disease has a physical cause and that treatment requires some form of physical intervention—pharmacology, surgery, radiation, physiotherapy, and so on. Each has a corresponding expert for diagnosis and treatment. Doctors and dentists handle medical problems. If psychological problems seem to be present, these are referred to psychologists or psychiatrists. Social problems are referred to social workers, and spiritual problems are shunted to a pastoral counselor. If the experts are Christian, this frame is only improved slightly. The belief systems of modern medicine, psychology, and social care are enhanced with a bit of prayer or a few Bible verses, but the underlying frame is the same—a biomedical, materialistic reduction of the human being into parts. The resulting framework looks something like figure 1.1 below.

Medicine deals with the body. Psychology deals with the mind. Religion deals with the spiritual dimension or soul (although this is dismissed or treated as optional by many medically trained people). And dysfunctional social relationships often fall between the cracks.

My dilemma was that my Christian faith informed me otherwise. The Bible speaks about healing persons and restoring them to wholeness. Genesis 1 and 2 describe how God created us as whole persons. Jesus taught that life consists of relationships (Matt 22:37–39) and health consists in healthy relationships. Other faiths describe similar concepts. How had medicine come to exclude the power of faith in healing the mind, soul, and spirit of sick persons? No one discussed this during the 1950s when I was trained, and I had no one to ask for help, neither in medical school nor in the church I was attending.

BODY
Hypertension, heart disease
Chronic pain or inflammation
Diabetes
Auto-immune disorders
Digestive problems
Malignancies
Many infections

MIND
Fear, worries
Anxiety, anger
Bitterness, resentment
Shame, guilt
Jealousy
Envy

SPIRIT
Poor self-image
Depression
Meaninglessness
Sense of rejection
Loneliness

RELATIONS
Dysfunctional relationships
Divorce
Abuse
Poverty
Unemployment

*Figure 1.1: The Western compartmentalized
understanding of health and human beings*

I was lodged in the upper left quadrant of this picture, doing my best with the limited physical technology we had to cure the diseases of those who came to the hospital. But I had nothing to offer to Baledi or to Papa Abraham Kilesa, or to the multitude of sick people with complaints of weakness, dizziness, insomnia, chronic and often vague headaches, intractable gastric symptoms, chronic pain syndromes, and so forth. My intuition informed me these were due to stress factors—broken relationships, fear, worry, guilt—but I had no idea how to find out the real causes or what to do about them should they be found.

In the Vanga Hospital we did offer a form of "spiritual care," but it suffered from the same problematic conceptual framework. A pastor functioned as hospital chaplain, giving short Bible messages each morning, briefly talking and praying at the bedside with sick persons, and offering salvation to all who would receive it. Yet he had no skills in discussing life issues with people or applying spiritual resources to the deep hurts in the minds and spirits of sick persons. I was doing physical care—curing malaria, fixing hernias, and providing symptomatic relief for aches and pains that had no discernible physical cause. No one knew how to care for the inner burdens of people—painful feelings, broken relationships, and deep levels of fear and shame. This dichotomy between physical care and psycho-spiritual care was painful, yet no solution was apparent in spite of prayer and the study of both medical texts and the Bible.

A God-Given Solution

In August of 1984 a young Congolese woman came to see me, Mrs. Matala Masieta. She had just completed her theological studies in Kinshasa, where she majored in hospital pastoral counseling. She came to see if she could be of help to us. After consulting with the hospital committee, we hired her, not as a chaplain, but as a pastoral caregiver. We avoided the word "chaplain" because of the many unhelpful connotations attached to it—a religious official in the hospital with the roles of prayer, preaching, and consoling the dying. We felt Mrs. Masieta would have different and far more effective roles, and we were not mistaken. She became our "heart doctor," bringing Jesus' healing of the broken heart and the wounded spirit to sick persons.

We physicians began referring to her many sick persons who were suffering from a variety of illnesses, and not just those with psychosomatic complaints. People with heart disease, gastritis, chronic infections, liver disease, arthritis, and other physical conditions went to her. She would take a history from each person—the illness, their personal story, and the stresses in their lives. She would then do a spiritual assessment to find out the nature of their faith. The vast majority claimed to be Christian; this simply meant they were members of a particular church.

Her concern, however, was a relational concern—did they have a personal relationship with God through the presence of the spirit of

Jesus in their lives? If not, she would explain this to them and how Jesus could not only give them eternal life but could also heal the problems of mind, soul, and spirit. Many asked Jesus to come into their spirit and would find the peace and joy that come from a new identity and the hope of eternal life. When this occurred, Mrs. Masieta would lead them back to the particular personal problems they had described and suggest, "Let's bring each of these problems to Jesus in prayer and ask him to remove them."

As this process took place, anxiety, fear, anger, bitterness, and a whole spectrum of negative emotions would be resolved, with the pain produced by those feelings replaced by an inner peace. A verse in the book of Proverbs—chapter 14, verse 30—became the theme verse for this ministry, and we put a framed placard of it in Kituba on the walls of our consulting rooms and wards: "Peace of mind makes the body strong. Envy is like a cancer" (GNT). With this approach to the "cure of the soul," we were finally seeing the medical view of a human being getting put back together.

A Striking Example

In 1986 John, a sixteen-year-old high school student, came to the hospital very ill with smear-positive tuberculosis. We hospitalized him and put him on our standard triple therapy—INH, streptomycin, and thiacetazone, then widely used in the tropics for TB therapy. We were not concerned about his outcome, for this regime, if carefully followed, had cure rates above 90 percent. However, after one month of direct observed therapy, John's condition was deteriorating. We assumed his TB bacilli were resistant to the antibiotics, so we switched him to our second-line treatment of rifampin, ethambutol, INH, and pyrazinamide, believing that would solve his problem. It did not, and within another couple of weeks it was clear John was dying, and we had no idea why.

Denise, a student nurse who was caring for him, talking with him, and listening to him, found out why. John had been cursed by his maternal uncle and knew he was going to die. When Denise explained this to me, I was dumbfounded. Asking about a curse was not part of my usual history-taking, nor did I have a clue about how to treat a curse. Mrs. Masieta entered the picture; she knew the treatment for this situation. She and Denise introduced John to Jesus, and John asked Christ to enter his life. He was now a Christian, and therefore I assumed our job was done. When he died of his tuberculosis, he would go to heaven. Wonderful! But Mrs. Masieta was not yet satisfied. She felt that he did not need to die of tuberculosis and that she knew what was impeding his healing.

She told John stories of what Jesus did. He healed sick people, walked on water, multiplied bread and fish, and even raised people from the dead. She then asked John who was more powerful—Jesus, or his uncle. When John recognized that the power of Jesus surpassed that of his uncle, she assured him he was now under the protection of Christ and his uncle's power to kill could no longer get through to him. She was treating his fear, and with success.

Next she tackled a much more difficult problem. She asked John if his uncle had done him wrong. "Of course," he replied. "He tried to kill me." She read to him the words of Jesus about forgiving those who do us wrong and asked John if he could forgive his uncle. This was difficult; how could he forgive someone who wanted him to die? She explained that forgiveness is not excusing or denying the reality of the offense. Rather, it is releasing the offending person into the hands of God, who is the only true judge. John was finally able to do that in prayer. He released his uncle to God and asked him to take away the anger and hatred in his heart toward his uncle. God did. Within a few days John's fever disappeared, his appetite returned, and he went on to a complete recovery, healed in body, soul, and spirit.

Mind-Body Research

By that time biomedicine was discovering much about the relationship between the psyche and physiology. Dr. Hans Selye in Toronto did fascinating studies on the effects of long-term stress on the body. He discovered that stress can cause much physical damage to many bodily systems—cardiovascular, digestive, musculoskeletal, and even the immune system. He related these to increased levels of certain hormones, especially adrenaline and cortisol (Selye 1984).

A new branch of medicine, psychoneuroimmunology, began working out the highly complex interrelationships between the brain, feelings and emotions, and the immune system. Brain cells (neurons) produce an array of neurochemicals, with a specific one produced for each emotional reaction. These neurochemicals circulate quickly throughout the entire body and affect the functioning of all our organ systems, including the immune system. The fear, anger, and hatred in his mind kept John's immune system suppressed and unable to cope with his TB. When Mrs. Masieta helped him turn those destructive feelings over to the Lord, his immune system rebounded and he was restored to wholeness (see Matthews 1999).

Spreading this Approach Elsewhere

We saw increasing numbers of people come to our hospital primarily because they now had a place where they could unload the heavy burdens they were carrying in their hearts. As the numbers of those wanting the "cure of the soul" grew, we had to train other caregivers to handle the load. This included some of our nursing staff and another full-time pastoral counselor. We introduced this approach to students in our medical training institute and found that some of them had real gifts of listening and of encouragement. We taught this to our family medicine residents to equip them to engage in this approach in the hospitals where they would be working.

Mrs. Masieta and I also went to our pastoral training schools and introduced pastoral students and their wives to an understanding of the role they could play in the healing of persons. It was clear to us that a team approach is essential for providing whole-person care—a team composed of health providers, pastoral caregivers, and even the administrative staff of health programs and churches.

We felt this approach to caring for the whole person under one roof should spread to other hospitals and health programs. We organized workshops in this approach to which health professionals and pastors from other hospitals and health programs around the country came. Eventually I taught this in other African and Asian countries. As the HIV/AIDS epidemic escalated, it became quickly apparent that this approach was of immense benefit to people infected with HIV.

Fear and Pain

God called us back to the States in 1996, and we settled in Berrien County, Michigan. With the help of Dr. Sherry O'Donnell, a gifted young woman internist, we began training volunteer lay people to become spiritual caregivers in the offices of Christian physicians. In the first group, as I was explaining what longstanding fear can do to us, a woman named Karen raised her hand and said, "I have a lot of fear in my life." She explained that her son had recently married a fine Christian girl, but the young woman refused to have anything to do with Karen and her husband. Now Karen was afraid even to contact her own son. All I could do at that point was offer prayer for her with the group, asking that God take the fear from her heart and replace it with his peace.

Thirty minutes later Karen raised her hand again. For the past three months she had had constant pain in her neck, shoulders, and upper arms. This restricted her movement, interfered with her sleep, and resisted the pain medicines prescribed by her family physician and the manipulations of her chiropractor. When we prayed, the pain suddenly disappeared, and now she could move her neck and arms in a complete range of motion.

I was unaware of her pain and had not prayed about that, and she had made no connection between her fear and the pain. But her adrenal glands knew she had fear and continued producing high levels of adrenaline that kept her muscles in a constant state of tension. When through our prayer she released her fear to the Lord, he removed the fear. The adrenal glands stopped producing a high level of adrenaline and the skeletal muscles could now relax. The pain never returned.

Depression, Anger, and Forgiveness

A man in his forties named Steve came to Dr. O'Donnell with a thirty-year history of depression. His depression began at age eleven, when his mother died of cancer. His father was not a good single parent, and Steve struggled for years in spite of a gamut of psychotropic medications. A question came into Sherry's mind, and she asked him, "Steve, have you ever forgiven your mother for abandoning you?" Steve was shocked and gasped, "No one ever asked me a question like that!" After some reflection, he replied, "Doc, I don't know. I will have to think about that."

He returned a week later and said, "Doc, you were right. I went to the cemetery and 'talked' to my mother. I told her how angry I had been because she left me, but as I realized how much she had suffered, I forgave her and said, 'We will have a long talk when I come to where you are.' An incredible burden fell from me at that point. Now, Doc, I don't need those medicines anymore. How can I get off of them?" Sherry weaned him off of them all and his depression never returned. Bitterness, resentment, and the refusal to forgive are causal factors in many chronic illnesses today, and even in some cases of depression. The joy people find when they release their anger to the Lord is amazing, almost matched by the joy we receive when we help them accomplish this. That is true healing.

Conclusion

Can whole-person care be given anywhere? Yes, wherever people are hurting "inside," and my impression is that such people are everywhere in the world. With wisdom, it can be given in any social, political, or religious context, and by anyone who understands the biblical worldview and what is now becoming evident through much research. Do we have time for it? Yes! With one key question, Sherry saved herself innumerable repeat and unsuccessful visits from Steve—he needed no more care because he was healed. I have written about this in my book *God, Medicine, and Miracles* (1999).

Dr. O'Donnell and I developed this model in Michigan, trained many spiritual caregivers, and produced a twenty-two-lesson DVD program so that health professionals and pastoral care people can learn this approach wherever they are. It is called *A Team Approach to Caring for the Whole Person* and is available from King University, Bristol, Tennessee (globalhealth@king.edu).

Seeing the fragments of medicine come back together has been a most gratifying experience, almost as gratifying as seeing people find healing for body, soul, and spirit. This confirms what the Apostle Paul wrote in his letter to the Ephesians, that God's plan is to bring all things together, both in the physical and the spiritual realms (1:10). Bringing medicine back together is part of that process, and we can play a role in it.

References Cited

Fountain, Daniel E. 1999. *God, Medicine, and Miracles.* Colorado Springs: WaterBrook Press.

Matthews, Dale A. 1999. *The Faith Factor: Proof of the Healing Power of Prayer.* New York: Penguin.

Selye, Hans. 1984. *The Stress of Life.* New York: McGraw-Hill.

NEW FRONTIERS
IN THEOLOGY
AND HEALTHCARE
MISSIONS

CHAPTER 2

Health, Healing, and Wholeness
Theological Reflections on Shalom and Salvation

Bryant L. Myers, PhD

The purpose of this chapter is to present a theological framework for a biblical understanding of health and wholeness and then to relate this frame to the practice of healing and healthcare missions. To build this theological foundation for health and wholeness, we need to do three things. First, we need a clear Christian anthropology—Who are human beings? Of what do they consist? What were they intended to be and do? And how do we, or does God, help us overcome the fact that we cannot be and do as God intended? This anthropology is derived from the creation account. Second, we need to explore the related theological ideas of shalom and salvation. Finally, we need to explore the implications of this theological work in terms of its consequences for the theory and practice of Christian health care that seeks healing, wholeness, and human flourishing.

This reflection ends with three main conclusions. First, human beings were created by God as relational beings, not autonomous individuals. Any understanding of shalom must begin here. Second, we are inseparably mind, body, and soul; human well-being or a sense of shalom is determined by the indivisible mix of all three. Third, human beings were always intended for health, wholeness, and flourishing—shalom is and was God's intent. In spite of the disruption of our sin, God calls us to participate in God's work of saving and healing. These conclusions require us to understand human health, wholeness, and flourishing relationally and holistically: when all of our relationships work for the well-being of our body, mind, soul, and community, all may flourish as human beings in the way that God intended. This is the essence of shalom, the central biblical metaphor for understanding a Christian account of health, healing, and wholeness.

The Creation Narrative

A Christian anthropology is the foundational underpinning for understanding the role of the church in its missional practice of saving and healing. On the one hand, we need to know who God is and what God is doing, and on the other hand, we need to know who human beings are and why they were created (Myers 2011, 50ff.). Until we are clear on both of these key theological ideas, our investigation into health and healing will be limited, shortsighted, and possibly flawed.

We need to begin with God. What is the God of the Bible like? What is God doing? Working from the creation account, the truth about God is that God is the creator, sustainer, redeemer, and restorer of creation (Gen 1:1,2; John 1:1–3; Heb 1:2,3). Furthermore, this three-in-one God is a relational God whose being is characterized by communication, peace, and love. A Christian understanding of health and healing rests on the truth about this relational God and the certainty of God's continuing project of redemption and restoration of God's struggling creation (Fountain 1989, 53ff.).

The first truth about human beings that is relevant to our conversation comes from the second creation account. *Adam* was created by God "from the dust of the ground," and God "breathed into his nostrils the breath of life, and *adam* became a living being" (Gen 2:7). We are of the earth and alive by the Spirit of God. We are whole persons—inseparably body, soul, and mind.[1] Paul's first letter to the Thessalonians reinforces

---

1   For the purposes of this paper I am setting aside the intriguing idea that there is really no such thing as mind and soul, and that, rather, the mind and soul are higher-level emergent properties of the complex human physical organism (Brown, Murphy, and Malony 1998). I believe the argument I am making works with either proposal.

this: "May God himself, the God of peace, sanctify you through and through. May your whole spirit, soul and body be kept blameless at the coming of our Lord Jesus Christ" (5:23). Any Christian understanding of human health and wholeness must reject the modern, Western idea that somehow human beings can be subdivided into three discrete elements. The idea of separate domains—medicine and the body, psychology and the mind, and evangelism and discipleship for the soul—does not stand up in the light of the biblical account (nor current scientific research for that matter; more on this later).

The second truth about human beings comes from the first creation account: "So God created human beings in his own image. In the image of God he created them; male and female he created them" (Gen 1:27 NLT). This has three important contributions to make to our conversation about health, healing, and wholeness. First, being made in the image of a three-in-one God and being whole persons suggests a more provocative question that is directly relevant to human health and well-being. In what way is the image of God "in us"? Biblical studies scholar J. Richard Middleton points out that for much of church history the image of God was understood as being reflected in our soul or mind—the image of God as an analogy of being. The modern worldview, which separates the material and spiritual, reinforces this view. Barth and Westermann challenged this reductionism and proposed a relational interpretation: the image of God as analogy for a more holistic, personal reflection of God (Middleton 2005, xxx). How, then, is the image of God present in our mind, body, and soul? We need to be open to the possibility that the image of God may also find expression in our material selves (more on this later).

The second consequence of human beings' being made in the image of a three-in-one God is that we are relational beings too. Our identity and vocation are embedded and expressed most fully in a family of relationships—our relationship with God, with each other, with those we call Other, with the natural world where we live, and within ourselves.

Emulating the triune God, our relationally embedded selves were intended to embody and express love, justice, and peace. In the garden, all of these relationships were without tension or flaw; there was food, water, beauty, and the presence of God in the afternoon. Health, well-being, and human flourishing were just how things were—all part of God's original intent (Fountain 1989, 90). It is from this anthropological foundation that Jesus articulates his greatest commandment—we are to love God and our neighbor as we love ourselves. The very drive to find ways to heal, accompany, and care for those who are unwell or not flourishing finds its source here in the creation account.

The third consequence is that we are made in the image of God for a specific purpose—to make God's creation fruitful and productive (Gen 1:27,28). Being made in the image of a creator God means we are intended to enhance and to partner with God in developing God's creation. Middleton asserts, "The human calling as *imago Dei* is itself developmental and transformational and may be helpfully understood as equivalent to the labor or work of forming culture or developing civilization" (2005, 89). Genesis 2 expands on this. The cosmic God of Genesis 1 becomes a hands-on, working, creation-improving God in Genesis 2 (Brown 2012, 23). God formed *adam* from the dust of the ground and later determined that *adam* should not be alone—relationality again. God placed *adam* in the garden to nurture the garden and make it productive—our vocation again. Finally, *adam* was given the responsibility to see the rational order in what God had created and then name the animals accordingly.

Being made in the image of rational, order-making God means that we were created to observe, reason, and figure out how God made us and how God's world works. Paul makes the same claim about Christ in his role as creator: "For in him all things were created: things in heaven and on earth, visible and invisible, whether thrones or powers or rulers or authorities; all things have been created through him and for him. He is before all things, and in him all things hold together" (Col 1:16,17).

This fact is the ultimate origin of all science—rational human beings figuring out how God created God's world. Furthermore, we are to act on and even create new things based on what we figure out. This is the foundational source of the exploding number of medical inventions and interventions that have emerged over the last two hundred years. We are clever and creative because we are made in the image of a clever and creative God. The potential to be healed and the means for us to discover how to heal are part of God's original intention. Thus, we are to use reason and investigation in ways that make the world more conducive to human well-being.

Finally, in the creation narrative, we must also take note of the fact that, upon completion, God announced that what God had created was very good. At one level, this means that creation was designed to work for the well-being of human beings. Health, well-being, and the means for human flourishing were built into the creation and into us. At another level, this also means that creation contains a God-created moral order. Being righteous matters to human well-being too. Furthermore, it means that we have a responsibility to engage in the increasingly complex and difficult ethical conversations that surround the science and practice of health today.

There is another meaning to the idea of the creation being very good. God's creation does more than just work well; God's creation was beautiful (Gen 2:9). Scripture reminds us that this beauty is a witness to God and reveals God's glory (Ps 19:1–4; Rom 1:20). This should alert us to the fact that human well-being is more than just a life without illness, psychological struggle, and spiritual emptiness. Being in God's creation and doing what God intends us to do makes us excited, happy to be alive, and full of joy. Music and worship were also part of the creation narrative (Gen 4:23,26). We need art, high culture, music, celebration, and worship, which take us beyond ourselves and give our lives cultural form and meaning. Beauty, art, aesthetics, and worship are relevant to human health, healing, and wholeness (Goizueta 2009).

Sadly, the biblical account from which we are deriving our Christian anthropology ends with human disobedience and separation from God. Bad human choices disrupted our relationships with God, with each other, with nature, and within ourselves. We no longer know who we are, nor do we live up to our vocation of tending God's creation. Our relationships no longer work for the well-being of all and too often work against it. Illness, psychopathology, and the worship of false gods join injustice, oppression, and violence in a fallen creation (see fig. 2.1).

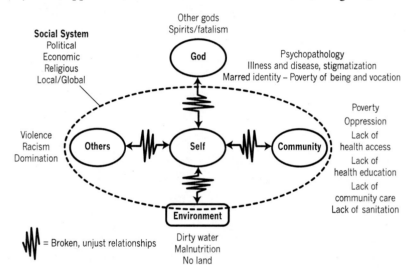

Figure 2.1: The impact of sin on health and wholeness

The consequences of the Fall are fairly obvious. A fruitful creation reluctantly sustains life (Gen 3:17), and only by hard, back-breaking work (Gen 3:19). Human life now ends in death (Gen 3:19). The relationship between men and women is disrupted and becomes unjust (Gen 3:16). Violence and murder enter the human story (Gen 4:8), as does the hunger for revenge (Gen 4:23). Human well-being is now a struggle and beyond the reach of human effort alone (Myers 2011, 65).

We need to take special note of the relational impact of sin and its consequences. The absence of health and well-being are not just biological or psychological, but relational as well. Thus, we must understand the task of seeking human health and well-being as a relational task that must go beyond the merely biological or psychological interventions suggested by modern science. It is theologically as well as practically important that the recent work in both medicine and psychology is taking the relational context of human beings more seriously (more on this to come).

We must also remember that God's love and grace remain in creation after the Fall. God made us our first clothes and prevented us from making the Fall permanent (Gen 3:22). God still speaks of us as being made in God's image (Gen 5:1), and even after the flood, God reaffirms the image of God in us and our vocation of being fruitful and productive stewards in creation (Gen 9:1,6). Our vocation remains, while our sin makes us flawed partners working alongside a faithful God.

Thus, our God-given mandate to make God's creation fruitful and productive for all and conducive to human flourishing continues in two important ways. First, we must remember that the human community is infused with both original sin and original good.[2] The impact of sin means disease of body, mind, and soul, but the impact of the original good means we can find ways to prevent, ameliorate, and even cure disease and damaged hearts. The only "disease" that is beyond our power to address is restoring our relationship with God and overcoming death, things only God can do. By creating us in God's image, God made it possible for us to figure out how to mitigate the impact of sin and work for the common good. Medieval religion historian Lynn White has argued that we might think of technological innovation, which would include our healing sciences and medical technology, as expressions of grace whereby God helps us cope with the effects of sin (1978, 13).

Second, contemporary research into medicine and psychology is leading us to understand the tremendous resilience that God has built

---

2   Our Roman Catholic brothers and sisters are much better at this than we Protestants are, especially those of us of the Reformed variety.

into human beings. Our bodies are designed to do what they can to heal themselves. Grace is already in place. Thus, working for health and wholeness is working with God on God's project to redeem and restore God's creation.

Shalom

Shalom, "peace," is an important biblical word and is the second major theological theme that we need to investigate. In the Old Testament, shalom is a concept that relates relationships to human well-being or wellness. Nicholas Wolterstorff describes shalom as "the human being dwelling in peace with all of his or her relationships: with God, with self, with fellows, with nature" (1983, 69). We flourish when our relationships are peaceful, a stance consistent with what we've already noted in the creation narrative.

Shalom (*šālôm*) is often used in a way that conveys an image of wholeness, unity, and harmony—of something that is complete and sound. Thus, relationships that reflect shalom also include the ideas of prosperity, health, and human fulfillment (Richards 1999, 479). This makes the idea of shalom highly relevant to a discussion about human health and well-being.

Nicholas Wolterstorff adds the ideas of justice, harmony, and enjoyment to capture the full biblical understanding of shalom (1983, 69ff.). Recalling Psalm 85, Wolterstorff reminds us that "Love and Fidelity now meet, Justice and Peace now embrace" (1983, 70). Relationships that are not just can never be peaceful. Therefore, shalom means just relationships (living justly and experiencing justice), harmonious relationships, and enjoyable relationships. Shalom means a healing and restoring community or society whose conditions encourage human flourishing.

Wolterstorff then takes the idea of shalom a step further. Yes, relationships must be just and peaceful, but God's shalom also incorporates the ideas of delight, enjoyment, and even fun.

> Shalom at its highest is *enjoyment* in one's relationships. To dwell in shalom is to enjoy living before God, to *enjoy* living in one's physical surroundings, to enjoy living with one's fellows, to *enjoy* life with oneself. (Wolterstorff 1983, 70)

Once again, worship, ritual, celebration, and having fun all become part of what God intends.

In the New Testament, the word *peace* (*eirēnē*) is used in a number of varied forms (Freedman 2000, 1021ff.). *Peace* is a frequent part of normal greetings. Peace is also used as an attribute for one's relationship with God. The Greek term is also used to refer to the absence of war or interpersonal conflict.

Of particular interest to us, the word for peace in the New Testament is also used to speak about personal well-being. In the Epistles, *peace* most often refers to the wholeness of restored relationships that Jesus brings to our relationship with God and others, "although this cannot be separated from the inner sense of well-being that accompanies them" (Richards 1999, 481). Peace is harmony with God, others, and within ourselves. This use of the word *peace* lines up nicely with the OT understanding of shalom and the lessons we have drawn from the creation narrative.

This brings us to the issue of what God is doing in the world—God's project of redemption and restoration. From the day we were driven from the garden, God has been at work to find a way home for us that satisfies the requirements of God's love and justice. This work culminated in the birth, death, and resurrection of Jesus Christ, the son of God. The kingdom of God entered human history and is now working toward God's final victory. Through Christ, the potential is now in place to restore all of our broken, strained, unjust, and unhealthy relationships—with God, within ourselves, with our community, with those we call Other, and with nature. This emerging, not-yet kingdom is full of health, healing, wholeness (fig. 2.2). It embodies shalom and is hence designed for human flourishing.

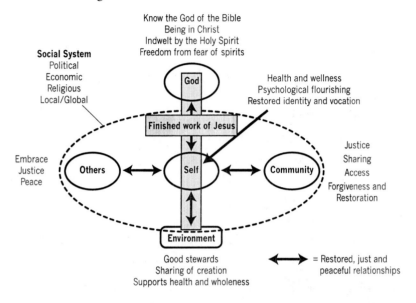

Figure 2.2: Salvation, shalom, health, and wholeness

This New Testament understanding of peace orients us to the future, to what God is doing and is going to do in human history. The ideas of shalom and what God is doing redemptively in the world are related, and thus human health and well-being are part of God's intent. "Because God's goal for humanity has always been to experience fellowship with him and in that fellowship to develop every human potential, 'peace' also speaks of health, completeness, and fulfillment" (Richards 1999, 481).

Newbigin reminds us that the church is to be the sign of God's kingdom in the world and that working for shalom is such a sign (1954, 67). Making the same point in eschatological terms, John Howard Yoder argues that the church is "called to be now what the world is called to be ultimately . . . a foretaste of the peace for which the world was made" (1984, 92, 94). Wolterstorff again: "Shalom in the world is both God's cause in the world and our human calling. . . . We are not to stand around, hands folded, waiting for shalom to arrive. We are workers in God's cause, his peace-workers" (1983, 72). This is the foundational grounding for a Christian mission that seeks to provide health and wholeness.

Wolterstorff continues to push the connection between peace and justice.

> An implication of this [line of reasoning] is that our work will always have the two dimensions of a struggle for justice and the pursuit of increased mastery of the world so as to enrich human life. Both together are necessary if shalom is to be brought nearer. Development and liberation must go hand in hand. (1983, 72)

This means that we must also work for access to affordable health services for all and do the research that leads to prevention, cures, and even eradication of disease. All are part of witnessing to the kingdom of God that is and is coming.

Saving and Salvation

We turn finally to the theological theme of salvation and the New Testament word "to save" (*sōzō*). We evangelicals sometimes think of Christ's saving work in narrow, vertical terms, speaking only about the restoration of our relationship with God through Jesus Christ, the saving of our souls. Of course, this is a central part of the meaning of salvation. But there is a bit more that is relevant to our conversation on missions of health, healing, and wholeness. Freedman suggests that we expand our understanding: "Salvation is a theme of much of the Bible. In the life of the Hebrew people, God is the one who delivers from oppression, trouble and destruction" (2000, 1154).

In the Old Testament, healing, peace, and salvation often go together. The Psalmist says, "Praise the Lord, my soul, and forget not all his benefits—who forgives all your sins and heals all your diseases" (Ps 103:2,3). Isaiah says of the coming Christ, "But he was pierced for our transgressions, he was crushed for our iniquities; the punishment that brought us peace was on him, and by his wounds we are healed" (Isa 53:5). In Jeremiah, God's promise to an exiled Israel again promises peace (*shalom*) and relates peace to healing: "I will bring health and healing to it [Israel]; I will heal my people and will let them enjoy abundant peace and security" (33:6). Salvation, peace, and healing occur together in seven of the seventeen deliverance passages in Isaiah (Stassen and Gushee 2003, 25).

In the New Testament, use of the idea of salvation is also broader than the narrow idea of souls being saved: "The NT speaks of salvation as deliverance from physical danger such as sickness, deformity, demon possession or death, or the 'evil one,' as well as deliverance from sin" (Freedman 2000, 1154). The Greek word *sōzō* is used when God or Jesus acts to deliver people from life-threatening danger. Examining the contexts related to Christ's healing miracles, "*sōzō* (save) means 'to restore the health and wholeness' (Matt 9:21,22; Mark 15:31; Luke 23:35,37,39)" (Richards 1999, 540). This expanded understanding of the idea of salvation and the use of the word *sōzō* caused E. Anthony Allen, the Jamaican psychiatrist and theologian, to conclude with his coauthors that "healing is inseparable from salvation under the reign of God" (1991, 8).

One final note ties salvation to the idea of shalom and restored relationships. Freedman reminds us that salvation is both individual and communal throughout the biblical text: "God's salvation is the reception of his steadfast love (*hesed*) and peace (*shalom*) in the life of the nation and the individual" (2000, 1154). In terms of shalom, Richards argues that "in most contexts, *sōzō* and *sōtēria/sōtērios* reveal God's action in Christ to deliver humanity from the powers of sin, death, and Satan, which drain life on earth of its joy and threaten each person with eternal loss" (1999, 541).

Implications for a Christian View of Health, Healing, and Flourishing

GOD, THE LOVING, EMPATHIC HEALER

Healing, restoration of shalom, and saving whole human beings are the work of God in human history and reflect God's love for us and our well-being. Health, wholeness, and human flourishing are part of what God has been working to restore through the redemptive work of Jesus Christ. Thus, we must remember that healing and restoration are God's mission, not ours. This has three important implications.

First, we must remember that our vocation is to be faithful witnesses to God's saving and healing, not successful healers. There is a temptation toward a messianic spirit among gifted, well-educated people who accomplish a lot of good in the world. We need to come to our mission as we are—weak, fallen, and fallible, not proud of our education or confident in our power to save and to heal. Furthermore, we pursue our mission in a fallen and unjust world. This implies that suffering is more the norm than the exception, both for those we serve and for ourselves. This is the basis for Rick Donlon's call to health workers to be prepared to take up their "crosses" and accept the price of serving as Jesus served (2012).

Second, sometimes healing takes place and sometimes it does not. Our Christian eschatology informs us that God's intended shalom will not be realized until after Jesus comes again. If the test of our healthcare missions is successful healing, then we will surely be disappointed some of the time, and this disappointment can lead down a road to frustration, burnout, and depression. We need a spirituality that helps us remember who we really are and who God is and thus sustains us as fallen practitioners in a fallen world.

Third, we must act like followers and disciples. Any mission of health and healing is simply us following after God, the only one who can save and heal. We must explain what we do and why we do it in these terms.

We need to appear as dependent people, neither as bringers of superior knowledge or healing power nor as self-sufficient individuals without weakness, need, or sin. We must point beyond ourselves to the source of any healing we bring. Any good that we do, we do because of our God and God's redemptive work in our lives, and we need to announce these facts. W. Meredith Long, a doctor of public health who has worked with African churches combating HIV/AIDS, reports the motto of a hospital in Kenya: "We treat. Jesus heals" (2000, 190). This invites those we serve to look beyond our medical, psychological, and spiritual gifts to their true source. At the end of the day, the credit for healing and the possibility of flourishing must go to God. Christian witness in healthcare missions rests on this fact (more on this in chap. 3).

GOD, THE SOURCE OF WHAT WE KNOW

As Christians, we are quick to say yes to this claim—and so we should. But it may help to unpack it a little more. It has some significant implications.

First, the biological, psychological, and spiritual resilience of human beings and their potential to heal is a consequence of our being made in the image of God. Long argues that "the effectiveness of all healing or preventative intervention depends upon the healing power that God designed in the human body as part of his created order. Jesus created the healing process in the body (John 1:1–3) and sustains it by his power (Heb 1:3)" (2000, 191).

Daniel E. Fountain, a long-time medical missionary to central Africa who passed away as this book was being written, extended this idea by arguing that the potential to heal is "built-in" to human beings (1989, 70). He points out that we have two kidneys but can function with one. Livers have far more cells than their function requires. We have inbuilt resistance to disease. The brain has remarkable self-healing power and psychological resilience. When we are wounded or ill, our body launches its own healing process. This potential for healing and well-being is evidence of God's grace built into us.

Second, we've already noted that God made an orderly world and that, because we are made in God's image, we can figure out how God's world works. Furthermore, the fact that we are made in the image of a creator God makes us creators too. Whatever we have discovered about the nature of disease, mental illness, and spiritual disorder, and however clever we've become in terms of prevention and treatment, it was made possible by God and the way God made us. This drives our continuing medical and psychological research to enhance or extend our knowledge of what God has already revealed to us. We are constantly surprised by what God has built into our body, mind, and soul that enables health and healing.

Third, the triune God understands and identifies with the sick. This is deeper than the love that God feels for every human being in God's creation. Long reminds us that "Christ is the only member of the Godhead who has ever been sick, tired, or injured—the only one who ever experienced the need for healing" (2000, 223). We can tell the sick that Jesus has been there too, and that the power that raised him from the dead is active in human history today, working to heal and save.

GOD INTENDS HEALTH, WHOLENESS, AND FLOURISHING

We have already noted that this is the intention for God's creation in Genesis 1 and 2. But what about the impact of sin? What are we to expect in a fallen world?

The biblical account is unambiguous: The eschatological vision in Isaiah 65 speaks of the restoration of joy and of no more weeping and crying. Infants do not die young, and the old live out their years. Mothers do not bear children doomed to misfortune. God answers before people call out. The lamb and the lion lie down together. This image of God's new heavens and earth points to shalom in concrete terms. Saving and healing are surely among the means of restoring God's creation.

The ministry of Jesus was framed in similar terms. Jesus announced that he came to preach good news to the poor, to proclaim freedom to prisoners and recovery of sight to the blind (Luke 4:18,19). When John the Baptist sent folks to see if Jesus was the Messiah, Jesus' response was, "Report to John what you have seen and heard: The blind receive sight, the lame walk, those who have leprosy are cleansed, the deaf hear, the dead are raised, and the good news is proclaimed to the poor" (Luke 7:22). In the clearest statement on the connection between saving and healing, Jesus declares his intention "that they [the world] may have life, and have it to the full" (John 10:10). Surely a full life is a flourishing life of peaceful and delightful relationships in all dimensions.

The vision of John in Revelation echoes this encouraging image of God's redeemed and restored world. There is no more death, mourning, or pain. God dwells once again among God's people. The seemingly valuable jewels and gold we fight over today are simply beautiful building materials, paving streets and decorating walls. In the new Jerusalem, there is life-giving water and healing for the nations. There is no temple, as the presence of God and the Lamb is enough—yet another expression of shalom.

We must conclude that it is God's intention that we work for health, wholeness, and human flourishing in this fallen world, emulating what Jesus did during his ministry on earth.

This also pushes us to deepen and extend our understanding of what constitutes human health and well-being. We all agree it is more than absence of disease, mental illness, or spiritual hunger. Being poor and living life on the edge of death is clearly not what God intends. Africans pray for a "life as well as the means to make life worth living" (Okorocha 1994, 79). But what does this more fully human life look like? This is a biological question, a psychological question, and a theological question all at the same time.

Biologically, human flourishing requires a healthy body and mind. But our theology tells us that there is more to being human than just being alive. Human beings, made in the image of God, should have choices as to what one does with one's self in the world. Amartya Sen calls these *capabilities*—the freedom to choose what one wishes to do and become. Sen argues that our education, physical health, and relationships are the human functionings that allow us to pursue the capabilities we value (1999, 74ff.). Thus, human freedom or human agency is also part of human flourishing.

We are expanding our answers to the question of what is human flourishing by shifting our focus to include those things that enable flourishing, not just focusing on the things that diminish it. Promoting well-being leads us to the fields of positive psychology (Keyes and Haidt 2003) and community psychology (Prilleltensky and Prilleltensky 2006). This also reminds us of the importance of the poetic side of life—celebrations, worship, art, beauty, and the like.

The question is also an economic and political one: What kinds of social systems and safeguards are needed to protect those who are too wounded or excluded to flourish? What must the domains of economics, politics, and civil society do to promote human well-being and flourishing of all? What kind of access to health and mental health services is necessary for a society to be declared just in God's eyes? What is the test of a society that promotes health and well-being? For the biblical prophets, the test was the well-being of the widow, orphan, and alien. If the "least of these" are doing well, the rest of society is probably doing well too.

Finally, and perhaps most importantly, this is a spiritual question. The biblical account is clear. We are made in the image of God, and this means that our best life is with God—a life of worship, becoming more like Christ, and being Christlike in the world.

Thus, we can conclude that whatever heals and restores body, mind, and spirit is part of the saving work of God toward the restoration of what God intended from the beginning—human flourishing in the midst of a flourishing creation.

HUMAN BEINGS ARE WHOLE PERSONS,
INSEPARABLY BODY, MIND, AND SOUL

We have already rejected the Greek and modern idea that there is both meaning and value in treating body, mind, and soul as three differing, unrelated domains.

Fountain has warned us repeatedly that ill health needs to be understood as more than a broken foot or a bleeding ulcer, a trauma victim or an addict who is self-medicating for a biochemical deficiency (1989, 33, 85ff.). If human beings are inseparably whole persons, then our approach to health and healing must reflect this fact. This suggests that Christian healthcare professionals need to move beyond just being doctors and psychologists who happen to be Christians and become what Anthony Allen calls "whole person health care givers" (1995, 19). Furthermore, we should no longer put the burden on the patient to figure out how to combine the gifts of a doctor, a psychologist, and an evangelist or spiritual director in order to get a whole-person treatment plan. This is why Allen calls for centers of integrated healing: "Mental health care should be in place. Spiritual health care (which includes the ministry of prayer, confession and absolution, spiritual direction, healing rituals, and congregational support) should become an integral part of primary healthcare and hospital facilities" (1995, 24).

The inseparability of mind, body, and soul is more than a shift in a philosophical idea; it is increasingly grounded in science. In his chapter in this book, Daniel Fountain points out that the medical effects of emotions such as anger, fear, and stress are biochemical in nature and thus linked to illness in the body. Jonathan Haidt, a social psychologist, has proposed that we have an innate set of moral intuitions that are embedded in our DNA and thus to the biochemistry of our brains that cause us to extend cooperative behavior outside our family or clan (2012). Justin Barrett, head of the Thrive Center at Fuller Theological Seminary, argues that we are born with an innate instinct in favor of believing in some kind of God (2012). Is it possible that our DNA softwires us with a bias in favor of loving God and neighbor? Neuroeconomist Paul Zak has studied oxytocin, which he calls the "moral molecule," and shown that it is the biochemical that triggers empathy, which is the basis of trust and compassion (2012). Cognitive psychologist Steven Pinker has argued that cognitive psychology, neuropsychology, and behavioral genetics have also radically undermined the body-mind-soul distinction (2002, 31–45). Psychiatrist Harold Koenig, head of Duke's Center for the Study of Religion/Spirituality and Health, and community psychologist Kenneth Pargament are demonstrating the connection between religious belief, spirituality, and human coping and resilience (Pargament 1998). The mind-body-soul distinction is not only unhelpful; it is getting in the way of a more holistic understanding of how medicine, psychology, and spiritual care fit together.

HUMAN BEINGS ARE RELATIONAL AND SOCIAL BY NATURE

Being made in the image of a relational God whose central emotional motivations are love and compassion means that human beings are relational more than anything else. We need to view health, healing, and wholeness through a relational and social lens.

The relational or social reality of disease comes through in the Gospels. To the beggar at the gate, Christ asks, "Do you want to be healed?" and the response is surprising: "I have no one to put me into the pool" (John 5:6–8,14 ESV). The root of the cripple's hopelessness is social alienation, not his illness. This connection between the social world of the sick person and his or her disease is repeated in Matthew's account of Jesus healing the leper (Matt 14). Jesus touches a leper, crossing the social boundary between the clean and the unclean, the included and the excluded, and the leper is healed. Jesus then tells him to go to the priest to do what Moses requires to rejoin the Jewish community. Healing and social restoration go together in the Gospel account.

Building on this relational or community view of human beings, we need to expand our methods in diagnosing and treating people who are ill.

Allen also suggests that we must be as curious about family and social life as we are about the presenting health problem of an individual (Allen et al. 1991, 14ff.). He calls for "whole person history taking, diagnostic formulation and treatment" (1995, 30).

Psychology is also moving toward an understanding of individuals as embedded relational selves, not autonomous individuals. Balswick and his collaborators have framed human development in terms of what they call the *reciprocating self:* "It is our belief that God's intention for individual (human) development is inextricably intertwined with our relationships to God and one another" (Balswick, King, and Reimer 2005, 49). Community psychology is leading us in the same direction by insisting that mental health is not just an issue of what's going on emotionally inside the patient, but that the social/political/economic environment of the patient is also critical to mental health. Isaac Prilleltensky focuses on the psychological impacts of social structures that work against human flourishing: "Human interactions are marred by disrespect, exclusion, humiliation, and erasure of identity" (2003, 19–34). This is a contemporary explanation of what happened to the cripple at the gate in the Gospel account.

Our relational nature also enlarges our vision for mission. Yes, individuals need to be saved and healed. But our relational or social nature also means that we must bring our social, political, and economic contexts into focus as healthcare missions opportunities too. If shalom and human flourishing are God's intention, then we need to work to create social systems that are supportive and conducive to this flourishing. Various political philosophies argue for differing ways to provide affordable health care for all, but the moral bottom line is the same: Is affordable health care available to all or not? Access to psychological care and support would seem unarguable as well. Thus, to support God's saving and healing mission, Christians need to vote for those who satisfy this requirement, and their churches need to work as part of civil society to do the same.

HUMAN BEINGS ARE CREATORS TOO

We need to further examine the theological idea that, having been made in the image of God, we are creators too. While we cannot create from nothing as God did, we can create from what God has made in God's creation. Since our vocation is to work for a world in which all human beings can flourish, certain conclusions follow.

First, we are intended and enabled by God to figure out how God's world works. Further, we are to do so in a way that results in saving, healing, and flourishing. Criticizing the medieval Scholastics at the beginning of the seventeenth century for their endless focus on reasoning from first principles, Francis Bacon called for a shift from reading God's Bible alone to also reading God's other book—nature. Bacon's goal was to see what could be learned to improve the human condition (1960, 23, 78). By the beginning of the next century, the resulting curiosity and creative research were driving the discoveries in modern medicine, agriculture, and economics. At the beginning of the twentieth century, psychology began its own research pilgrimage.

Second, we need to explore the idea of where the image of God resides in the human being. For too long, we've assumed it was simply a connection between the spirit of God and the spirit of human beings. The modern worldview and our struggle with evolution and "the survival of the fittest" make us uncritically comfortable with this view. But earlier, I've made the case for the inseparability of body, mind, and soul, and thus I wonder if we need to reexamine this assumption. Could the image of God also find expression in our body, even in our genes? Is it possible that elements of the image of God might be embedded by God in our evolutionary history? As long as evolution and genes means the big, smart, and strong survive, and the weak die off, evolution is problematic from a Christian perspective in terms of explaining moral or other-centered behavior. But there is new information that suggests there may be more to the evolution story than we know.

ROLE OF THE CHRISTIAN COMMUNITY

Our relational understanding of health and wholeness leads us to examine the role of the Christian community in health and healing. We've already noted that the mission of the church is to seek, to save, and to heal. But there is more.

Long reminds us that we, the church alone, have the good news that Jesus died and rose so that we could experience reconciliation in all of our relationships—with God, within ourselves, with our community and those we call Other, and with God's created order (2000, 229ff.). Thus, reconciliation must be a mark of Christian mission. We are back to shalom again.

The church is to be a caring community bearing one another's burdens (Gal 6:2) and rejoicing with those who rejoice and mourning with those who mourn (Rom 12:16). We are to be a therapeutic community that heals its own (Jas 5:14) and those around us: "Stretch out your hand to heal and perform signs and wonders, through the name of your holy servant Jesus" (Acts 4:30). We are a suffering community with a healing message:

> We always carry around in our body the death of Jesus,
> so that the life of Jesus may also be revealed in our body.
> For we who are alive are always being given over to death
> for Jesus' sake, so that his life may also be revealed in our
> mortal body. So then, death is at work in us, but life is at
> work in you. (2 Cor 4:10–12)

Long calls us to be "healing communities of shalom" (2000, 71). Allen and colleagues call us to mobilize our members to see themselves as "village health workers or community organizers" (1991, 36).

Allen and his coauthors go on to argue persuasively that the church can be a healing community in ways that are difficult for secular institutions (1991, 34ff.). For the excluded or marginalized, the church can be a community of belonging and fellowship, an essential ingredient to social health. The church has access to the gifts of the Holy Spirit and can speak of the work of Jesus—the ultimate and most complete source of healing. Finally, we are a praying community with resources far greater than the material and psychological alone (Long 2000, 232; Allen et al. 1991, 232; Fountain 1989, 63). (More on this in chap. 15.)

Conclusion

Healing, wholeness, and communities of human flourishing are at the center of the biblical text and the gospel itself. This is the message of the creation narratives, and it is the meaning of shalom, a crucial part of the salvation offered through Jesus Christ. In the beginning and at the end of history, we are to be in loving, just, peaceful, and enjoyable relationships with God, within ourselves, with our communities and those we call Other, and with the whole of creation. This is the mission of God and thus is our mission, too.

References Cited

Allen, E. Anthony. 1995. "Wholeness, Salvation and the Christian Health Professional." In *Transforming Health: Christian Approaches to Healing and Wholeness,* edited by Eric R. Ram. Monrovia, CA: MARC (World Vision).

Allen, E. Anthony, Kenneth L. Luscombe, Bryant L. Myers, and Eric R. Ram. 1991. *Health, Healing and Transformation: Biblical Reflections on the Church in Ministries of Healing and Wholeness.* Monrovia CA: MARC (World Vision).

Bacon, Francis. 1960. *The New Organon and Related Writings.* Edited by Fulton H. Anderson. New York: Macmillan.

Balswick, Jack O., Pamela Ebstyne King, and Kevin S. Reimer. 2005. *The Reciprocating Self: Human Development in Theological Perspective.* Downers Grove, IL: InterVarsity Press.

Barrett, Justin L. 2012. *Born Believers: The Science of Children's Religious Belief.* 1st Free Press hardcover ed. New York: Free Press.

Brown, Warren, Nancey Murphy, and H. Newton Maloney. 1998. *Whatever Happened to the Soul? Scientific and Theological Portraits of Human Nature.* Philadelphia: Fortress.

Brown, William P. 2012. "Manifest Diversity: The Presence of God in Genesis." In *Genesis and Christian Theology,* edited by Nathan MacDonald, M. Elliott, and G. Macaskill. Grand Rapids, MI: Eerdmans.

Donlon, Rick. 2012. "The Truth about Suffering." Christian Community Health Fellowship website (posted January 1), https://www.cchf.org/resources/h-and-dthe-truth-about-suffering/ (accessed February 5, 2015).

Fountain, Daniel E. 1989. *Health, the Bible and the Church.* BGC Monograph. Wheaton, IL: Billy Graham Center.

Freedman, David Noel, ed. 2000. *Eerdmans Dictionary of the Bible.* Grand Rapids, MI: Eerdmans.

Goizueta, Roberto S. 2009. *Christ Our Companion: Toward a Theological Aesthetics of Liberation.* Maryknoll, NY: Orbis.

Haidt, Jonathan. 2012. *The Righteous Mind: Why Good People Are Divided by Politics and Religion.* New York: Pantheon.

Keyes, Corey L. M., and Jonathan Haidt. 2003. *Flourishing: Positive Psychology and the Life Well-Lived.* Washington, DC: American Psychological Association.

Long, W. Meredith. 2000. *Health, Healing and God's Kingdom: New Pathways to Christian Health Ministry in Africa.* Carlisle, CA: Regnum.

Middleton, J. Richard. 2005. *The Liberating Image: The* Imago Dei *in Genesis 1.* Grand Rapids, MI: Brazos.

Myers, Bryant L. 2011. *Walking with the Poor: Principles and Practices of Transformational Development.* Revised and updated ed. Maryknoll, NY: Orbis.

Newbigin, Lesslie. 1954. *The Household of God: Lectures on the Nature of the Church.* New York: Friendship.

Okorocha, Cyril. 1994. "The Meaning of Salvation: An African Perspective." In *Emerging Voices in Global Christian Theology,* edited by William A. Dyrness, 59–92. Grand Rapids: MI: Zondervan.

Pargament, K. I., B. W. Smith, H. G. Koenig, and L. Perez. 1998. "Patterns of Positive and Negative Religious Coping with Major Life Stressors." *Journal for the Scientific Study of Religion* 37: 710–24.

Pinker, Steven. 2002. *The Blank Slate: The Modern Denial of Human Nature.* London: Penguin.

Prilleltensky, Isaac. 2003. "Poverty and Power." In *Poverty and Psychology: From Global Perspective to Local Practice,* edited by Stuart C. Carr and Tod Stratton Sloan, 19–44. New York: Plenum.

————, and Ora Prilleltensky. 2006. *Promoting Well-Being: Linking Personal, Organizational, and Community Change*. Hoboken, NJ: John Wiley.

Richards, Lawrence O. 1999. *New International Encyclopedia of Bible Words*. Grand Rapids, MI: Zondervan.

Sen, Amartya. 1999. *Development as Freedom*. New York: Knopf.

Stassen, Glen Harold, and David P. Gushee. 2003. *Kingdom Ethics: Following Jesus in Contemporary Context*. Downers Grove, IL: InterVarsity Press.

White, Lynn, Jr. 1978. *Medieval Religion and Technology: Collected Essays*. Berkeley, CA: Center for Medieval and Renaissance Studies.

Wolterstorff, Nicholas. 1983. *Until Justice and Peace Embrace*. Grand Rapids, MI: Eerdmans.

Yoder, John Howard. 1984. *The Priestly Kingdom: Social Ethics as Gospel*. Notre Dame, IN: University of Notre Dame Press.

Zak, Paul J. 2012. *The Moral Molecule: The Source of Love and Prosperity*. New York: Dutton.

CHAPTER 3

Announcing the
Whole Gospel
Health, Healing, and
Christian Witness

Bryant L. Myers, PhD

We treat; Jesus heals.
MOTTO OF TENWEK HOSPITAL, KENYA

The purpose of this chapter is to examine how evangelism and Christian witness can find a seamless and integrated home in Christian medical mission. What makes medical missions Christian at the end of the day? At heart this is a worldview issue in which the modern worldview's separation of the material and the spiritual seems to support separating medicine and psychology from evangelism and spiritual things.

We need to begin with the simple and obvious affirmation that being Christian means being a witness. By definition our faith is a missionary faith. The noun *gospel* means "message" or "good news." Messages are not messages unless they are announced, and hoarding good news to oneself is not terribly consistent with loving your neighbor as you love yourself.

When Christians say that they accept Jesus as their Lord and Savior, they are also saying that they intend to announce this fact in every facet of their lives and by every means available to them: by life, deed, word, and sign. For a Christian, being a witness is integral to who we are and what we believe. This, of course, includes medical missions. I am assuming that we all agree that this is a legitimate point of departure.

My intention in this chapter is to take the conversation to a deeper level. We need to explore four different areas relating to Christian witness and medical missions:

- When are we witnesses?
- To what and whom are we witnessing?
- A twofold worldview challenge
- A different way of thinking about proclamation

When Are We Witnesses?

Sometimes I am not sure that we think hard enough about this business of being witnesses. Sometimes we think there are two choices: being witnesses or not being witnesses. This is not true. We are always witnesses to something. The only question is, to what or to whom are we witnessing?

Let me tell you a story by way of illustration. In Uganda, after a large relief response, I visited the program about a year after the response had ended. A lot of good things had been done. Children looked healthy and decently nourished. The health huts still had government staff in them with a decent stock of essential drugs. The people recalled the work of World Vision and their Tanzanian Christian staff with affection. "You came when we needed help," they said. So far so good.

As I met and talked with some local people, I was introduced to a little boy. "What's his name?" I asked. "World Vision," I was told. Surprised, I continued on only to meet five more young children named "World Vision" before the day had ended. I later learned that when someone saves the life of a member of your family, it is the local custom to rename your child after the one who did the saving. I was pleased that World Vision had such a positive reputation, but deeply troubled that the credit for saving children was going to World Vision and not to God. Credit was not going to whom credit was due.

We need to be concerned about who gets worshiped at the end of a health program. World Vision's Jayakumar Christian has said that whatever the people perceive that the agency puts at the center of its program will tend to be what the community puts its faith in when the program ends. If we act as if medical technology is the key element of the program, technology will be worshiped as the key to healing. If the health agency, its experts, and its resources appear to be the central feature of the program, the health agency will become the object of worship. In one case in India, it was discovered that World Vision had been added to a tribal community's list of gurus—those who have answers the community does not have. A small pile of stones became a prayer site to keep this new guru happy and helping the community. If money is the focus, then money is perceived to be the key to health and healing. Whatever we are perceived to put at the center of our medical mission programming is our *de facto* witness.

This is the first challenge to Christian witness in the context of doing medical missions. You are always witnessing. You will have to listen to those you serve to find out to whom or about what you are witnessing. This leads me to my second point.

To What and Whom Are We Witnessing?

My second point has to do with a very basic question. As Christians, what is the content of our witness? About what or whom exactly are we supposed to be witnessing?

In the third chapter of Mark's Gospel, Mark tells us that Jesus "appointed twelve . . . that they might be with him and that he might send them out to preach and to have authority to drive out demons" (vv. 14,15). When they went out on their first solo ministry outing, Mark reports, "They went out and preached that people should repent. They drove out many demons and anointed many sick people with oil and healed them" (Mark 6:12,13).

I take this to be an articulation of the whole gospel of Jesus Christ. It begins with "being with Jesus." Mission activists of all types too often jump over this "being with" part to get to the "doing" work of healing, casting out, and preaching. This is dangerous for our spiritual, mental, and physical health; developing a spirituality that enables us to sustain our mission, however, is a topic for another time.

I find it helpful to picture this description of the gospel as a pyramid (fig. 3.1). The top of the pyramid is being with Jesus, life in Christ indwelt by the Holy Spirit. Each of the corners of the pyramid is one aspect of the gospel: *preaching*—the gospel as word; *healing*—the gospel as deed; *casting out*—the gospel as sign. I choose this metaphor because we cannot break off a corner of a pyramid and still have a pyramid. All we'd have left is a broken pyramid. For the gospel to be the gospel, all four aspects must be present—life, deed, word, and sign.

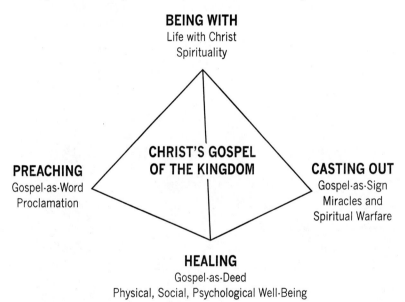

BEING WITH
Life with Christ
Spirituality

**CHRIST'S GOSPEL
OF THE KINGDOM**

PREACHING
Gospel-as-Word
Proclamation

CASTING OUT
Gospel-as-Sign
Miracles and
Spiritual Warfare

HEALING
Gospel-as-Deed
Physical, Social, Psychological Well-Being

*Figure 3.1: The whole gospel of Jesus Christ
(Myers 2011, 101)*

Kwame Bediako, a Ghanaian theologian who recently went home to be with the Lord, sat with me one evening in Accra, and we talked about the meaning of the whole gospel. He voiced a concern about Western theology that I had heard him state on other occasions.

> You Western folk can be silly sometimes. You think that
> if you cut up a dog and study its parts, you then under-
> stand what a dog is. Even worse, you sometimes sound as
> if you believe that by putting the parts back together in
> their proper places, you have a dog again. But you don't.
> You have a dead dog. When you decided to take the dog
> apart in the first place, you lost sight of the most im-
> portant thing—the fact that the dog is a living being.
> (Bediako 1996)

Living beings lose their life and meaning when we disassemble them. An eagle is only fully understood as an eagle when it soars in the sky. When we separate gospel-as-deed from gospel-as-word from gospel-as-sign, we lose the life and truth of the gospel.

There is something else we need to note. No aspect of the gospel is the whole gospel in and of itself. Words are ambiguous until deeds clarify the meaning of the words. After all, larger numbers of people in America claim to be Christians, yet social behavior research reveals that most behave in society in ways indistinguishable from non-Christians (Sider 2005). This why we tend to identify a Christian by the congruence between what one says and what one does.

Similarly, good deeds are also ambiguous. We don't know how to interpret deeds fully until the doer announces the motive and meaning behind his or her good deed. Buddhist and atheist healthcare workers can be just as effective and professional as Christian practitioners. Only words can clarify the fact that our medical missions are done because we follow a Lord of life and wholeness who demands that we seek to save and heal the broken and the lost.

Paul missed this key point in Lystra (Acts 14:8–18) and learned an important healthcare missions principle. After healing the lame man with no mention of the name of Jesus, he found himself the focus of an enthusiastic crowd that wanted to sacrifice a bull to him as the incarnation of a Roman god. He then tried to overcome his miscommunication—"We, too, are only human like you"—and point-ed to God as the one whom they should be worshiping.

Finally, signs are ambiguous as well. Not all miracles come from God. Satan can counterfeit miracles too, the Bible tells us.

Word, deed, and sign must all work together as a living consistent message, pointing to the activity of the living God. This is why a holistic understanding of the gospel is so important. Medical good news alone is not the same as gospel good news.

A Twofold Worldview Challenge

Another story to set the context for my third area of concern: I visited a child survival project in West Africa in the 1990s. The immunization coverage was excellent, and there were indicators that suggested that the incidence of childhood diseases would soon be on the decline. I was introduced to the local village healer, a shaman of excellent reputation. I wondered how he felt about this child survival project; after all, it was clearly a threat to his work, his role in the community, and possibly his livelihood.

"How do you feel about this program?" I asked. "Wonderful!" he re-plied. "I have learned so much." "About what?" I continued. "Well, I now know that there are six demons that make children sick of which I knew nothing until World Vision's program began," he proudly reported. Six immunizations meant six demons, it seems.

World Vision's healthcare staff responded instantly. "No, the immu-nizations have nothing to do with demons. They are just good science," they confidently explained.

This reveals a worldview problem of some complexity. A primal worldview has come in contact with the modern Western worldview, and there is a breakdown in communication. Paul Hiebert, a highly gifted anthropologist who recently passed away, provided us with a simple dia-gram (fig. 3.2) to help us understand what is going on (Hiebert 1982).

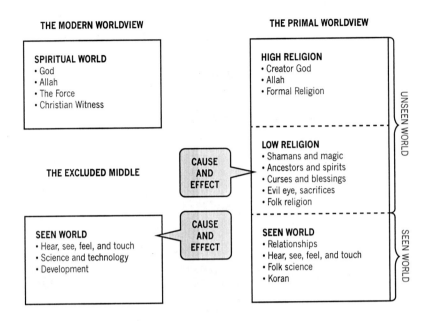

Figure 3.2: Cause and effect according to worldview
(Adapted from Myers 2011, 8)

For the shaman, cause and effect for illness are located in the unseen world that Hiebert calls "low religion," the supernatural world of magic, curses, demons, angry ancestors, and the like (fig. 3.2). It follows that effective immunizations must mean that six demons have been unmasked and made powerless to harm children.

For the healthcare staff, educated into the modern Western worldview, especially through their medical education, cause and effect are located in the material world where things can be seen, felt, touched, measured, and studied, a world quite separate and distinct from the spiritual world. Immunizations are simply the result of good science.

This worldview conflict has two important consequences. First, Christian medical professionals may find themselves living as functional atheists. While they believe in Jesus, worship God, read their Bible, and go to church on Sunday, all of this takes place in the spiritual realm and usually on Sunday or after work. But Monday to Friday, the Christian healthcare worker operates in the material realm of science. Daniel Fountain has pointed to this dilemma too: "We are Christian when we 'witness to patients,' go to church or give an evangelistic message. But when we practice medicine, we are 'professionals' and this has little rapport with Christian faith" (Fountain 1989, 3).

A second major consequence also arises from these conflicting worldviews. Allowing the shaman and the local people to continue with their primal worldview intact is neither true nor good for developing their understanding of what makes them healthy in the future. But replacing this explanation with a modern Western worldview is neither biblical nor Christian.

The underlying problem is that most Christian healthcare practitioners don't have a way to do anything other than offer the rationale that immunizations are "just science." We in the West, and particularly those of us trained in the sciences, do not require God or the gospel as part of the explanation for why our science is effective. God disappeared from our explanatory schemes for science over two hundred years ago. Our professional training has equipped us to be messengers of a secular explanation for illness, health, and healing.

The effectiveness of all development technologies—health, agriculture, water management, disaster mitigation, and so forth—can reinforce this worldview problem in primal cultures. Augustine Musopole, a Malawian theologian, reports that the more successful the development intervention, the greater the reinforcement of the primal religious worldview: "The more education, the better the job, the larger the house, the more you have to protect and the greater the temptation to witchcraft" (Musopole 1997).

We need to remember that whenever a surgery spares the life of a child or children no longer die young, people will wonder how this came to be. Without an explanation, the primal worldview provides an animist explanation. "Thus ended the surgical drama," Daniel Fountain tells us with reference to an Indian villager stunned and confused by a modern surgery, "a thyroidectomy in modern medical parlance, but a battle between the gods and the evil spirits when seen through the eyes of an Indian villager" (1989, 24). If the modern healthcare professional reduces the good news to "just science," the explanation is a secular one. Either way there is a witness—and it is not to the gospel.

We need to figure out how to work in primal cultures in a way that does not reinforce primal religious explanations for disease and healing. Yet there is another, possibly deeper challenge: how we understand and interpret our Western medical knowledge. For this latter point, I do not see an easy way out of this conundrum. We in the West are so thoroughly locked into our material, biological, scientific view of the world that it is hard to see a way to for us to reimagine the effectiveness of our science with God as part of the explanation. I suspect the way out of our dilemma may come from our brothers and sisters in the South.

A Different Way of Thinking about Proclamation

The fourth challenge has to do with the traditional framework of evangelism or Christian witness. In the traditional understanding of evangelism, unreached people are assumed to have a problem of which they are not aware—they have not heard the gospel. From this perspective, it is natural for the evangelist to assume the role of answer-giver. Furthermore, there is an unstated assumption that the evangelist knows something about the future of the audience that the audience does not know; namely, their ultimate destination if they do not believe.

At the most foundational level, these claims are true. Christians do believe a truth that non-Christians do not know or share. We are called to share this gospel news even if people are not aware they need it. Further, Christians do believe that life eternal is only possible by believing in Jesus Christ as Lord and Savior. Yet there is a fine line between being faithful to these beliefs and a subtle, sinful shift toward an attitude of superiority or even arrogance.

There is always the danger that we may act, not as undeserving recipients of a gift, but as people with something that makes us superior, expressing what Kosuke Koyama called the "teacher complex," something that Koyama felt damages the attractiveness of the gospel: "The Spirit of Christ does not support the spirit of greed to conquer others and self-righteousness to demonstrate our superior piety" (1993, 293).

If done sensitively and without arrogance, this "go and tell" frame for Christian witness may be appropriate for a church or traditional church planting agency, but I am not sure it is a good fit for an agency with a development agenda. Going and telling cuts across the idea of the community needing to take responsibility for addressing its own healthcare needs now and in the future. It works against the notion of beginning where the community is and helping the community find answers to its own questions. Initiative and power are with the outsider; control is external. This is especially true when the "go and tell gospel" arrives in a Land Rover, accompanied by highly educated medical professionals and a large program budget. Since most of us don't believe in "go and tell" development, we need to be concerned about "go and tell" evangelism.

So is there a way out of this dilemma? I was greatly helped by Lesslie Newbigin, a long-time missionary to India and one of the great missiologists of the last century. In his classic *The Gospel in a Pluralistic Society* (1989), Newbigin calls our attention to the book of Acts and its account of the evangelism and the growth of the early church. Examining these stories, Newbigin calls our attention to an interesting pattern. Evangelism, the saying of the gospel, is often the second act, not the first.

When Peter gives his first public proclamation of the gospel, we are told that three thousand believers were added that day. Yet his sermon was a spontaneous reaction; it was not preplanned. Peter begins his articulation of the gospel by saying, "Let me explain this to you" (Acts 2:14). What was the "this" that needed explaining? The people of Jerusalem are amazed to "hear [the disciples] declaring the wonders of God in our own tongues" (Acts 2:12). This powerful act of the Holy Spirit demanded an explanation. Peter's message was in response to a question asked by the crowd who had just witnessed the Pentecost event.

The second articulation of the gospel in Acts follows a similar pattern. After Peter heals the crippled beggar at the temple gate, a crowd gathers, astonished at the sight of the former cripple walking around and praising God. Peter once again finds himself needing to clarify the situation. "You Israelites, why do you wonder at this, or why do you stare at us, as though by our own power or piety we had made him walk? The God of Abraham, the God of Isaac, and the God of Jacob, the God of our ancestors, has glorified his servant Jesus" (Acts 3:12,13 NRSV). Once again Peter's declaration of the gospel is in response to a question provoked by evidence of God's healing activity.

The same pattern emerges again in the story of Stephen. His opportunity to share the gospel's recomposed history of Israel in Acts 7 comes about not by plan, but through his being falsely accused as a result of the Holy Spirit doing "great wonders and signs among the people" (Acts 6:8). As a result of Stephen's preaching in front of the Sanhedrin, a Pharisee named Saul hears the gospel for the first time. God acts and the gospel is then proclaimed. Evangelism is the second act.

In each case, the gospel is proclaimed, not by intent or plan, but in response to a question provoked by God's healing and saving activity in the community. There is an act that demands an explanation, and the gospel explains this act. As Newbigin put it, "Something has happened which makes people aware of a new reality, and therefore the question arises: What is this reality? The communication of the gospel is the answering of that question" (Newbigin 1989, 132).

This framework suggests that we can also think of evangelism as the work that God does through us as long as we are acting in ways that provoke questions to which the good news of Jesus Christ is the answer. This framework calls for us to do our work of medical missions in a way that provokes questions about our mission, motives, and effectiveness.

Our lives and the way we do our work must be eloquent, pointing to something that is beyond us and beyond our science.

This kind of approach provides an alternative frame for Christian witness that solves my concern about "go and tell" evangelism in the context of development or medical missions. When water is found in the desert, when children no longer die young, when water no longer makes people sick, something has happened that needs an explanation. When healthcare professionals come to poor villages and everyone there knows they could be making more money and their children could go to better schools in the city, this odd behavior provokes a question to which the gospel is the answer.

There is a lot to like about this frame for Christian witness in the context of doing medical missions. First, people ask questions as a result of witnessing something they do not expect or understand. The initiative lies with them. This avoids the complaint, attributed to Paul Tillich, that it is wrong to throw answers like stones at the heads of those who haven't asked a question. Second, the burden is on us as Christians, not on the people. If the people do not ask questions to which the gospel is the answer, we can no longer dismiss them, saying, "Their hearts were hardened," and walk away feeling good that we have proclaimed the gospel. Instead, we need to get down on our knees and ask God why our lives and our work are so unremarkable that no one has raised a question related to what we believe.

For medical mission practitioners, the challenge is serious indeed. We must do our work and live our lives in a way that calls attention to the new Spirit that lives within us. We need to relate to people, be transparent, and promote our health and healing in a way that creates a sense of wonder. We must live out a spirituality that makes our lives unusual. Dorothy Day is reported to have admonished her readers to "live a life so mysterious that the only adequate explanation is the presence of a living, loving God."

There is anecdotal evidence that this approach can bear fruit. World Vision hired a Christian public health specialist to hold clinics in five West African villages. She would visit one village a day and move on to the next one, completing her circuit each week. When the program was being designed with village leaders and the local government, a local mullah hovered nearby, listening in on the discussions. At one point, he became very animated and spoke out harshly: "I know about you Christians and your offer to help us with our health needs. You Christians use health care as a trick. You really want to take our children away and give them to your God, Issa. You are missionaries, not health workers."

The woman listened carefully and finally made a promise: "I love Jesus Christ and am here to help your people because of that love. But, I promise you, I will never mention the name of Jesus Christ while I am in your village!" The mullah agreed to the weekly clinic on this condition. Did she do the right thing? Can any Christian, especially a missionary, make such a promise? How does the gospel get declared under an oath of silence?

Every Tuesday, the woman showed up and opened her simple clinic. As she drove up, the mullah also arrived. He sat under a tree on the other side of the dusty road. He watched the woman as she treated her patients; all day he watched her. He only left when she did.

Almost a year later, in the late afternoon, the mullah stood up, crossed the road and spoke to the woman for the first time. "I have been watching you!"

"I know," she replied with a smile. The mullah went on, "You have kept your promise. You have never talked to anyone about your Issa. I can tell that you truly love my people and that you want to help them. Can you tell me more about this Issa?"

Summing Up

We have explored four areas that raise interesting questions related to health care done in the context of Christian mission. First, I underscored the fact that we are always witnesses to something—to our effective medical science, to a primal worldview, or to the gospel. This raises the question of whether or not we are carrying out our mission like dependent people, relying on a God who saves and heals.

Second, we asked, to whom and what are we witnessing? I made a proposal for a holistic understanding of the good news of Jesus. This understanding begins with our being with Jesus, and this "being with" empowers us to witness by life, deed, sign, and word.

Third, we grappled with a worldview challenge in terms of competing understandings of cause and effect. Are we combating a primal worldview that gives credit to spirits and demons? Are we explaining the "miracles" of our healthcare healing with God as part of the explanation?

Finally, we looked at a different model of proclaiming the gospel. Are we living lives and doing our missional work in a way that provokes questions to which the gospel of Jesus Christ and his kingdom are the answer? Do we answer those questions when asked?

References Cited

Bediako, Kwame. 1996. "Biblical Perspectives on Transformational Development: Some Reflections." Paper read at World Vision Development Training and Education Workshop, October 4–9, Lilongwe, Malawi.

Fountain, Daniel E. 1989. *Health, the Bible and the Church*. BGC Monograph. Wheaton, IL: Billy Graham Center.

Hiebert, Paul. 1982. "The Flaw of the Excluded Middle." *Missiology* 10 (1): 35–47.

Koyama, Kosuke. 1993. "Extending Hospitality to Strangers: A Missiology of *Theologia Crucis*." *International Review of Mission* 82 (321): 283–95.

Long, W. Meredith. 2000. *Health, Healing and God's Kingdom: New Pathways to Christian Health Ministry in Africa*. Carlisle, CA: Regnum.

Musopole, Augustine. 1997. "African Worldview." Paper read at Changing the Story: Christian Witness and Transformational Development, at World Vision International, Pasadena, CA.

Myers, Bryant L. 2011. *Walking with the Poor: Principles and Practices of Transformational Development*. Revised and updated ed. Maryknoll, NY: Orbis.

Newbigin, Lesslie. 1989. *The Gospel in a Pluralist Society*. Grand Rapids, MI: Eerdmans.

Sider, Ronald J. 2005. *The Scandal of the Evangelical Conscience: Why Are Christians Living Just Like the Rest of the World?* Grand Rapids, MI: Baker.

CHAPTER 4

Health Missions to Children in Crisis
Theological Contributions for Better Practice

David H. Scott, PhD

An unacceptable number of children today are forced to live in conditions that jeopardize their survival, health, and well-being. This is a failure to honor the dignity that God has bestowed on them. Some of these children are also subjected to social forces and the choices of others that confine them to unspeakable abuse, neglect, and suffering. It is incumbent upon Christ's church to ensure that we are improving the lives of these little ones. This is not an option. We were instructed to care for "the least of these."

At the same time, as Christians who take the Bible and our theology seriously, we also need to go beyond the technical quality of our health work in mission directed at children and be sure that it is theologically informed and shaped. In other words, we need to be sure that we act theologically as well as professionally in our health missions work related to children.

In this chapter, after a brief snapshot of global child health statistics, I will review a relatively new theological framework, called "Understanding God's Heart for Children," that emerged out of the work of Christian practitioners and theologians who were committed to caring for children at risk. I will argue that this tool may also prove useful to health professionals responding to the needs of children everywhere.

Child Health in Global Perspective

It is difficult to definitively measure child health on a global scale. The reliability (or even the existence) of vital data-gathering systems varies widely, as do the specific factors that impact the health of children from nation to nation and community to community (Ahmad, Lopez, and Inoue 2000). However, based on the data we do have, we can be confident that children are healthier today than ever before in the history of the world (You, Jones, and Wardlaw 2011).

The internationally preferred method of measuring child health is child mortality, which is the number of under-five deaths per 1,000 live births.[3] Over the past sixty years, child mortality has decreased by two-thirds. The major driver was the world's response to the United Nation's fourth Millennium Development Goal, which called for a reduction in child mortality to 30 by 2015. Current estimates suggest this goal will be reached partly because two-thirds of these fatalities are due to preventable causes such as pneumonia (18% of all under-five deaths), diarrhea (11%) and malaria (7%) (United Nations Children's Fund 2012, 2).

It is also important to note the connection between child mortality and indicators of chronic poverty. Where there is chronic poverty, young children struggle to survive. For example, children born into families in the lowest 20 percent of household income globally were twice as likely to die before the age of five as those born into the top 20 percent of incomes (You, Jones, and Wardlaw 2011, 11). Poor families, who either cannot afford or have little access to health resources, are going to struggle to respond effectively to the health needs of their children. Similarly, child malnutrition and starvation are more common among those with fewer financial resources.

---

3   While not all countries produce this data, by 2000, 171 out of the 189 participating UN member states were able to report figures on child mortality (90.5% of the total), whereas in 2012, 187 of the 193 member states were able to do so (96.9%) (Ahmad, Lopez, and Inoue 2000; United Nations 2013; You, Jones, and Wardlaw 2011).

The link between child health and poverty is self-reinforcing. A UNICEF report argues that "just as low income is a contributing factor to poor health and malnutrition, so poor health and malnutrition are key reasons for the persistence of poverty" (2001, 19). This is especially true when considering the health of children, since the malnourished and stunted children of today will be fathers and mothers who are likely to struggle with the nutrition-related difficulties of their own children in the future.

Undernutrition accounts for at least one-third of child deaths since inadequate nutrition results in greater susceptibility to other diseases and undermines the body's defenses to fight disease. Twenty-five percent of malnourished children around the world—162 million of them—suffer from stunting (inadequate height for age), while 99 million are underweight (inadequate weight for age) (Thompson et al. 2013).

The good news in the West is that undernutrition is much less of a problem, but the deep irony is that obesity among children in the West has become an equally serious health concern and is also poverty related (see also chap. 5 in this book). Over the last three decades, the percentage of obese and overweight children under eighteen in the United States has almost tripled. Among two- to five-year-olds, obesity has increased from 5 to over 10 percent. Furthermore, among children under five who live in low-income families, the obesity rate jumps to 14.8 percent (Banghart 2012, 5). Poverty increases the likelihood of obesity, while obesity, in turn, creates a strong likelihood of greater health challenges later in life.

This brief glimpse of the global child-health picture does not address other factors that impact children's health worldwide. Not included here are such significant and widespread health concerns as the availability of clean water, abuse and maltreatment of children, compliance with immunization schedules for young children—the list goes on. However, the real tragedy of each of the above statistics is that they are preventable. Therefore, as the people of God we are compelled to act.

The Role of the Church

While Christians cannot help but be concerned about these overwhelming numbers, it is often deceptively easy to believe that these problems are the responsibility of governments, international organizations, or the private health sector. After all, all the statistics collected above were collected and maintained by a public entity—either government-led or government-funded (UNICEF, WHO, UN, etc.). There is a temptation to assume that they will accordingly take responsibility for the response. This temptation is augmented by the fact that we tend to suffer from a lack of what Gary Haugen calls "compassion permanence," the ability to retain and remember the suffering of others (2009).

There are three reasons why such a perspective is both ill-informed and inadequate. First of all, the biblical record makes it quite clear that the church, as the people of God, has a responsibility to care for those in need, especially orphans and poor children. While we reasonably expect that governments and NGOs will be at the center of caring for the health of children, we are mistaken if we believe that the church has no contribution to make and thus can sit on the sidelines.

Second, ignoring these realities and delegating the response is a luxury that only the church in the West can afford. Local churches in the Global South are typically much more aware of these needs since these children are in their pews and in their neighborhoods. In addition, local churches are often the delivery system, sometimes the only delivery system, for much of the relief and development health work that is currently taking place in the Global South.

Finally, we need to remember that many of the largest and most effective international NGOs that are working with children are Christian organizations (World Vision, World Relief, Compassion International, Tear Fund, etc.), which often partner with local churches. In fact, given the relative ubiquity of local churches and their Christian holistic body/mind/soul worldview, we have reason to wonder if churches do not have something unique to offer that is not available from governments and NGOs.

Therefore, the considerable challenges that children face globally are issues that the church worldwide must necessarily be engaged in addressing. Given this challenge, I want to move on to the issue of theology and what we need to learn about God's heart for children.

Why Theological Reflection?

Much of the human rationale undergirding public concern for children at risk is built on two fundamental motivations: self-preservation and sentimentality. [First, most people understand that the children of this generation are the adults of the next one. In order to safeguard the future of our species, we must address the needs of the world's children today.] This argument undergirds the fundraising appeals of governments, the United Nations, and NGOs. Second, these appeals have an emotional element grounded in how we feel about children who are in distress. Happy children make adults feel good. Sad, suffering children make adults feel bad.

The shortcomings of both motivations are apparent. While appeals to long-term preservation of the species make for compelling arguments in books and global summits, in the face of immediate crises of today, the future is often forced to wait. Conflicting priorities, economic recessions, tensions between nations, and other unexpected events divert us from the urgent need of sick children, especially when these children are invisible and far away. The Millennium Development Goals were established in hopes that national long-term commitments would help us overcome distractions and seemingly more urgent priorities.

The flaws of the second human motivation for helping children in crisis are similarly apparent. It is easy to find enthusiasm for children when looking at a picture of a child or reading a heartbreaking story about their innocence. But a roomful of crying, hungry, or manipulative children can quickly have the opposite effect. Real children have dirty diapers, head lice, and adolescent identity struggles. Street children may steal your wallet. Sentiment-based appeals on behalf of children will inevitably preference those children who engender the best feelings in adults. As a result, those with more difficult or emotionally painful challenges are less likely to get the attention—both in policy and in practice—that they need.

A Christian theology for responding to the needs of children in crisis can draw from a much deeper set of motivations, and might have the potential to inform our practices and strategies as well. The problem is that many Christians who work with children don't have much of a theological foundation. Instead, much well-meaning Christian work with children is based on a very narrow set of biblical texts with little in terms of a theological foundation. As a result, the lived or implicit theology of this Christian work is too often indistinguishable from that of its secular counterparts. A cursory review of the websites of Christian organizations working with children illustrates a distressing shortage of theological content and a heavy reliance on proof texts.

To a certain extent this is understandable. If "theologically in-formed" Christian work with children means two kinds of degrees—a professional degree in health care, education, social work, or a related field, and a second degree in theology—we cannot expect that many will take this path. This is especially true in a field that is not known for of-fering particularly compelling salaries (if any are offered at all).

So what then does one do when faced with what appears to be a very unhelpful choice?

A Framework for Understanding God's Heart for Children

In an intentional response to this problem of a lack of theologically in-formed theory and practice for aiding children in crisis, a conversation began among practitioners and theologians. The eventual outcome was the development of what is called the "Understanding God's Heart for

[Children Framework.] Rather than entertaining the idea that a theology for working with children could be developed in an ivory tower, the goal was to create a means by which Christians working with children around the world could be enabled to consider the insights they drew from Scripture as they pursued their work and then also theologically framed their practices, most of which were derived through empirical processes. This conversation began as a local seminar with workers in Manila in 1999, but over time grew to become an international dialogue of theologians and Christian childcare workers.

Rather than seeking a set of doctrines, the framework was designed to highlight theological themes and concepts, drawn from biblical and systematic theology, that promised relevance for work with children. It was hoped that this framework would function as a tool for practitioners to apply in their daily work among children (McConnell, Orona, and Stockley 2007, 3–4). Therefore, the "Understanding God's Heart for Children Framework" should not be understood as a replacement for existing biblical theology, but rather as an extension of it designed to highlight possible theological insights relevant to working with children.

The framework took the shape of seven affirmations, each of which draws on a focused set of biblical texts and Christian doctrines with special significance to work with children. Once exposed to the framework, practitioners are encouraged to reflect more deeply on the significance of the seven statements individually, and on the new theological insights that are produced by combining them in new ways. As a result, rather than seeing this as a completed theological work, the original authors offered it as a conversation starter.

Consistent with that purpose, I have two intentions for this chapter. First, I am going to show how this framework might assist those whose vocation is the health of children. As I introduce the seven affirmations, I will highlight those elements that I feel may be most applicable for medical professionals in their missional work with children.

Second, I am proposing that Bryant Myers's multidimensional and relational understanding of the nature of poverty (especially in light of his discussion of Wolterstorff's work on shalom earlier in this book) may have some useful additions to contribute to the "Understanding God's Heart for Children Framework" (chap. 2 in this volume; Myers 2011). Specifically, Myers's articulation of the nature of poverty as being relational as well as his formulation of God's intent for human flourishing in each of these dimensions (God, self, community, environment, and other) seems potentially useful.

AFFIRMATION 1: GOD CREATES EVERY UNIQUE PERSON AS A CHILD WITH DIGNITY.

The first affirmation of the "Understanding God's Heart for Children Framework" begins with our theological understanding of who children are. Drawing on the classical Christian doctrine of the *imago Dei* (image of God), our work with children must reflect a fundamental and positive-leaning understanding about the full personhood of children. Since children are fully human, it follows that God cares about every aspect of a child's well-being—their spiritual, physical, emotional, and social selves. This is critically important for medical missions, since it argues against any dualistic formulations of mission that separate the spiritual from the physical and emotional components of a child's personhood. Since many medical health practitioners are specialists, who have extraordinary expertise in a particular area of child health, this is a critical reminder that the holistic health and well-being of a child is really the main goal.

At the same time, this affirmation lays the groundwork for the second affirmation—to see human personhood as fundamentally relational (more on this below). Being made in the image of a relational triune God requires that we attend to social dimensions of health. Not coincidentally, Myers begins his understanding of poverty from the same doctrine, and offers an extended discussion of human dignity that is drawn from his reflections on the *imago Dei* (Myers 2011, 61–62).

Deeper reflection on our theology of human dignity offers two additional insights. First, this affirmation provides a more theologically rigorous basis for appreciation of children. This affirmation provides an antidote to the aforementioned sentimental conception of children since it grounds a justification for caring for their health not in adult belief in the innocence of children but in the dignity that God bestowed on children. This, in turn, leads to the idea of children not just as image-bearers, but as rights-bearers as well (Marshall and Parvis 2004; Scott 2007). Once we acknowledge this, we dare not think of providing emergency medical care for children as being out of our own goodness. We must do it because God created children with dignity, and therefore we are responsible to God to preserve and encourage the healthy flourishing of young human life.

Second, this affirmation helps to bridge some of the "us-them" distinctions that adults too easily reflect in their interactions with children. The dignity of children is identical to the dignity of the adults who are working with them. As a result, we should avoid situations where the health of children is placed in competition with the health of adults. Rather, concern for the health of children should be an integral part of concern for the health of an entire community.

AFFIRMATION 2: CHILDREN NEED PARENTAL LOVE IN A BROKEN WORLD.

The second affirmation introduces the two theological themes of family and sin. While at first glance these two themes may seem disparate, the overall structure of the framework necessitates their close affiliation. I will discuss each of these themes in turn, and then discuss how the two relate to each other.

Marcia Bunge, professor at Gustavus Adolphus College, who has written extensively on the theology of children, has explored how theological perspectives on parenting have changed over the history of the church, reflecting changing theological convictions (2001). Similarly, over the past century, anthropologists have grown to appreciate the diversity of parenting approaches used from culture to culture, and how each is designed to raise children to be successful within their contexts as adults (LeVine and New 2008). Because of this diversity of parenting approaches and understandings, affirmation 2 does not attempt to endorse any particular parenting style, but instead makes the deeper claim that God's intent is for children to be born into healthy families and to experience the love of their parents over the course of their lifetimes together.

Furthermore, the Bible is clear about the responsibility of children to obey their parents and about parents' responsibility to love and nurture their children. As a result, the second affirmation helps everyone working to address the medical needs of children to remember that at least part of their role is facilitating healthy mutual support and responsiveness between parents and children and vice versa. Parents, especially new parents, often need help in understanding what their babies and young children need—what their cries mean and how their needs should best be met. Children also need reminders to follow their parents' instructions, especially as they get older.

This second affirmation also places special emphasis on the particular challenges of working with children when their parents are either not present or not available. For example, in a relief effort—a time when children are often separated from their parents—getting parental consent can be difficult or impossible. However, reestablishing and reinforcing the links with a child's primary caregiver should be of paramount importance, even though sometimes this can appear to be a distraction in the midst of more urgent treatment matters.

Seeing parents more as obstacles than assets to children's health and well-being is sometimes the awkward case in emergency situations. During the 2012 earthquake in Haiti, the harrowing stories of well-meaning Christians attempting to facilitate international adoptions rather than support birth families is a stark reminder of this. Rather, we need to constantly keep the theological importance of parent-child bonds before us in order to adequately support the authority over their children that God has given to parents.

The theology of sin and its implications is particularly awkward to think about when it comes to children. Yet the doctrine of sin and its impact is a critical component of Christian understanding of the human condition, and this includes understanding God's heart for children. We must be able to deal with the reality of sin and suffering, both as they are experienced by the children we serve and as something that the children themselves are capable of inflicting on others. We must also understand sin and suffering in a way that more fully appreciates the depths of God's love for us as demonstrated by Christ's sacrifice.

Affirmation 2 also offers the opportunity to think theologically about the different kinds of sin that exist, ranging from the personal to the structural. Each of these types of sin and how God addresses them are important topics for Christians working for the health of children.

The personal sins of the child or young person may have an impact on his or her health. This can take the form of engaging in risky behaviors like alcohol or substance abuse, or neglecting to brush their teeth as directed. Children need to be guided sensitively to an understanding that actions have consequences and that better choices in behaviors increases well-being. However, this must be coupled with an awareness of God's forgiveness as well as children's ability to repent and change in order to make better choices in the future (Willmer 2009).

Theological reflection can also help us see that structural sin is present within family structures as well as within society as a whole. A ready example of structural sin that affects children can be seen in the previously mentioned epidemic of childhood obesity in the United States. Any response to this dilemma, if the impact of a medical intervention is going to take hold, must take into account family patterns of eating and exercise as well as the marketing temptations of the food industry.

In addition to a consideration of family structures that tend towards sin, medical practitioners must also consider those societal structures that impact the health of children. Sometimes access to food or water is made possible only for the wealthiest in a society. In other cases, having a particular skin color or speaking with a particular accent makes access to health care more difficult. A Christian consideration of the sins that affect children must take these concerns into account and work to see these wrongs made right.

Interestingly, Christian professional healthcare providers have more reason than most Christians to reflect carefully on the relationship between illness and original sin. Myers describes the impact of the Fall as leading to "widespread deception, distortion, and domination in all forms of human relationships—with God, within one's self (and family), within the community and between others, and with the environment" (Myers 2011, 64). A robust understanding of original sin has to account for all manner of birth defects, chronic illnesses that affect children, and other accidents that are part of being human. Furthermore, these explanations must sometimes be offered in the face of explanations for suffering that would try to lay the blame on the actions or choices of the child or immediate family members, much like the blind man in John 9:2,3. At the same time, these can be excellent opportunities for testimonies of faith in God and his ability to bring good out of even the worst evil.

By the same token, our consideration of human sin must also recognize that some health problems are the direct result of human choice. Countless injuries and illnesses due to abuse or neglect create the need for many medical responses, but these are too often the result of an entirely different kind of sin.

The juxtaposition of the themes of parenting and sin in this second affirmation reminds us that parents are not only a child's first source of love and nurture; they are also the source of a child's first experiences of sin and suffering. Furthermore, while the dual themes of the second affirmation cannot provide the same kind of starting point for our theological understanding of children that is provided by appreciating the dignity imparted in the *imago Dei,* these two new themes press tightly up against that first one in importance. When we consider children, we must balance our understanding of their depravity with an understanding of their dignity, and both of these must be considered within their relationship with their parents and community. As a result, health providers need to recognize the frequent brokenness of this vital parent-child relationship, while also seeking insight for how they can help redeem the relationship.

AFFIRMATION 3: GOD GIVES CHILDREN AS A GIFT TO WELCOME AND NURTURE.

While affirmation 1 asserts that God is the original creative force for every child, and affirmation 2 calls our attention to the vital role that parents play in the lives of their children, affirmation 3 takes us another step by reminding us that God is the one who places children with their parents. This stands in contrast to the more humanistic or modern assumption that children are merely the biological result of adult procreative impulses. This affirmation reminds us that children are intended not as burdens, but as gifts from the hand of YHWH.

However, perhaps the most important theme in this affirmation is the observation that the biblical account places the responsibility to welcome and nurture children not just on a child's parents, but also on the extended family and the larger community:

> It is a privilege to join with children in celebrating their uniqueness, valuing childhood as formative for all of life. Family, friends, church, and the local community are responsible for creating an environment that promotes children's well-being. (McConnell, Orona, and Stockley 2007, 95)

This emphasis on the child's embeddedness in family and community is an important distinction, since it highlights a broader web of relationships of accountability and reciprocity than what is implied within the nuclear family structure, which tends to dominate many Western understandings of childhood. The affirmation is a call to communities to remember and embody their responsibility to welcome and nurture all of the children in their midst. The pattern for these relationships flows from the ideals of community spelled out in the Pentateuch. Another important source is the mutually supportive faith community embodied in the Acts 2 church.

The good news is that many community health workers see this as a primary domain for their engagement. They get to see, better than most, the resources and responsibilities of communities. As they work towards community-wide immunizations or try to ensure the dissemination of critical preventive education lessons, they can help to instruct other practitioners on how to best engage with the webs of extended relationships that surround every child.

AFFIRMATION 4: SOCIETY HAS A GOD-GIVEN RESPONSIBILITY FOR THE WELL-BEING OF CHILDREN AND FAMILIES.

At first glance the fourth affirmation appears to be strikingly similar to the third, since it also emphasizes communal responsibility for children. However, once again the explanatory paragraph helps to make the uniqueness of this affirmation more distinct.

> All children and families live in society and are dependent on institutions for health care, shelter, access to social services, safe drinking water, information, and safety. The church must collaborate with these institutions for the common good, and if they fail, the church must speak and act with and on behalf of the vulnerable. (McConnell, Orona, and Stockley 2007, 133)

Therefore, the emphasis in this affirmation is on societal and political structures—the institutions, such as schools and governments, that sustain communities and families at different levels. This affirmation goes on to emphasize the role of churches to advocate for children in order to ensure that governments and other societal structures fulfill their God-given responsibilities towards children, such as in the provision of basic health care for all children. The biblical support for this affirmation comes from the same sources mentioned in affirmation 3, but focuses on statements around the provision of justice and the equitable distribution of resources through such measures as the Year of Jubilee.

This affirmation is also important for medical professionals, since in many cases the ways that they serve are either part of a government's provision for the health needs of children, or a compensation for the failure of societies to address these needs. This affirmation also provides the basis for missional healthcare providers to engage in advocacy on behalf of children, to ensure that all children have access to those resources that could facilitate improved health.

Taken together, affirmations 1 through 4 can be seen as moving from the child as an individual created by God, through the concentric circles of parents, community, and society, not unlike the ecological systems theory of Urie Bronfenbrenner (1979). This helps us see how God has ordained and established expectations for each of these entities. In turn this should remind those working with children of the opportunities that each entity has for helping children. But perhaps more importantly, it moves the focus of healthcare providers' emphasis beyond the confines of an examination room and reminds them of their responsibility to encourage health at each of those levels of a child's world.

This structure is also strikingly similar to Myers's model of poverty, which emphasizes multiple relationships, even though Myers does not employ the same kind of concentric circles implied by the "Understanding God's Heart for Children Framework." There are other minor differences as well. Where the first affirmation asserts the child as the central figure in view, Myers begins with the individual self—adult or child. Since Myers is not specifically looking at children, he does not place the same emphasis on family and parents. Instead, he emphasizes both "community" (as in affirmation 3) and "those who are other," both of which are implicit in affirmations 2 through 4. Myers even identifies the "social system" in his model, which is analogous to affirmation 4 and its focus on societal structures (2011, 144).

AFFIRMATION 5: CHILDREN ARE A PROMISE OF HOPE FOR EVERY GENERATION.

The fifth affirmation shifts our attention away from the Bronfenbrenner-influenced structure of the first four statements. Having established the social embeddedness of children in families and societies, the framework shifts its attention to the passage of time and its impact on children. While adults do age over time, the relatively swift development and maturation processes that children undergo sharpen our focus on the passage of time. This aspect of the "Understanding God's Heart for Children Framework" stands out as an important addition to Myers's understanding of poverty and reminds us that children and youth play some of their most unique roles in their families and communities simply by being young people. Thus, this dimension of childhood can be a rich source for theological reflection that remains largely untapped in the history of Christian theology. I would like to highlight three ideas that are important for grasping the significance of this affirmation.

First, affirmation 5 reminds us that children exist both as part of a generation and as part of every generation in history. This generational understanding echoes the child sociologist William Corsaro, who reminds us that childhood exists in a dual fashion, both in the life of an individual child, and as an institution with continuity throughout the history of a society (2013). Biblically, we see many examples of children being presented as part of their generation. Some prominent ones are the presentation of children as part of a family lineage (i.e., the "begat" passages) and the several observations around generational sin that suggest that in some way children will experience the impact of their parents' wrongdoings. The application of this latter insight is especially appropriate when we observe the ways in which many of the health choices of parents and grandparents continue to frame the worldviews and choices of their future generations.

Second, this affirmation points to the hope that children represent for many parents, who want to see their children experience a better and more fulfilling life than they had as parents. While for some parents, the prospect of another child to care for is a burden that they only begrudgingly bear, for other parents the arrival of a child serves as a powerful incentive to exercise disciplines and restraints, in the hope that their children will experience a better childhood than their own. Another way of observing this insight in practice is in the ways parents invest in their children as a means of helping their whole family escape the trap of poverty. In some cases this is represented by the practice of pulling children out of school so that they can work to support the survival of their families. In other cases, parents scrimp and save in order to provide the best enrichment and educational opportunities for their children, in hopes that one day they will be able to return the favor by finding more lucrative careers.

Yet no matter how this desire is manifested in the lives of children, each of these is merely a metaphor for the eternal significance of the one hope represented by the Christ child. Even the cries of Adam upon meeting his children (Gen 4–5) are merely echoes of this one, eternally hopeful birth. Jesus Christ came as a child, in fulfillment of the prophecy of Isaiah 51, and was the only person able to finally address the sin of humanity that separates us from God. It is this child alone who is the true hope of every nation and every generation (McConnell, Orona, and Stockley 2007).

Third, this affirmation also reminds us of the very temporal nature of childhood. Inherent in the presentation of a child's needs is the urgency of seeing them met. Children grow and change more rapidly than adults. Medically, this means that they have greater potential for rapid recovery. But it also means that interventions must be timely. This is encapsulated well in the words of Chilean poet Gabriela Mistral: "Many things we need can wait. The child cannot. Now is the time his bones are formed, his mind developed. To him we cannot say tomorrow, his name is today."

For healthcare workers, this affirmation is profoundly encouraging. It reminds us that every act to support the health and sustainability of a child is a step towards increasing the hope of families and communities. It is a recognition that the work we do is not just for the present moment but for the future as well.

AFFIRMATION 6: GOD WELCOMES CHILDREN FULLY INTO THE FAMILY OF FAITH.

The sixth affirmation considers children in the context of church, and it affirms their full inclusion in faith communities. This is an important theological reminder, since in many contemporary church contexts the protection of adults from children as worship distractions is prioritized over the children's own participation in worship. In contrast, this affirmation challenges church leaders to think about children in terms of what they can provide for their faith communities through the exercise of their spiritual gifts and their unique contributions to worship.

This affirmation places the strongest emphasis on child participation of any so far. In order to be welcomed *fully*, it must be presumed that children have the capacity to function as church members in ways that are analogous to adults. Of course, the supporting paragraph for this affirmation also asserts that any participation of children should take a child's developing capacities into account. However, it intentionally does not limit the extent of that inclusion, to allow for the possibility that a child's gifts and abilities might surprise even the most closed-minded adult.

Whereas healthcare professionals might not typically be concerned with the healthy functioning of churches, affirmation 6 helps enliven the possibility of seeing churches as partners in the pursuit of the health of children. For example, Susie Howe has described how Bethany Children's Trust has been able to mobilize and train churches to identify and support people living with HIV/AIDS in Rwanda (McConnell, Orona, and Stockley 2007). Furthermore, as churches increasingly see children as full participants, they might be able to encourage even their youngest members to help identify those with needs and provide the welcome for others that churches are charged with providing.

AFFIRMATION 7: CHILDREN ARE ESSENTIAL TO THE MISSION OF GOD.

The assertion that children are essential in mission has a twofold meaning in the seventh affirmation. First, it identifies children as worthy and in need of the life-giving message of the gospel. It affirms that young people have the capacity of genuine knowledge of God, and sees mission to children as an important strategic focus for the church. Second, consistent with the themes of participation identified in affirmation 6, this last affirmation proposes that children be seen as agents of the gospel—as missionaries—themselves. However, the fact that this is the last affirmation also suggests that all of our approaches for mission with children need to take into account each of the other truths identified in the previous six. Only by considering each of these insights can we begin to develop truly ethical and God-honoring forms of mission.

This insight is just as true for Christians who pursue the holistic health of children for missional purposes. While we eagerly seek to see every child know the holistic love of Christ, we must also be sure that our practices reflect a careful consideration of the fullness of God's heart for children and his sovereignty over their young lives. And it reminds us that the purpose for which we work towards the health of children is not merely to extend or enrich their lives—it is to serve God's mission in the world.

THE IMPORTANCE OF THE ENVIRONMENT

While the "Understanding God's Heart for Children Framework" is very helpful and addresses a wide variety of issues related to children, there is one important topic that a comparison with Myers's understanding and *shalom* helps to show. Specifically, while the seven affirmations hint at the importance of the environment to the well-being of children, it is nowhere as explicit in this regard as Myers's description. It may be possible to see environmental concerns as embedded in the first affirmation, which focuses on the creation narrative for much of its biblical support, but the discussion that has emerged from this affirmation so far has seldom emphasized the importance of creation care as much as it has emphasized the dignity and priority of human life as the pinnacle of creation (2011). Given the significance of environmental degradation globally and the frequent challenges related to sanitation and clean water that impact the poor, it is essential that we address this dimension more directly.

Final Comments on the Framework

In drawing these various ideas together we can begin to see a slightly different theological model for Christian engagement with child poverty from either Myers's model or the "Understanding God's Heart for Children Framework" as a whole. Children, like adults, can be seen as being in a cluster of relationships: with themselves, God, their communities, and their environment. Furthermore, extending Myers's model, it may be helpful (as the seven affirmations do) when considering children to break down "community" into subsections of "church" and "society" as well, since there are important and distinctive things that can be said about each of these relationships. However, when considering children we must remember that all of these relationships, including the child's relationship with him- or herself, are mediated by their relationship with their parent(s) or other primary caregiver. This is precisely why it is so tragic when a child is orphaned, either figuratively or actually. It is also why parental abuse or neglect can be so destructive for a child.

Furthermore, Myers's concept of marred identity provides important nuance for each of these relationships as well. Extending the themes of affirmation 2, the concept of marred identity reminds us that children suffer when their relationships are marred by sin: when parents, or communities, or governments fail to protect them, or when the environment has been so polluted that clean water is impossible to find. But thankfully, the model also points to what is needed and what God's idea of shalom is for each of these relationships as well—that children would not only experience a transformed sense of identity within each of these relationships, but that they would also realize their vocation in each— that they have responsibilities towards others, and within each of these relationships they have the potential to flourish. What is perhaps even more exciting is that within each of these relationships they have the potential to act as signs and active participants, even as participants in mission.

The Collaborative Challenge of Children at Risk

The work of this chapter has been to take the focus of our work with children away from the very complex and technical task of providing medical care for them for long enough to engage our theological imagination. While we began with fairly standard reporting of facts and statistics, we continued by painting a biblically informed picture of what God might intend for childhood to be so that we can then use that picture to enhance and deepen the Christianness of our work.

If Christian medical mission efforts intend to pursue the heart of God for God's children, they must move past a narrowly clinical approach that focuses only on children's physical health (a repeated theme in this book). Effective missional work with children must understand children as holistic (body-mind-soul) beings who are made in the image of God and yet who are also fallible beings. We need to see children as embedded human beings who are members of families, communities, churches, and societies. Furthermore, we need to see them as actors in formation who need to become able in time to make their own choices and solve their own problems. Equally important, children who are properly cared for and empowered can become vital participants in the task of mission to their own generation.

In addition, we need to make every effort to partner with others—both those doing work that is similar to ours and those whose work is complementary. This is the only way the broad spectrum of children's needs can be met in a comprehensive way. Above all, we need to remember that the reason we are doing this is not because we are more knowledgeable, more sacrificial, more strategic, or more compassionate. Rather, providing health and healing to the least of these—the children—is what God expects us to do.

References Cited

Ahmad, Omar B., Alan D. Lopez, and Mie Inoue. 2000. "The Decline of Child Mortality: A Reappraisal." *Bulletin of the World Health Organization* 78 (10): 1175–91.

Banghart, Patti. 2012. *Comprehensive Obesity Prevention in Early Childhood: Promising Federal and State Initiatives.* New York: National Center for Children in Poverty. Available at http://www.nccp.org/publications/pdf/text_1058.pdf.

Bronfenbrenner, Urie. 1979. *The Ecology of Human Development: Experiments by Nature and Design.* Cambridge, MA: Harvard University Press.

Bunge, Marcia J., ed. 2001. *The Child in Christian Thought.* Grand Rapids, MI: Eerdmans.

Corsaro, William A. 2013. *The Sociology of Childhood.* 4th ed. Thousand Oaks, CA: Sage.

Haugen, Gary A. 2009. *Good News about Injustice: A Witness of Courage in a Hurting World.* Updated 10th Anniversary Edition. Downers Grove, IL: InterVarsity Press.

LeVine, Robert Alan, and Rebecca S. New, eds. 2008. *Anthropology and Child Development: A Cross-Cultural Reader.* Blackwell Anthologies in Social and Cultural Anthropology 11. Malden, MA: Blackwell.

Marshall, Kathleen, and Paul Parvis. 2004. *Honouring Children: The Human Rights of the Child in Christian Perspective.* Edinburgh, UK: Saint Andrew Press.

McConnell, Douglas, Jennifer Orona, and Paul Stockley, eds. 2007. *Understanding God's Heart for Children: Toward a Biblical Framework.*

Colorado Springs, CO: Authentic; published in partnership with World Vision.

Myers, Bryant L. 2011. *Walking with the Poor: Principles and Practices of Transformational Development*. Revised and updated ed. Maryknoll, NY: Orbis.

Scott, David H. 2007. "Theological Dignity and Human Rights for Children." In *Understanding God's Heart for Children: Toward a Biblical Framework*, edited by Douglas McConnell, Jennifer Orona, and Paul Stockley. Colorado Springs, CO: Authentic; published in partnership with World Vision.

Thompson, Andrew, Monika Blössner, Elaine Borghi, Juan Feng, and Johan Mistiaen. 2013. "Joint UNICEF – WHO – The World Bank Child Malnutrition Database: Estimates for 2012 and Launch of Interactive Data Dashboards." World Health Organization. http://www.who.int/nutgrowthdb/jme_2012_summary_note_v2.pdf?ua=1 (accessed August 20, 2014).

UNICEF. 2001. *We the Children: Meeting the Promises of the World Summit for Children*. New York: UNICEF.

United Nations. 2013. "Growth in United Nations Membership, 1945–Present." http://www.un.org/en/members/growth.shtml (accessed November 4, 2013).

United Nations Children's Fund. 2012. *Pneumonia and Diarrhoea: Tackling the Deadliest Diseases for the World's Poorest Children*. New York: UNICEF. Available at http://www.childinfo.org/files/Pneumonia_Diarrhoea_2012.pdf.

Willmer, Haddon. 2009. "Child Theology and Sin." In Toddling to the Kingdom, edited by John Collier, Marcia J. Bunge, and William Carter Prevette. London, UK: Child Theology Movement.

You, Dhanzhen, Gareth Jones, and Tessa Wardlaw. 2011. *Levels and Trends in Child Mortality: Report 2011*. New York: United Nations Children's Fund. Available at http://www.childinfo.org/files/Child_Mortality_Report_2011.pdf.

NEW FRONTIERS IN HEALTHCARE MISSIONS PRACTICE

CHAPTER 5

The Slow-Motion Disaster in Healthcare Missions
Will the Churches Respond?

Arnold Gorske, MD, FAAP,
and Bryant L. Myers, PhD

> When Jesus commissioned his disciples to
> heal, he was not addressing a graduating
> class of the healing profession. He was laying
> an obligation on all those who follow him.
> **FIRST DIRECTOR OF THE CHRISTIAN MEDICAL COMMISSION**

This chapter combines two concerns and then sounds a call to action.[4] First, the church has been in the healing business for over two thousand years. Yet in the modern era the responsibility for health and healing has largely been relocated to the sphere of hospitals and clinics run by health professionals. As a consequence, the church seems to have forgotten the healing part of its vocation, except for the healing of lost souls. The second concern is that there is today an emerging slow-motion health disaster that began in the West and is now spreading to the newly emerging economies in the Global South. For the first time in the history of health, obesity and smoking are among the leading causes of disease and death in the world (Chan 2011).

This chapter is a call to action on the part of local churches to respond to this new threat on the world's healthcare landscape. The first piece of good news is that these health challenges are something that

---

4   The authors are especially indebted to John H. Bryant for his contributions to this chapter and the references he graciously provided. We also need to thank Beth Snodderly, Vicki Hesterman, Grace Tazelaar, Peter Yorgin, and Rick Donlon for assistance in the preparation of this document.

local churches can and should do something about. This slow-motion disaster is driven by lifestyle choices that are an obvious and natural focus for Christian discipleship. The second piece of good news is that tools and ideas are available that are ideally suited to enable churches, as community-based organizations, and their congregants, as lay people, to recover the church's healing vocation in their communities. The Community-Based Health Screening and Education approach has been around for almost forty years. It was developed in part by Christian medical missionaries and is based on biblical principles. While it never took hold in the churches as was hoped, it is nonetheless even more ideally suited to addressing today's slow-motion disaster.

The only question is whether churches today will recover their forgotten vocation as healers, as restorers of shalom.

A Slow-Motion Disaster

Recently, the WHO director-general spoke to the General Assembly of the United Nations to call the world's attention to what she termed a "slow-motion disaster" (Chan 2011). This slow-motion disaster is a pandemic of a variety of noncommunicable diseases caused by obesity[5] and smoking. It is a profound irony that obesity has become as prevalent a threat to children today as malnutrition (WHO 2002). This looming disaster is said to be in "slow motion" because the health impacts of obesity and smoking result in chronic disease that leads to death over time. Contrary to common belief, these diseases are no longer restricted to adults. For example, obesity-related "adult onset" diabetes was renamed "type 2" diabetes because it is now occurring in our children (Rosenbaum and Lamas 2011).

In addition to the impact on people's health and well-being, we must also take note of the financial consequences of this slow-motion disaster.

5   Research has linked obesity to heart disease, stroke, high blood pressure, type 2 diabetes, breathing problems, gallstones, osteoarthritis, certain cancers, and numerous other preventable conditions (U.S. Department of Health and Human Services 2010).

"In the absence of urgent action, the rising financial and economic costs of these diseases will reach levels that are beyond the coping capacity of even the wealthiest countries in the world" (Chan 2011). Furthermore, these consequences will fall primarily on the poor and undermine current development efforts. This behavior-induced epidemic "constitutes one of the major challenges to development throughout the world in the twenty-first century . . . which threatens the achievement of internationally agreed development goals" (United Nations 2011).

The causes of these noncommunicable diseases are different from those of preventable diseases that have been the traditional focus of healthcare missions. The root causes of obesity and smoking are not medical. The consequences of these diseases lie with medical professionals,[6] but prevention cannot. Behaviors such as an unhealthy diet, inadequate exercise, smoking, and misuse of alcohol are lifestyle problems. Many have spiritual roots. All involve personal choice. Calling people to healthy choices and a healthy lifestyle is a values issue as much as it is an educational one.

This is where the church enters the picture. The church, if it is fulfilling its vocation as healer in its community—as a restorer of shalom—has both resources and a grassroots reach that the medical establishment lacks. The church needs to step up to its historic mission role in health and well-being once again. The purpose of this paper is to make the problem clear to the churches and to provide some guidance as to how to fulfill this role today.

A LOOK BACK FOR THE WAY FORWARD

The Christian ministry of healing belongs primarily to the congregation as a whole, and only in that context to those who are specially trained. If healing is understood . . . ,

---

6   It is also important to understand that medicines provide only temporary symptomatic treatment and cannot cure conditions such as atherosclerotic heart disease, high blood pressure, or type 2 diabetes. The only cures for these diseases have been due to healthy lifestyle changes, not medical or surgical treatment.

it will be clear that the entire congregation has a part to play in it. By its prayer, by the love with which it surrounds each person, by the practical acts which express its concern for every [person], and by the opportunities which it offers for participation in Christ's mission, the congregation is the primary agent of healing. At the heart of this healing activity lies the ministry of the Word, Sacraments and prayer. (McGilvray 1981, 34)[7]

The introduction of this book outlines the continuing history of the church in healing and seeking human well-being since the time of Christ. In fact, most of modern healing and health care arose within the Judeo-Christian tradition. It was only with the arrival of modern medicine in Europe, as part of the Enlightenment, that health provision slowly became a scientific, nonreligious activity increasingly provided by trained health professionals and hospitals. The assumption that health and medicine came only from professionals resulted in the churches and their congregations of lay people moving to the health sidelines.

The beginning of a correction to this trend emerged in the 1960s. The biblically based concepts of shalom and "complete" or "holistic" health and well-being, derived from the church's healthcare missions experience, had an important but not always recognized influence on the World Health Organization (WHO). The principles of WHO's Alma-Ata Declaration in 1978 and its innovative call for a collaborative, integrated, holistic[8] approach to health were significantly influenced by the efforts of Dr. Carl Taylor, a member of the Christian Medical Association and a long-term missionary to India (Taylor et al., 2008).

7   From *The Quest for Health and Wholeness* by Dr. James C. McGilvray, the first director of the Christian Medical Commission. Although last revised in 1981 and no longer in print, this excellent book is now available free for downloading (see references) and remains essential reading for all Christians.

8   "Holistic" refers to care of the whole person—body, mind, and spirit. For Christians this integrates religion and health care. For secular folk, it acknowledges the role of emotional and social factors, as well as the spiritual nature of human beings without necessarily recognizing the role of religion.

A reasonable reading of history supports the claim that the current WHO standards and guidelines on primary care and development are based in part on the work of our Christian missionary and faith-based organization efforts in the 1960s and 1970s.

When one looks at the work of WHO and Christian medical missions over the last forty years, the focus was largely on the Global South and the urgent effort to reduce deaths from preventable diseases. Immunization campaigns along with water and sanitation efforts were responses to halt the spread of communicable disease, while improved agricultural production, nutrition training, and extension of community-based health care to the rural poor and those living on the margins in cities increased the capacity of people to resist and then respond to disease. The strategy called for preventing the diseases of people first and only then for treatment. This emphasis put the churches and other faith-based organizations at the front line in carrying out what was called *primary health care*.[9] This was a good and proper thing to do, and Christian medical missions and the church were very much central to this effort. But something new has emerged, and it less clear that the church is fulfilling its calling in response today.

Although the underlying diseases are different, the missions healthcare dilemma faced by the Christian Medical Commission forty years ago and the slow-motion healthcare crisis now facing the world and the worldwide church are fundamentally the same: Then, as now, the unaffordable costs and the inability of hospitals and curative care to reduce the incidence of disease are unarguable (McGilvray 1965, 1981;

---

9   Primary health care has been defined as "essential health care based on practical, scientifically sound and socially acceptable methods and technology, made universally accessible to individuals and families in the community. It is through their full participation and at a cost that the community and the country can afford to maintain at every stage of their development in the spirit of self-reliance and self-determination" (WHO 1978). Today, the Christian understanding of primary health care extends to spiritual well-being and the entire context of poverty and its impact on human well-being. Thus, it is described by some as transformational development (Taylor 2008; Myers 2011; Fountain 1990; and others).

Paterson 1998a, 1998b). Just as was the case forty years ago, what is most important is keeping patients out of hospitals in the first place (Chan 2008; WHO 2008a, 2008b). An emphasis on prevention is critically needed and is fairly simple to do. The question is whether or not churches will take up once again their responsibility for seeking the shalom of their congregations and communities.

While it is true that a number of larger Christian agencies, such as the Adventists (www.adventistsinstepforlife.org), and large churches, such as Saddleback (www.danielplan.com), have begun to implement programs that incorporate a number of the Christian Medical Commission principles with excellent results, these tend to be exceptions. This slow-motion disaster requires that every church and every congregation assume its responsibility for healing and seeking the shalom of its congregation and community. There are two central questions. First, will the churches recover their historic role as healers? Second, what approach to a healing ministry will they follow, especially for smaller congregations whose resources are limited? Is there a simple, low-cost approach that can be followed? The good news is that a tool and procedures proposed forty years ago hold a great deal of promise in the face of this slow-motion disaster.

A Simple Approach to Community- and Church-Based Healing

What is this biblical, evidence-based, holistic approach that held such promise in the Global South some forty years ago? The Community-Based (church-based) Health Screening and Education approach was developed over forty years ago to assist churches and their communities to "save lives and prevent suffering" through prevention. Sadly, most churches failed to take up the challenge then, so powerful was our belief in the West that health and well-being are the purview of professionals. Will it be different today?

In introducing this tool, there is a temptation to believe that it is too simple, even simplistic—that it is not technical enough. But we need to remember one basic fact: 70 percent of most disease burden is preventable, according to WHO (2008b). Again, prevention can address as much as 70 percent of the world's disease burden. And how is prevention best done? The information for prevention is simple and is best communicated personally. Most of us learned prevention from our mothers, after all. Prevention is the work of lay people, the work of loving one's neighbor by sharing important information that can prevent disease. The idea of prevention done by lay people is the central principle behind Community-Based Health Screening and Education.

WHY CHURCH BASED?

First, because it is part of Christ's call to mission for his church. The church, with its foundation of love, belief, prayer, the Word, sacraments, and Christian fellowship, was created for healing (McGilvray 1965, 1981). Churches and their congregations have the vocation and the gifts necessary to assume their share of the responsibility for the health of their own communities. Each congregation and its healthcare providers must be convinced that this is part of their Christian vocation.

The second reason for being church based is that good health prevention must be embedded at the community level. In an assessment of the impact of the WHO Alma-Ata Declaration and its emphasis on primary health care as a result of input from the Christian Medical Commission, an article in the medical journal *Lancet* concluded, "The missing link in the translation of the principles of Alma-Ata from idealism to practical, effective strategies has been the failure to integrate the perspective of personal and public health. *The future of health care* generally, and primary care specifically, depends on the integration of personal health care and public health *at the level of the local community*" (van Weel, De Maeseneer, and Roberts 2008, 871–72). What community-based institution is better placed to help create this connection with the local community than its churches? And whose vocation is that of being a healer in the community—the restorer of shalom?

What then can community-based organizations like churches do to fulfill this important role? They are not made up of healthcare professionals, after all. Most cannot afford to run clinics, nor is it clear that churches should run clinics. The answer is to focus on what they can do. Churches and their congregations can focus on disease prevention and health promotion. After all, communities, churches, and families are the foundational level of the WHO Health Services Pyramid—communities, then clinics, and only then hospitals. The Community-Based Health Screening and Education approach was designed for this level of the WHO Pyramid. Tools like Community-Based Health Screening and Education can enable the local church, regardless of its size or resources, to reassume its responsibilities for the provision of biblically based, holistic (body, mind, spirit) health and healing for its members and its community—the quest for shalom.

But would this provision by the churches really contribute to reducing the slow-motion disaster? The simple answer is yes. Eighty percent of premature heart disease, strokes, and diabetes, along with 40 percent of cancers, can be prevented by three simple things: a healthy diet, adequate exercise, and avoiding tobacco. This simple message saves lives, and it does not take health professionals to spread this good news.

WHAT IS COMMUNITY-BASED HEALTH SCREENING AND EDUCATION?

The approach was developed to enable community-based organizations, such as churches, to deliver simple messages of preventive health to members of the community. The goal is to assist the church and its communities, both urban and rural, in their collaborative efforts to resolve their most important healthcare problems with the goal "to save the most lives and prevent the most suffering."

The Community-Based Health Screening and Education approach is a flexible approach. It can be implemented in a wide variety of ways by even the smallest and poorest of churches. It can range from a simple healing prayer ministry with education/support groups, to more complex approaches with local community health fairs, to short-term missions to other countries.

The Community-Based Health Screening and Education approach is a simple, easy-to-use, participatory, evidence-based program for prevention. The good news is that implementing the Community-Based Health Screening and Education program is extremely simple and requires very basic training. All the training materials for leaders and for the community are available online.[10] One simply reads, discusses, and applies.

While promotion of this simple approach is needed, it is also important to note that churches are not limited to the Community-Based Health Screening and Education approach for health promotion and prevention. Churches and communities with adequate resources are also encouraged to create their own education materials. It is critical, however, for whatever prevention approach is used to be holistic, evidence based, and driven by the work of the Christian Medical Commission and WHO guidelines.[11]

WHAT KIND OF HEALTH SCREENING?

Health screening is simple and easy to do. It is often done by minimally trained lay people with little formal education (see notes 6 and 7 in this chapter). But this work is always done with the assistance of healthcare providers in the congregation or working alongside it and works

---

10   The complete Community-Based Health Screening and Education guidelines (twenty-two pages), as well as evidence-based lessons, are available free for downloading through the Health Education Program For Developing Countries (HEPFDC) website: www.hepfdc.info. The program guidelines come from the Christian Medical Commission, WHO, and the U.S. Department of Health and Human Services. See "Health screening" and "Participatory approaches."

11   All church- or mission-based health efforts must meet international standards and guidelines. The WHO is the "directing and coordinating authority for health . . . setting norms and standards, articulating evidence based policy" (Gorske 2012; Best Practices in Global Health Missions 2010).

collaboratively with other local healthcare providers. Where these professional resources are unavailable, the congregation can limit its focus to health promotion and disease prevention.

The health screening information reflects WHO's three key factors in prevention: A healthy diet, adequate exercise, and not using tobacco. A healthy diet and adequate exercise can be monitored through simple height and weight measurements. Blood pressure and pulse rate can also be tracked. Questions about the amount of exercise and use of tobacco go along with four simple questions on critical symptoms. All of this information can be tracked on a simple card, a copy of which goes home with the patient. This health tracking allows for follow-up work to be scheduled and alerts the promoters when professional health services need to be arranged. When a health problem arises that requires assistance from a trained professional, the participant is helped to find and go to a clinic or other health service provider.

WHAT KIND OF EDUCATION?

The health education of this approach is equally simple—promoting prevention through better choices of food, exercise, and minimizing risky behaviors. But there is an important nuance in terms of how this education takes place. The Community-Based Health Screening and Education approach is built on the same participatory approach to health education that was emphasized by our Christian missionary mentors. Dr. John H. Bryant, the first chairman of the Christian Medical Commission and US representative to Alma-Ata, argued that "the initial objective might be to involve the community in deliberations that would lead to a particular health care programme but the greater objective would be to establish as an ongoing community process the problem-solving cycle, which might also be called the cycle of self-determination" (McGilvray 1981, 90).

So the central motif of Community-Based Health Screening and Education is a participatory learning and problem-solving process that enables individuals, families, and communities to assume responsibility for improving their physical health and thus empowering their ministry of seeking shalom. The church-based setting and the Christ-centered holistic approach to healing are essential to this empowering process. What might this look like?

The invitation to a health screening event includes a copy of WHO's "Three Things" diagram, which reminds people that three simple things can prevent a very large proportion of disease. Before the event, people are already asking themselves, "What are the three things we can to do prevent major disease?" As the patients wait in line to register, church-based health promoters use the "healthy food, regular exercise, and no smoking" materials to draw out answers from the people on culturally appropriate ways to move in these directions as well as listening for the resources they have or may need to make these changes.[12]

Health screening and education can be done after a church service or before a prayer meeting or any other time that people tend to be around the church. Doing health screening measurements means that people are gathered and are often standing in line. The person filling out the health screening record has a one-on-one opportunity to deepen health knowledge through participatory learning. People can be gathered into small groups to work together on how best to promote healthy eating, regular exercise, and prevention of smoking. They know their context better than we do, after all. Bible studies can reveal the call of God for us to steward our bodies as well as our souls.

The lay people delivering these simple messages are supported by a simple set of instructions in a Provider Guidelines and Patient Counseling

---

12 Numerous additional biblically based guidelines with participatory lesson plans to enable the church to assist the community in its quest for shalom are available. For examples for communities worldwide, see the Global CHE Network website: http://www.chenetwork.org/.

folder.[13] People teaching each other at the simplest level of health education make a difference if prevention is your goal.

IS THIS A PROFESSIONALLY SUPPORTED PREVENTION?

Yes, and this is very important. The Community-Based Health Screening and Education program is part of the lowest tier in the WHO health
pyramid—communities, churches, and families. It is at this bottom level
that most disease prevention education takes place. But this part of the
health pyramid must meet professional standards in order to be accepted
by the next two higher levels of the health pyramid—clinics and health
centers and then hospitals. If it is not, then coordination is very difficult
and patients suffer.

What is not generally known is that evidence-based WHO reports
have given even the simple church-based interventions for the epidemic of noncommunicable diseases the very highest possible rating for
effectiveness.

> (Health) behavior can be influenced especially in . . . re-
> ligious institutions. . . . Effective interventions . . . are
> planned and implemented in collaboration with reli-
> gious leaders and congregational members using pastoral
> support and spiritual strategies and that include group
> education sessions and self-help strategies. (WHO 2009)

SHORT-TERM MEDICAL MISSIONS

As enthusiasm and support for long-term medical missions in the church
has waned, the phenomenon of short-term medical missions has taken
hold in North American churches. Each year, thousands of Christian
healthcare professionals travel to developing countries to share their
knowledge and skills by serving the sick and poor. The best of these trips
have seamlessly integrated the gospel message and healing works. The
poor receive much-needed medical care, while the Christian healthcare

---

13   Available free for downloading through the Health Education Program for
Developing Countries (HEPFDC) website: www.hepfdc.info.

professionals often experience a renewed relationship with God while on short-term medical missions.

The goals and means of short-term medical missions vary widely. They can be geared to healthcare education for professionals, church planting, health surveys, demonstrations of new techniques, church-based health education, and curative care clinics. In chapter 9 of this book, Michael Soderling provides additional warnings and encouragements for short-term medical missions, but there is one weakness that needs attention here.

Sadly, there is another trajectory that is less helpful. There has been a recent shift to a drug-based short-term missions approach (Gorske 2009). This represents a critical, foundational change to Christian missions and health care. Although effective medicines, with appropriate safeguards in place, do benefit patients in the short term, the overall effect of ill-advised or culturally insensitive drug-based treatment on the quality of health care, as well as the beliefs and values of both patients and communities, can be devastating (Seager 2012; Seager, Seager, and Tazelaar 2010; Gorske 2009).

Our patients on the mission field in the Global South, due to language barriers and illiteracy, have little or no access to any of the written safeguards we are used to in the West or understanding of harmful side effects. To make things worse, we often have returned home before drug-related problems arise. WHO reports that worldwide, "50% of patients fail to take medicines correctly," and there are numerous unnecessary deaths on and off mission fields due to this risk factor alone (WHO 2004–2007). This issue is central to medicine's ethical demand that we do no harm.

Community-Based Health Screening and Education is an approach that can be used by any church or long-term mission in any country, and one that takes us in another direction away from the dangers of drug-based short-term missions. Promoting the use of Community-Based Health Screening and Education in short-term medical missions allows us to incorporate the standards of our Christian missionary mentors and evidence-based medicine to optimize all the potential benefits of medical short-term missions, without the harm. The individual team members, not drugs, are short-term missions' greatest asset.

Conclusion

Community-Based Health Screening and Education was developed to enable local congregations, regardless of size, wealth, resources, or location, to fulfill the mission of healing to which their Lord calls them. A slow-motion disaster is sweeping the world, and more than anything else it takes simple prevention education and value-focused discipleship. Congregations must begin to reassume their biblical healthcare responsibilities to their communities, and they must do so *urgently*.

References Cited

Best Practices in Global Health Missions. 2010. "International Standards and Practice Guidelines and Health Missions." Last updated June 30. Available at http://centerforhim.org/wp-content/uploads/2013/07/IntStds26PG+30Jun10.pdf.

Chan, Margaret. 2008. "Return to Alma-Ata." *Lancet* 372 (9642): 865–66. doi:10.1016/S0140-6736(08)61372-0.

———. 2011. "Noncommunicable Diseases Damage Health, Including Economic Health." Address at the High-Level Meeting on Noncommunicable Diseases, United Nations General Assembly. New York: United Nations, September 19. Available at http://www.who.int/dg/speeches/2011/un_ncds_09_19/en/.

Fountain, Daniel E. 1999. *God, Medicine & Miracles: The Spiritual Factor in Healing*. Wheaton, IL: H. Shaw Publishers.

Gorske, Arnold L. 2009. "Harm from Drugs in Short-Term Missions: Review of the Medical Literature." Best Practices in Global Health Missions (A project of the Center for the Study of Health in Missions). Available at http://www.csthmbestpractices.org/resources/Harm+From+Drugs+in+Short-term+Missions.pdf.

———. 2012. "EBM [Evidence-Based Medicine], the Church and Development." Global Missions Health Conference (GMHC).

Overview available at https://www.medicalmissions.com/learn/resources/ebm-in-development.

Health Education Program for Developing Countries (HEPFDC). 2009. "Health Education Program for Developing Countries" website: www.hepfdc.info.

———. 2011. "Community Health Screening and Education (CHS&E)." Health Education Program for Developing Countries. http://hepfdc.info/files/CHS_EGuide.pdf.

McGilvray, J. C. 1965, 1981. The Quest for Health and Wholeness." German Institute for Medical Missions. Available at http://difaem.de/fileadmin/Dokumente/Publikationen/Dokumente_AErztliche_Mission/webThe_Quest_for_Health_and_Wholeness.pdf.

Myers, Bryant L. 2011. *Walking with the Poor: Principles and Practices of Transformational Development*. Revised and updated ed. Maryknoll, NY: Orbis.

Paterson, Gillian. 1998a. "The CMC Story 1968–1998 P2-18." *Contact* 161/162: 2–18. Available at http://www.oikoumene.org/en/what-we-do/health-and-healing/con161162_p218.pdf.

———. 1998b. "The CMC Story 1968–1998 P32-57" *Contact* 161/162: 32–57. Available at http://www.oikoumene.org/en/what-we-do/health-and-healing/con161162_p3257.pdf.

Rosenbaum, Lisa, and Daniela Lamas. 2011. "Facing a 'Slow-Motion Disaster'— The UN Meeting on Noncommunicable Diseases." *New England Journal of Medicine* 365 (25): 2345–48. doi:10.1056/NEJMp1112235.

Seager, Greg. 2012. *When Healthcare Hurts: An Evidence Based Guide for Best Practices in Global Health Initiatives*. Bloomington, IN: AuthorHouse.

Seager, G., C. Seager, and G. Tazelaar. 2010. "The Perils and Promise of Short-Term Healthcare Missions." *Journal of Christian Nursing* 27 (3): 262–66.

Taylor, Carl E. 2008. "Christian Health Workers and Empowering Communities for Lasting Change." Global Missions Health Conference, Louisville, KY, November 13–15.

U.S. Department of Health and Human Services. 2010. "Overweight and Obesity Statistics." *NIH Publication Number 04–4158*. Available at http://www.cdc.gov/obesity/data/adult.html.

van Weel, Chris, Jan De Maeseneer, and Richard Roberts. 2008. "Integration of Personal and Community Health Care." *Lancet* 372 (9642): 871–72. doi:10.1016/S0140-6736(08)61376-8.

United Nations. 2011. "Political Declaration of the High-Level Meeting of the General Assembly on the Prevention and Control of Non-Communicable Diseases." September 19.

World Health Organization (WHO). 1978. "Declaration of Alma-Ata." Statement drafted at the International Conference on Primary Health Care, September 6–12, Alma-Ata, USSR [Almaty, Kazakhstan]. Available from http://www.who.int/publications/almaata_declaration_en.pdf (accessed February 10, 2015).

———. 2002. "Childhood and Maternal Undernutrition." Chap. 4 in *World Health Report.* Geneva.

———. 2004–2007. "WHO Medicines Strategy." Geneva.

———. 2008a. "Building from Common Foundations: The World Health Organization and Faith-Based Organizations in Primary Healthcare." Edited by T. Karpf and A. Ross. Geneva.

———. 2008b. "The World Health Report 2008: Primary Health Care Now More Than Ever." Geneva.

———. 2009. "Interventions on Diet and Physical Activity: What Works, Summary Report." Geneva.

CHAPTER 6

Kingdom Health Care
and the Urban Poor

Katy White, MD, MPH, and
Kathleen Henry, PA-C

If we are truly interested in improving people's health, kingdom health
care must work toward access to affordable health services for people
who are excluded from our system of health services. One in every five
adult individuals in the United States has no usual source of health care,
despite the United States being one of the most medically advanced
countries in the world (CDC/NCHS 2011). A mountain of data shows
that people in material poverty are much more likely to have limited
or no access to health care, and that people without health insurance
in the United States have poorer physical health and less access to primary preventive care, treatment of acute conditions, and management
of chronic illnesses (Hoffman 2009; UCLA Center for Health Policy
Research 2012; CDC/NCHS 2011). Why can't we, as Christians in the
twenty-first century, reclaim the call of the early church and our king,
Jesus, to seek shalom among those with the greatest health needs?

INTRODUCING NOREEN

I (Katy) first met Noreen just out of my residency training for family practice. She lived in the inner-city neighborhood by our clinic in
South Central Los Angeles. She was one of eight children from a family
with multiple fathers and a history of abuse and neglect. I had never
seen a thirty-six-year-old patient like her: heart disease, diabetes, asthma,
obesity, high cholesterol, allergies, thyroid problems, anemia, an STD,
depression, and anxiety. One of the first things I did as her doctor was

tell her to get her affairs in order to prepare for what seemed to be an almost certain early death. Over the eleven years I have known Noreen, she has lost three siblings to heart attacks (each under age fifty), survived two open heart surgeries, endured weight loss surgery, gone to over two hundred specialist appointments, and taken (and forgotten to take) thousands of medications.

It can safely be said that Noreen lacked shalom in every dimension of her life. She didn't know Christ personally, her extended family relationships were filled with division and fighting, and the main place where she felt successful and productive (work) was a dust-filled environment that was seriously harming her health. Recently, her life became even more financially unstable since her husband lost his job, forcing the whole family out of their home. However, she still has a strong sense of vocation, something she shares with many resilient mothers in deep poverty—she has always sought to care for her children, prioritizing them even over her own health.

From the very beginning I was overwhelmed by Noreen's needs. But time and time again God reminded me that my job was not to fix Noreen but to be a healing presence in her life. So I listened to Noreen share her sufferings and cried with her over her losses. She followed me to the two other inner-city clinics where I have worked. I shared the gospel with her and prayed with her to receive Christ as her Savior. I invited her repeatedly to take more ownership over her health, and applauded her baby steps. I am amazed that she can manage, at least some of the time, to remember to take eighteen medicines a day and go to specialist appointments while living in a garage and caring for three children with no stable source of income. She and I, patient and provider, have both succeeded and failed to find shalom. Medically, we have succeeded, because she is alive when other family members of hers are not. But we have also failed in that many of her medical problems, especially asthma and diabetes, remain completely out of control. Overall, I know she has found more shalom than pain because of her increased ability to love and express gratitude.

Noreen's clearest images of shalom are the beauty of the relationship I have with her and the attractiveness of her unashamed need for God. She knows she is broken. She knows she needs God's grace. She hugs me regularly and tells me that she loves me, even after I chastise her for taking poor care of herself. She knows that I care deeply about her, because she has seen me cry out of frustration and sadness over her life. What she values the most, I think, are my prayers for her. Sometimes I get rushed and forget to pray, but as I walk out she asks timidly, "Can you pray for me?"

At first, Noreen represented the "other" to me—a sick, overweight person whose life was a mess and who felt powerless to pull it together. At times, even now, I choose to distance myself from the depth of her suffering and brokenness. But when I am seeing and hearing clearly, I see her as a child of God, needing him. And she is beautiful. God asks me to give her his blessing, and through her I experience his healing presence.

SHALOM THROUGH KINGDOM HEALTH CARE

While Noreen's medical needs might be more complex than most, her suffering is typical of hundreds of millions of people throughout the world, who because of their poverty and living circumstances have needs that go well beyond traditional medicine. Despite the brokenness of our world, health, wholeness, and shalom have been part of God's design since creation and continue as God's intention now. Jesus expressed the inbreaking of the kingdom of God through his healing, his compassion, his love, his incarnational presence, and his development of disciples and the church. In this chapter we present a picture of "kingdom health care" that is Christ-centered and Christ-directed, following the principles and practices of Jesus.

Jesus healed emotional, spiritual, and social needs in addition to healing physical ailments. When he spoke with the Samaritan woman at the well, he addressed her sin, her loneliness, her need for companionship, and her desire for truth (John 4:1–26). When Jesus healed the paralytic in Capernaum in Mark's Gospel, he forgave his sins as well as healing his body (2:1–12). Jesus also healed people who were ostracized from society, including an "unclean" bleeding woman (Mark 5:25–34), the daughter of the Syro-Phoenician woman (Mark 7:25–30), and a blind beggar (Luke 18:35–43). Each of these lived on the margins of society. Like the ministry of Jesus, kingdom health care must be holistic, addressing the social, mental, and physical needs of people, and, most importantly, the spiritual need for reconciliation with God.

The example of kingdom health care was also a distinguishing mark of the early Christian church. Gary Ferngren, author of *Medicine and Health Care in Early Christianity,* notes that health care was a major contribution of the early church:

> The Christian church . . . developed ideas of philanthropy which began in the local church and culminated in the creation of the hospital in the 4th century. . . . We know that in the middle of the 3rd century there were about 1,500 widows and distressed people, including the sick, the poor and orphans, in the city of Rome that were taken care of by the churches in Rome. No program like it existed anywhere in the ancient world. (Shorb 2011, 20)

JESUS AND THE EXAMPLE OF THE EARLY CHURCH

The incarnation of Jesus was the compelling example of God coming close to us, living as we live, feeling what we feel. Jesus gave people access to his personal time and presence. The idea of "God with us" suggests that kingdom health care should be physically located in communities of need, and that the health providers should be part of the community, not just visiting the community during working hours.

Partnering with local churches is a critical part of kingdom health care. Christian healthcare providers may recognize the spiritual illness in people's lives, but our many constraints on time, resources, and gifts do not allow us to lead a person through the spiritual healing process, nor is it our job to be the source of community that we all need. For this important kingdom work, we must turn to local Christian churches. We can invite the people we serve through health care into "a nurturing community of faith [that] can best provide the thrusts of evangelism, discipleship, spiritual accountability, and relationships by which disciples grow in their walk with God" (CCDA 2012). A healthy local church can be a profound agent of shalom through helping transform interpersonal relationships and promoting involvement in the larger community.

Those in kingdom health care soon realize the need to be connected beyond just the local church, however. The overwhelming health needs in our country and the brokenness of our healthcare system require a broader response. The Apostle Paul not only started but maintained a network of local communities throughout what is now Turkey and Greece, often meeting with them in person as well as encouraging them by letter to "be strong in the Lord" (Eph 6:10). In the same way, in kingdom health care we can join with like-minded fellow servants to form a prophetic community of healthcare providers across the nation and the world. One such network is the Christian Community Health Fellowship (CCHF), a national organization whose mission is to "encourage, educate and equip Christians to live out the gospel through health care among the poor." CCHF calls Christians to step out of "usual medical care" settings to focus their care on the poor, uninsured, and underinsured. CCHF envisions a movement of God's people who choose daily to promote healing in marginalized communities in the name of Jesus. Miguel's story below illustrates the need for and the possibilities of kingdom health care.

SHALOM THROUGH INCARNATIONAL PRESENCE AND SHARED COMMUNITY

I (Kathy) came to Los Angeles from the Midwest to work as a physician assistant and live incarnationally among the urban poor as a part of InnerCHANGE, a Christian order among the poor. Although I wanted to work with women and young girls, after two male colleagues left for sabbaticals, a different opportunity literally knocked on the door sporting a bald head and baggy pants. I was introduced to Miguel and invited to tutor him, which I did while integrating short Bible stories and prayer into our times.

What a world I encountered when I got to know Miguel! He was only eighteen years old, but he already had known twenty-five young men shot in his 'hood. He grew up in a building with a history of forty counts of neglect against its landlord. InnerCHANGE ministry teammates who lived there had spearheaded a major rehabilitation project that restored the building, making it a relatively safe place for the first time in years. Early on I took him shopping for slimmer pants to replace baggy ones for job interviews. Leaving the store he was caught shoplifting.

His high school counselor said Miguel would never get better than a C. As I worked with him on his homework, I realized that he would concoct false people and events for his writings and was ashamed to name real pain in his story. We worked on owning what is true, and we began to see change.

I remember celebrating Miguel's first B, and a year later, his first A. Since Miguel was considered to be at the "bottom of the ladder," his grades inspired everyone in his building to improve. Gradually, I began to wonder if his eyesight was hindering his studies. A visit to my clinic confirmed my suspicions. I accompanied him through the complex public insurance system like a mother would a son, since his mother couldn't read or write and spoke only Spanish. He was initially diagnosed with keratoconus[14] and given contacts. He had too much discomfort to wear them. Later, after a time of fasting and prayer, I sensed the need to push harder despite the fact that he no longer had public insurance. We went to UCLA and found that his vision was now 20/200! The specialist leaned forward and asked Miguel, "How have you been functioning?"

---

14   Keratoconus is a degenerative disease of the eye causing thinning of the cornea; it can cause progressive deterioration of vision.

He was offered promising experimental surgery, which would be free in exchange for allowing a promotional video to be filmed.

The day of surgery, I was informed that the video was cancelled because Miguel was so nervous he was stuttering. We would now have to pay up front. It had taken so much to get here. I knew that friends far away were praying and fasting on this day and there was no going back. In a step of faith, I wrote a check for the entire amount, but I didn't tell him. The very next day, as I drove him down the 10 freeway to his post-op appointment, he burst out with joy, "Hey Kathy . . . that sign says 'Wilshire Boulevard'!!!" Then, as thousands of dollars for his surgery poured in from people and churches across the country, Miguel came to see not only 20/30, but also God's loving provision.

Inspired, Miguel and his brother enrolled in medical assistant training five nights a week for seven months. I tutored them and they completed their certificates. Miguel's brother has been employed at a local hospital for ten years. Miguel got a job alongside me at the main community clinic serving our neighborhood. Serving his community through his vocation pumped up his self-esteem. He experienced healing, love, and purpose. He began to recover his true identity as a child of God because someone had whispered "shalom" into the noisy city.

The boys had not been in their jobs quite a year when their single mother had concerning symptoms. She came to our clinic, and after her wildly high labs returned, I accompanied her through the system that would evaluate her fastest—the Los Angeles County General Hospital emergency room. After nine hours enduring a waiting room full of boisterous, psychotic outbursts, we were finally seen. She died three weeks later of a rare, aggressive abdominal cancer.

Over the years, a community of Christians involved with Inner-CHANGE has had the privilege of walking with Miguel like family. This person I once thought of as "other" is now like a son to me. On Mother's Day, he always calls. Two years after his surgery he invited Jesus to live and lead in his life. He has become a person of faith and character—the kind of person who would take a bullet to protect someone.

Those we serve who are poor live in many contexts that need transformation. As we live in close relationships among the poor, we more effectively advocate for and become a part of the healthy community we all need in order to grow. Just as Miguel insisted that his real name be used for this story, I insist that his transformation and my own are "real evidence" of the slow yet powerful shalom that can grow through Christ, as healthcare professionals bring the kingdom among those they serve.

Barriers and Breakthroughs in the Midst of Brokenness

So far we have examined elements of kingdom health care that bring shalom. Kingdom health care is Christ-based and Christ-directed, holistic, incarnational, focused on those with the least access to health care, and rooted in Christian community. We have listened to two stories of individuals journeying toward shalom as a result of kingdom health care. But not enough kingdom health care is happening. What are the barriers we experience as healthcare providers seeking shalom for and with the urban poor?

A lack of an honest and substantive understanding of the struggles faced by people in poverty is one significant barrier for most of us as healthcare providers, since we typically hold positions of relative power and affluence. A recent study published in the Canadian *BioMed Central* notes "a lack of provider understanding of the lived reality of poverty, leading to a failure to collect adequate data about patients' social circumstances, and to the development of inappropriate care plans" (Bloch, Rozmovitz, and Giambrone 2011, 4). Even if we don't live in the community of the patients we serve, a first step toward understanding the reality of our patients' poverty is to truly listen to them. We need to hear about how many buses they took to get here, which medicines they never took because they couldn't afford them, how many people are squeezed into the home in which they live, and whether their job loss brought a change in their housing. We need to understand the real situation of our patients.

A second barrier is emotional distance. Even if we acknowledge an eviction, a job loss, domestic violence, or a tragic gang drive-by shooting, we often distance ourselves from the pain. To some degree we erect a barrier because we need emotional margin, to "do our jobs" and "see more patients." We break through this barrier by entering the pain of our patients. As Jesus wept at Lazarus's tomb, we are called to mourn the brokenness of one another's lives (John 11:35). John Perkins, civil rights activist, summed up the challenge of our call: "Great leaders for social change . . . gotta enter the pain of the people . . . and they bear that pain with the people in the pain" (2009). We can offer to pray for them, and we can speak a blessing over them. We can take a hand and look them in the eye and say, "I am so sorry that your mom died in Mexico and you could not be there." We can weep with those who weep—even if it is briefly.

A third barrier is limited progress in the face of ongoing suffering, continuing brokenness, and overwhelming need. For seven years we have dreamed of opening a faith-based clinic in South Los Angeles, where the health care needs are staggering—over two million uninsured people in Los Angeles, and one geographic section of South Los Angeles with over 600,000 people and only one hospital. But this has still not happened. There are patients for whom and with whom we have prayed, fasted, and pleaded for healing of their shattered relationships and terrible chronic illnesses. Yet many continue to suffer.

Father Greg Boyle, who has devoted his life to working among gang members in Los Angeles, redefines success in the context of this relationship:

> You stand with the least likely to succeed until success is succeeded by something more valuable: kinship.
> You stand with the belligerent, the surly, and the badly

> behaved until bad behavior is recognized for the language
> it is: the vocabulary of the deeply wounded and of those
> whose burdens are more than they can bear. (2010, 179)

Father Boyle further warns us of the dangers of overemphasizing successful outcomes:

> Funders sometimes say, "We don't fund efforts; we fund
> outcomes." We all hear this and think how sensible, practical, realistic, hard-nosed, and clear-eyed it is. But maybe
> Jesus doesn't know why we're nodding so vigorously. . . .
> If success is our engine, we sidestep the difficult and belligerent and eventually abandon "the slow work of God."
> (2010, 179)

Another barrier in our vocation is our own personal need for healing and shalom. We bear personal costs in this work. The pay is often sacrificially low. Our parents and families of origin, out of fear, hesitate or even refuse to visit us in the inner city, which limits our hosting special family times with them with our own children on our turf. I (Kathy), being single, know the challenge of finding a spouse who shares a heart for the urban poor. We both know colleagues who struggle with post-traumatic stress disorder or depression, as sharing loss and violence weighs heavily. We have competing needs to seek shalom with our family, children, spouse, or a dear friend. There are times to step back from the trenches, to fortify ourselves, even if this limits our impact on shalom through health care. Without personal shalom in our lives, it is difficult to move toward shalom among others.

As we complete our thoughts on the barriers we experience in seeking shalom for and with the urban poor, let us share two stories modeling kingdom health care. Courageous leaders moved into the neighborhood, entered the pain of the people, and formed communities of shalom. They faithfully endured over time and continue to creatively break through barriers.

In the mid-1980s, Art Jones, MD, moved into Chicago's west-side ghetto and began a clinic affiliated with a church plant, barely making any money. As volunteers from the church community literally broke the ground to renovate an old Cadillac dealership to build the new clinic complex, visitors to the small new church caught a vision of shalom coming to the community through this joint ministry. Over time more clinicians came to work in the clinic, many living in the neighborhood, and the leadership intentionally and patiently raised up local leaders from the neighborhood to join the ministry. Lawndale Christian Health Center (a Federally Qualified Health Center) now has forty-eight healthcare providers, treats 140,000 patients a year, has a beautiful fitness center in an energy-efficient building, where people can come and safely exercise for a minimal cost, and runs a café with healthy food in a neighborhood where few such options exist. The affiliated Lawndale Church hosts addiction recovery programs and is brimming with transformed lives. Places like Lawndale demonstrate prophetic shalom, inviting neighbors into a more peaceful community and inspiring clinics across the country to not just "treat sick patients" but create systemic opportunities for people to be healthier in mind, body, soul, and spirit.

Christ Community Health Services (also a Federally Qualified Health Center) in Memphis, Tennessee, began as a dream of four newly graduated physicians who wanted to serve the medically underprivileged. After two years of fundraising and working hospital shifts to raise money, they saw their first patient in September 1995, and moved their families into the nearby ghetto neighborhood. Their services now include comprehensive medical and dental services with 127,000 clinic visits in one year, mobile care for the homeless, HIV/AIDS care, pastoral care, and multiple outreach programs. But what draws most students and trainees to Memphis is the chance to live incarnationally and build shalom with staff and patients: they stay in the community of need alongside other professionals, participating in house churches with staff and patients together, helping in the community garden, and building relationships with their neighbors.

We invite you to participate in kingdom health care. While starting a large faith-based community clinic seems like an overwhelming endeavor, even projects like these start with stories like Noreen's or Miguel's and with people like us taking steps of faith over time, investing our careers and lives in the kingdom among the poor. We invite you to learn a patience that leans into the God of the big picture and the God who does "not despise the day of small beginnings" (Zech 4:10). Small beginnings that bear the heartbeat of shalom can make a world of difference for those urban poor who experience its transformation and healing.[15]

References Cited

Bloch, Gary, Linda Rozmovitz, and Braden Giambrone. 2011. "The Barriers to Primary Care Responsiveness to Poverty as a Risk Factor for Health." *BioMed Central Family Practice* 12 (62), June 29, Toronto, Canada. doi:10.1186/1471-2296-12-62.

Boyle, Gregory. 2010. *Tattoos on the Heart: The Power of Boundless Compassion.* New York: Free Press.

Centers for Disease Control/National Center for Health Statistics (CDC/ NCHS). 2011. National Health Interview Survey. "Table 78. No usual source of health care among adults 18–64 years of age, by selected characteristics: United States, average annual, selected years 1993–1994 through 2010–2011." Available at http://www.cdc.gov/ nchs/data/hus/2011/078.pdf (accessed July 2012).

Hoffman, Catherine. 2009. "Health Insurance and Access to Health Care." Video tutorial.

---

15   For more resources, see the websites of Christ Community Health Services (www.christcommunityhealth.org); the Christian Community Development Association (www.ccda.org; see especially "Church-Based," sixth of the eight key components under About > CCD Philosophy); Christian Community Health Fellowship (www.cchf.org); Esperanza Health Center (www.esperanzahealthcenter. org); the InnerCHANGE division of Church Resource Ministries (www.innerchange. org); and Lawndale Christian Health Center (www.lawndale.org).

Myers, Bryant L. 2011. *Walking with the Poor: Principles and Practices of Transformational Development*. Revised and updated ed. Maryknoll, NY: Orbis.

Perkins, John. 2009. "John M. Perkins in Conversation with Charles Marsh: Let Justice Roll Down." The Project on Lived Theology, University of Virginia. Available at http://archives.livedtheology.org/node/1360.

Shorb, John. 2011. "Medical Outreach: A Pillar of the Early Church: Q & A with Gary Ferngren." Church Health Reader. Available at http://chreader.org/medical-outreach-early-church/.

UCLA Center for Health Policy Research. Web copyright 2012. "Health Profiles 2009." Available at http://healthpolicy.ucla.edu/health-profiles/profiles/Pages/HealthProfiles2009R.aspx.

CHAPTER 7

Restoring Shalom
The Impact of Trauma around the World

Ana Wong-McDonald, PhD

The impact of trauma on a global scale is immense and largely unrecognized. Sixty countries around the world, and more than one billion people, have been affected by trauma in the form of war, ethnic conflict, torture, or terrorism (Mollica 2011b). Preliminary research suggests that 1 in 7 people experiences trauma in some form worldwide (Hill and Edman 2012), contributing to the staggering statistic that 450 million people suffer from some form of mental disorder globally, with 1 in 4 persons meeting the criteria for mental illness in a lifetime (Mollica 2011b).

Trauma is "the experience of violence and victimization including sexual abuse, physical abuse, severe neglect, loss, domestic violence and/ or the witnessing of violence, terrorism or disasters" (National Association of State Mental Health Program Directors 2006). The traumatic event overwhelms a person's ability to cope and disrupts one's "physical, relational, and environmental autonomy and [causes a] loss of safety and physical integrity" (Yassen and Harvey 1998). Trauma may involve a single incident or it may be chronic.[16]

Although not all individuals exposed to trauma develop post-traumatic stress disorder (PTSD), for many, impaired social functioning, decreased life satisfaction, and poor somatic health are typical forms of

---

16 Although the field of traumatic stress distinguishes between acute (single incident) and complex (repeated or prolonged) trauma, this chapter discusses trauma in general terms, including both categories, as both types are commonly encountered in medical missions.

negative outcome resulting from severe traumatic stress (Lazarus and Folkman 1984). Additionally, survivors may develop other difficulties such as depression, addictions, and self-destructive behaviors (Chassman 2012). Finally, trauma can mar the sense of self and severely impair individuals' relationships to God, others, their community, and the environment. In short, trauma shatters shalom (Wolterstorff 1983), as people can no longer dwell in peace within their relationships.

Despite the ubiquitous nature of trauma, it is an area that remains unaddressed in most mental health, primary care, and medical mission systems. In too many places in the world, it is not part of routine assessment. When healthcare recipients report trauma, many have not been taken seriously or have been told that it is not relevant to their presenting problems. Traumatic experiences and resulting difficulties are often not considered in diagnoses or treatment plans (Chassman 2012; Mollica 2011a; Richardson 2011). In medical missions, patients may present with somatic complaints, while the main cause for the symptoms is one relating to mental health (Richardson 2011).[17] The issue of trauma must be addressed to prevent treatment that misses the mark, necessitating multiple return visits to clinics. The assessment of trauma must be included in our health ministry of care for persons.

This chapter describes the magnitude of trauma in the United States and around the world. It highlights the Adverse Childhood Experiences study and discusses its finding that the root of many psychiatric disorders, health risk behaviors, physical diseases, and social ills has been traced to trauma (Felitti et al. 1998). A brief summary of the devastation in countries that are most affected by trauma is presented. Although there are resilient individuals who are able to emerge relatively unscathed from trauma, the focus of the chapter is on how best to minister to persons who suffer from the deleterious effects of trauma and how to assist

---

17   The American College of Gastroenterology, for example, found a link between chronic trauma and adult irritable bowel syndrome (2011).

them in restoring shalom with God, themselves, the environment, and the community.

Trauma in the United States

Seventy percent of Americans, or 223.4 million, have experienced some form of traumatic event at least once in their lives (Rosenthal 2012). Traumatic events include any form of abuse, mugging, assault, catastrophic illness or injury, neglect, abandonment, community and school violence, bullying, immigration, racism, rape, invasive medical procedure, accident, or natural disaster. Among public mental health patients with severe mental illness, 51 to 98 percent have been exposed to trauma, with most having experienced multiple traumas (Mueser et al. 1998, 2004). Exposure to trauma has been associated with PTSD, anxiety, depression, psychosis, personality disorders, dissociation, suicidal tendencies, risky sexual behaviors, and substance abuse (Goodman et al. 1997).

ADVERSE CHILDHOOD EXPERIENCES (ACE) STUDY

With over 17,000 adult participants and spanning over a decade, the Adverse Childhood Experiences (ACE) study is the largest study to examine the impact of childhood trauma on long-term disease, disability, chronic social problems, and early death (Felitti et al. 1998). The study examined early-life adverse experiences in ten areas, including (a) emotional, physical, and sexual abuse, (b) physical or emotional neglect, (c) not being raised by both biological parents, and (d) household dysfunction (such as domestic violence and whether a household member was imprisoned, chronically mentally ill, in a psychiatric hospital, or misused alcohol or drugs). Occurrence in any one area during the first 18 years of life is scored as one point.

Results indicated that the higher the score (at four or more points), the greater the likelihood for diseases, at-risk behaviors, and disabilities later in life. One in every 6 participants in the study had an ACE score of four or more, and 1 in 9 had a score of five or more. Women were

50 percent more likely than men to have experienced five or more areas of adverse experiences. The researchers, Felitti and Anda, interpreted this as "a key to what in mainstream epidemiology appears as women's natural proneness to ill-defined health problems such as fibromyalgia, chronic fatigue syndrome, obesity, irritable bowel syndrome and chronic non-malignant pain syndromes" (2010). They concluded that "we now see these as . . . artifacts resulting from medical blindness to social realities and ignorance of the impact of gender" (2010).

Participants who experienced four or more types of trauma have been found to have higher incidences of neurological problems, health risk behaviors, disease and disability, and maladaptive social behaviors in adulthood. Neurobiological ailments include brain abnormalities, rage, hallucinations, depression, panic and anxiety, impaired memory, flashbacks, and dissociation. Health risk behaviors include smoking, overeating, drug and alcohol abuse, promiscuity, and interpersonal violence. Physical ailments such as heart disease, cancer, lung disease, emphysema, asthma, liver disease, skeletal fractures, having six or more somatic symptoms, and HIV/AIDS were linked to trauma. Moreover, maladaptive social problems such as homelessness, prostitution, delinquency, violence, criminal behavior, inability to sustain employment, re-victimization as rape or domestic violence victims, and long-term use of health, correctional, and social services were traced to high incidences of adverse childhood experiences (Felitti et al. 1998; Jennings 2004).

Adults with an ACE score of four or higher, in comparison to adults with an ACE score of zero, were found to (a) be three times as likely to have depression, (b) be over five times as likely to struggle with alcoholism, (c) be over eight times as likely to be a victim of rape, and (d) have higher rates of psychotropic medications prescribed. Children with a score of four or more were almost ten times as likely to attempt suicide as children with no trauma. A male child with a score of six had a 46 percent increase in the likelihood that he would become an intravenous drug user later in life. Four or more incidences of ACE accounted for

64 percent of adult suicide attempts and 80 percent of child/adolescent suicide attempts. On average, adults with a high score had twice the death rate of adults who had no adverse childhood experience. Finally, children exposed to six or more ACE died on average at age 60, whereas children without ACE died at age 79 (Jennings 2011; Felitti et al. 1998). Trauma in the early years of life paves the way for disability, at-risk behaviors, addictions, more trauma, social ailments, and early death.

EFFECTS OF TRAUMA ON ADULTS

Research on the deleterious effect of trauma on adult functioning, health, and well-being is ample (Collins et al. 2010). National epidemiological studies of PTSD indicate that approximately 50 percent to 90 percent of Americans have experienced one or more traumatic events; 10 to 20 percent of those exposed will meet the diagnostic criteria of PTSD;[18] and up to 68 percent will develop some symptoms of the disorder, though not enough to meet the diagnosis (Norris and Slone 2007). Not only are the urban poor more likely to experience multiple traumas, they are also more prone to develop trauma-related symptoms that affect their overall functioning (Breslau et al. 1999; Cooper-Patrick et al. 1999; Kessler et al. 1999). Constant worry about hunger, violence, illness, accidents, finances, and discrimination reduces physical and mental health (Wadsworth and Santiago 2007) and the ability to live at peace within one's environment.

Consequences from living under prolonged or multiple traumatic events, especially those that are interpersonal in nature (Collins et al. 2010), extend beyond the symptoms of PTSD. Sufferers are often left with impairment in self-image and identity, poor affect regulation, low self-esteem, guilt, expectations of rejection and loss, and anger and aggression. For some, prolonged trauma can lead to dissociation,

---

18   Symptoms include reexperiencing the event as in flashbacks and nightmares, avoidance of reminders of the trauma and numbing, and increased arousal as evident, for example, in difficulty sleeping and exaggerated, startled response.

various addictions, binging and purging, and self-mutilation (Briere and Spinazzola 2005).

Trauma around the World

Reports outside the United States paint an even wider canvas of causes of trauma. They include poverty, disease, natural disasters, war and torture, terrorism, organized crime, civilian violence, human trafficking, and rape and sexual abuse (Leppaniemi 2004, 2009; Ray 2008). The most impacted geographic regions share common characteristics, such as depleted resources, severe poverty, and poor infrastructure, which deter intervention and relief. The areas that are most severely affected include South Sudan, Democratic Republic of the Congo, Cambodia, Haiti, and Gaza (Gouge 2012).

Two decades of civil war in South Sudan, unrest on its borders, and forced migration resulted in 1.9 million deaths and up to 4 million people becoming homeless. In a study of 1,242 adults in Juba, the new capital of South Sudan, more than one-third of the respondents met the diagnostic criteria for PTSD, and one-half met that for depression. The most frequent causes for trauma were related to combat and the unnatural death of a family member or friend. Men, refugees, and those who were forcibly displaced from their homes were more likely to have experienced eight or more traumatic events (Roberts et al. 2009).

The Democratic Republic of the Congo has lost more than 5 million inhabitants due to war and conflict since 1996. Systematically, civilians were robbed, raped, massacred, displaced, and conscripted as warlords vied for power and territory (Stearns 2011). In the Great Lakes Region, about 1.7 million women were raped, while over 3 million women suffered intimate partner sexual violence (Peterman, Palermo, and Bredenkamp 2011). The aftermath of these atrocities includes unwanted pregnancies, sexually transmitted diseases and HIV/AIDS, bodily injuries, cervical cancer, PTSD, panic attacks, dissociative disorders, sleeping disorders, self-blame, self-injury, and suicide (Clifford 2008).

Cambodia is a source, transit, and destination country for human trafficking. Cambodians are trafficked for sexual and labor exploitation in Thailand, Malaysia, Macao, and Taiwan (HumanTrafficking.org). Between 30,000 and 60,000 children are involved in the sex trade each year (Isaza 2010), and 90 percent of prostitutes are sold into brothels by their parents as a means of financial support (Jeter 2010). Although research on the health consequences of human trafficking in Cambodia is limited, one review of nineteen studies from Nepal, India, Thailand, and Cambodia revealed that trafficked women and girls display a high level of physical and mental ailments. Headaches, back pain, stomach pain, and memory problems were common. High levels of anxiety (48.0%–97.7%), depression (54.9%–100%), and PTSD (19.5%–77.0%) were also found utilizing mental health screening instruments (Oram et al. 2012).

Haiti's 9.7 million inhabitants have been traumatized by the 2010 earthquake and the loss of family and friends, disappearance of jobs and infrastructure, homes left in ruin, fear and violence in tent camps, political turmoil and poverty, and the lack of adequate health care (Center for Mind-Body Medicine). The disaster left 316,000 people dead and 1.5 million homeless (Leger 2012). After the earthquake, many Haitians reported having "earthquake shock," a persistent sensation that the ground is still shaking, resulting in a racing heart and chest pains. Although this symptomatic response to trauma is rather common, many were unaware that it is a physiological expression of psychological pain (Sontag 2010).

In Gaza, trauma is a way of life. Decades of political unrest and war have left Gaza in ruins and demolished community infrastructures. The January 2009 war alone left tens of thousands of homes destroyed (IOM 2009); 50,000 people homeless (BBC 2009a), 400,000 to 500,000 without running water, and one million without electricity (BBC 2009b); and acute food shortages (WFP 2009). Gazans frequently experience depression, flashbacks, insomnia, and anxiety. Since the feelings are overwhelming, they often suppress them, resulting in psychosomatic problems (Karabat 2010). The Gaza Community Mental Health

Program Research Department surveyed 374 children and found that each child had witnessed 12.8 traumatic events, 98.7 percent said that they were not safe at home, 29.9 percent showed moderate PTSD reactions, and 61.5 percent showed severe and very severe PTSD reactions (Thabet 2010).

The devastation in the world from trauma is immense due to its multifaceted nature. Aside from the depletion of resources and destruction of community infrastructure, trauma impacts the mind, leading to mental illness; invades the body, ushering in chronic disease; and ruptures the spirit, severing significant relationships. In a meta-analytic study of 161 articles representing 81,866 refugees and other conflict-affected persons from 40 countries, torture was the strongest factor relating to PTSD, and repeated exposure to trauma was the strongest factor linked to depression (Steel et al. 2009). Richard Mollica, professor of psychiatry at Harvard Medical School and director of the Harvard Program in Refugee Trauma at Massachusetts General Hospital, found that individuals exhibiting symptoms of these mental disorders were found to later develop psychosomatic conditions (Psychosomatics 2003) leading to higher rates of physical disability (Mollica et al. 2009) and somatic complaints including diabetes, hypertension, heart disease, and stroke (Mollica et al. 1993). He commented that it took him twenty years working with traumatized people around the world to put trauma on the top of the list of the medical information to be obtained from patients (Mollica et al. 2011a). In addition to the psychological and physical impact, trauma hits the human spirit by severing connections to what is significant in life. Death, loss, betrayal, and violation cut at the heart and redefine human existence.

Restoring Shalom in the Aftermath of Trauma

RECONCILIATION WITH GOD

Spiritually, trauma has the potential to erode and distort one's relationship and trust with a loving God. It can usher in doubt as to whether God is truly benevolent and has the best plans and intentions for human lives (Jer 29:11). Common questions that trauma victims ask include, "Where was God?" and "Why did he allow this to happen?" If we are to discuss the restoration of shalom, we must begin with God, who is the originator of reconciliation and the healer of trauma. He reconciled the world to himself through Christ and gave us the ministry of reconciliation (Rom 5:10,11; 2 Cor 5:18,19; Col 1:20, 22). To restore relationships with self, with others, and with the world, we must start with the relationship with God (Acts 17:28).

The core issue for sufferers of trauma revolves around God's goodness and his love for them. Scriptural passages about the character of God such as Psalm 103:2–5,11–14; Matthew 9:35,36; 1 John 4:9,10; and 1 Peter 5:7 can be important in reminding believers who God is (Hill et al. 2009). When we are in turmoil, we need to remind ourselves that God is "compassionate and gracious . . . slow to anger, abounding in love and faithfulness, maintaining love to thousands, and forgiving wickedness, rebellion and sin" (Ex 34:6,7). His love for us is so complete and powerful that no matter what happens, whether we experience trouble, trauma, illness, hardship, unemployment, loss, or injury, or even if we are the perpetrators of such (e.g., as a soldier in a war), it cannot separate us from the love of God (Rom 8:35,39).

Although the Bible tells us that trials, hardships, and suffering are not uncommon for God's people (Matt 24:21; Acts 14:22; 1 Thess 3:4; Jas 1:2; 1 Pet 4:12,13) and that we can expect abuse, violence, trauma, persecution, and even death (Matt 10:17–25), God promises that he will be present with us through it all and empower us to overcome (Ps 34:19; Isa 41:10; 43:2; Heb 13:5,6). It is common for humans to ask for sickness, tribulation, and suffering to be removed. In his wisdom, God does not always do so (2 Cor 12:7–9). The biblical solution is to persevere and to overcome evil with good (Rom 5:3; 8:37; 12:21). God's ultimate answer to the problem of evil and suffering is Jesus Christ. God came in the flesh to endure trauma and atrocity to a degree that was unmatched by anyone else in history. Jesus took the sins of the world upon himself, suffered betrayal, violence, and rejection, and overcame.

Although Jesus may not have experienced the same types of affliction as some trauma victims (e.g., rape), there is a kind of universality in suffering. Because of Christ's passion, we can say that he experienced the existential harm of betrayal, rejection, humiliation, and violation, and hence Christ can identify with trauma survivors (Cloud 2012). Victims can be consoled that because of his experience on the cross, Christ understands. Moreover, Jesus knows the parts of the sufferers that they do not even know or understand. His words in Matthew 25:40 indicate that he completely identifies with the least of his brothers and sisters. Jesus is Immanuel, the God who is with us (Matt 1:23). Trauma victims can be comforted in the fact that Jesus walks beside us in our pain and completely understands.

To the question, "Where was God?" the answer is that God was with us and continues to be with us in our suffering. To the question, "Why did God allow this to happen?" considerations are manifold, including human free will, the work of Satan, the testing of our faith, and God's sovereignty to accomplish a greater purpose beyond our understanding (Hicks 2006). Although we may not be able to fully grasp the reason during our earthly lives, through the work of Christ (Rom 8:32), we can trust that God's intention for us is benevolent, to prosper and not to harm us (Jer 29:11), and to bring us into reconciliation with God (Col 1:20; Heb 2:17). When we recognize that God is our greatest ally and not our enemy, we can then run toward God rather than away from him for healing and restoration (Adsit 2008). It is only within God's embrace that we can begin to learn that joy and pain are not mutually exclusive

(Hab 3:17,18) and that no matter what has happened, God can bring goodness out of the greatest devastation (Rom 8:28). He reigns sovereign on the throne (Rev 4:2).

RESTORING THE SHATTERED SELF

Trauma shakes the core of personhood, as it disrupts people's understanding of who they are and their understanding of how the world works. "Terror is the definitive response to trauma, characterized by internal disorganization and disintegration, shattered assumptions, and feelings of self-annihilation" (Abernathy 2008). Many survivors suffer a shock in their definition of self and consequently become disillusioned about their identity.

Severe losses, such as losing body integrity, livelihood, job, or family or societal role, or forced migration, threaten one's self-identity and create role confusion. When survivors can no longer maintain roles that are consistent with their self-definitions, their self-images are undermined (Thoits 2003). Women in particular may feel "impure" or that they have become "damaged goods" from rape or body defacement. Tragically, in communities like the Democratic Republic of Congo these messages are often reinforced in that husbands support the rejection of women as a result of rape and disease (Trenholm, Olsson, and Ahlberg 2011). When assumptions about the self and the world are shattered (Janoff-Bulman 1992), when survivors are confronted with a sudden sense of mortality (Taylor 1983), and when valued roles and meaningful pursuits are lost (Charmaz 1993), individuals often can no longer live at peace with who they have become. Shalom is lost.

Individuals make sense of experiences and integrate events into their life narratives for identity construction (McAdams 1993). "Identity is . . . a sensible result of one's life story" (Gergen and Gergen 1988). After a traumatic incident, people enter into meaning-making to regain a sense of coherence. The treatment for trauma is to help survivors integrate the terrifying and incomprehensible into their self-concepts. Life events initially experienced as alien and imposed from outside onto passive victims must become integrated into the individuals' histories and life experiences (Van der Kolk, McFarlane, and Van der Hart 1996). As they rethink and retell their stories, survivors gain new meaning and insight, their conceptual frameworks of the world change, and they can emerge with transformed selves (Brennan 2001) and renewed acceptance of life.

The integration of trauma with the injured self is exemplified by Christ. When Jesus took the sins of the world upon himself, he was forever changed. Sin, suffering, and death were taken into God, and the scars left on the slain Lamb are eternal (John 20:27; Rev 5:6). Of course, what he absorbed was also transformed. Sin was overcome, evil was broken, and the sting of death was withdrawn. Just as the Resurrection changed the darkness of death, so the scars that Christ eternally carries are both hideous and radiantly beautiful at the same time (Hicks 2006, 82). The mark of trauma was transformed by Christ into glory, and he is also forever changed by it. He became the only person in the universe who can open the scroll in Revelation chapter 5. "He is worthy not because he created the universe . . . [or] because he rose from the dead. He is worthy because he was slain" (Johnson 2004, 168).

Following the model of Christ, when we absorb suffering into ourselves, we are forever changed. When we accept pain into our life stories, when we forgive, and when we transcend the past, a new self can emerge, integrating darkness with light. Instead of being overcome by trauma, the power of Christ helps us to overcome evil with good in our hearts and in ourselves (Rom 12:21).

Finally, our new self is integrated with and renewed by our identity as revealed in the Bible (John 3:1; Rom 5:1; Eph 2:5; Col 2:6–10). Old truths take on new meanings as we gain a deeper understanding of God's promises after major losses and pain. The result is a transformed self, with greater maturity, a healthier self-love, increased empathy and acceptance for others, and a more intimate walk with God.

BEING AT PEACE IN THE WORLD AROUND YOU

Trauma steals a person's sense of safety and control. In the wake of trauma, one no longer assumes that he or she is invulnerable or that the world is orderly and just (Reiker and Carmen 1986, 362). "To feel threatened, helpless, and out of control is a vital attack on the capacity to be able to count on oneself" (Van der Kolk, McFarlane, and Van der Hart 1996, 15). The context in which one lives feels like a dangerous place that is beyond the victim's capacity for self-defense. The loss of personal agency[19] results in fear, avoidant behavior, anxiety, intrusive memories, and hyperarousal.

To restore a sense of control, treatment begins with making the environment safe and predictable.

> Immediately after people have been traumatized, the emphasis needs to be on self-regulation and on rebuilding. This means the reestablishment of security and predictability. It also means active involvement in adaptive action, such as the rebuilding of damaged property, engagement with other victims, and active engagement in the physical care of oneself and other survivors. . . . The initial response to trauma needs to consist of reconnecting individuals with their ordinary supportive networks, and having them engage in activities that reestablish a sense of mastery. (Van der Kolk, McFarlane, and Van der Hart 1996, 425)

Establishing a regular routine, seeing the same faces, and being informed of any changes or new procedures ahead of time allows survivors to feel that they are more able to cope with the world.

Shalom is lost when people no longer feel safe in their environment. To regain a sense of safety, we must first return to our primary source of sustainment, to the anchoring presence of Christ within. When our

---

19 Personal agency refers to one's capability to originate and direct actions for given purposes. It is influenced by the belief in one's effectiveness in performing specific tasks as well as by one's actual skills (Zimmerman and Cleary 2006, 45).

inner self is rooted in Christ, nothing in the environment can shake us. This is why shalom with God is foundational for all other relationships. When our inner being is grafted and built up in him (John 15:5), we can say with faith, "In God I trust and am not afraid. What can mere mortals do to me?" (Ps 56:4). We can rest in the confidence that, amidst calamity, we are safe. Although "the earth give way and the mountains fall into the heart of the sea" (Ps 46:2), because God is within us, we will not fall (Ps 46:5). Our true life in Christ in the vertical dimension upholds, anchors, and sustains us despite what may happen in the horizontal dimension (e.g., earthly events and trauma).

A second way of feeling safer in our context comes when we learn to recognize triggers[20] in the environment that may bring about feelings of anxiety and panic. With the help of a godly counselor, we put away fruitless worries that are not based on reality. We evaluate every thought by the truth (Anderson 1990) and do not entertain thinking that is not based on the Word or on current reality. For example, a combat veteran may be triggered from hearing the sound of firecrackers. A person may recite God's word of comfort and protection while reminding himself of the current truth that he is not in the war zone but on safe soil. During this process, spiritual warfare may be necessary (Eph 6:12–18), and we take captive every thought to make it obedient to Christ (2 Cor 10:5).

Finally, we integrate spiritual practices into relaxation techniques such as slow deep breathing, visualization, distraction, and calming self-talk. For example, when a survivor becomes triggered, she may utilize the spiritual practice of singing hymns to distract and comfort herself. A combination of several techniques with spiritual interventions is very helpful for deescalating hyper-aroused persons. When one begins to feel symptoms of anxiety or panic, he may start breathing slowly and visualize that Jesus is with him in the room, while reciting to himself Scripture

---

20 Being "triggered" refers to responses from traumatized persons when they are reminded of a traumatic event by something in their environment. Individuals may experience physiological and/or psychological symptoms such as sweating, heart-racing, flashbacks, and feelings of distress and doom.

verses about God's love and protection. The entire healing journey needs to be permeated by prayer. Before, during, and after the interventions, the individual prays for God's empowerment, deliverance, and protection, and for the peace of God to guard her heart and mind in Christ Jesus (Phil 4:6,7).

RECONCILING WITH OTHERS AND WITH THE COMMUNITY

In the aftermath of trauma, assumption and belief in a safe and orderly world are shattered. Basic trust in the goodness of other people dissipates, resulting in withdrawal, isolation, and paranoia. Shalom with other people and with the community is disrupted. Moreover, ongoing trauma may lead to distorted perceptions of "others"[21] as expendable objects, resulting in anger, abuse, and more violence for vengeance or as reenactments of the trauma. When wounded people no longer feel that they are worthy beings created in the image of God, they may generalize the distortion in perceiving that others are no longer valuable as well. Moreover, repercussions of trauma extend beyond the perpetrator and victim into the community as a whole. In the Democratic Republic of Congo, many rape victims are abandoned by their husbands, ostracized by their communities, and blamed for the sexual violence (Meger 2010). The lack of social acknowledgment and support is experienced as a second trauma (Raphael et al. 1996). The victims are rejected by the people closest to them, leading many to develop depression and PTSD (Pham et al. 2010).

In contrast, if the environment encourages and supports the person, pathology can be avoided. "A supportive response from other people may mitigate the impact of the event. . . . In the immediate aftermath of . . . trauma, rebuilding of some minimal form of trust is the primary task" (Herman 1992). In a study of firefighters, perceived social support

---

21 "Others" in the sense of not being part of us or our group (Myers 2011). "Others" are seen as people different from us, including those of a different race, socioeconomic status, or tribal group.

was associated with resilience from developing symptoms of depression and PTSD (Hoge, Austin, and Pollack 2007). As long as social support remains intact, people are relatively well protected against even catastrophic stressors, as not all trauma survivors develop PTSD (Van der Kolk, McFarlane, and Van der Hart 1996, 432).

Connection and affiliation protect against the damage of trauma. One central issue in treatment is the provision and restoration of social support (Raphael 1986). Some form of group therapy is often considered the treatment of choice for traumatized individuals. Fellow victims provide an effective bond, as shared experiences can provide a sense of communality. Among sufferers with similar experiences, most survivors who are at first reticent to speak are eventually able to share their stories. Reengagement begins first with a small group. When a sense of safety is reestablished, individuals are freed to gradually generalize and to slowly reconnect with their community and the greater world (Van der Kolk, McFarlane, and Van der Hart 1996, 433).

In certain areas where group treatment may not be available, healing may begin with connection to one caring person, such as a healthcare worker, pastor, or missionary. The restoration of shalom cannot happen when an individual is isolated (Eccl 4:9–12; Mark 2:1–12), as we are all members of one body (1 Cor 12:12–26). With support, survivors may engage in the challenging work of mourning what was lost (Matt 5:4), forgiving the damage suffered (Matt 6:14,15), forgiving and accepting their perpetrators and those perceived as "others" (Myers 2011, 61), seeking God's forgiveness for offenses committed (1 John 1:9), making amends where appropriate, reconciling broken relationships, accessing and accepting help from the community, and finding new and meaningful roles in society as contributing individuals (2 Cor 1:3,4).

Conclusion

Trauma hits the core of human existence by severing relationships. It has the potential to usher in doubt about the goodness of God, destroy self-concept, and shatter one's trust with the environment, with others, and with the community. Although these areas have been presented separately, they are interconnected. Healing in one dimension helps to facilitate and promote healing in another. Our relationship with God is the foundation and source for restoration of all other relationships. We are not able to find real life and true shalom without being in relationship with God (Acts 17:28). God's empowerment through the work of the Holy Spirit enables us to forgive and reconnect with other people (John 15:5). In turn, support from caring individuals can help us to reconnect with God and help to bring about a sense of safety to start trusting and reengaging with the world (Gal 6:2; Prov 17:17).

Trauma care can be summarized as having three stages. First, safety and stabilization must be established.[22] Interventions include finding physical and emotional safety, accessing primary care and mental health services, receiving psycho-education and spiritual education, and having immediate and ongoing spiritual support. The second stage involves trauma processing and resolution. The survivor comes to terms with the pain and loss with the support of a godly counselor. Profound mourning and grieving may emerge as the individual revisits the trauma and integrates avoided emotions. Work may include reinterpreting the trauma in light of Scripture, restoring one's identity through God's word, reestablishing spiritual activities, and forgiveness. The final stage is integration and reconnection as the person seeks a new and meaningful role in society, negotiates relationships with family and significant others, and reengages with the environment and the community with renewed energy and hope.

The essence of shalom is the ministry of reconciliation, beginning with God, who reconciled us to himself through Christ and gave us the

---

22   For a description of Psychological First Aid, used for initial stabilization after a traumatic event, see http://www.ptsd.va.gov/professional/manuals/manual-pdf/pfa/PFA_2ndEditionwithappendices.pdf.

ministry of reconciling the lost[23] to God, restoring God's image within the self, reconnecting with others, and mending what was broken in relationship with the world (2 Cor 5:18,19). The goal of the ministry of reconciliation is to help survivors transcend their trauma so that they may emerge with a stronger walk with God, a renewed identity and calling, and a greater appreciation for life and love for other people. Inspirational testimonies from people who have overcome great adversity and trauma are plentiful and can be used as encouragement for those who are recovering.[24]

Finally, we wait with anticipating hope that shalom and love will be restored in all our relationships when a great multitude from every nation, tribe, people, and language stand before the throne and in front of the Lamb (Rev 7:9), and

> he who sits on the throne will spread his tent over them.
> Never again will they hunger; never again will they thirst.
> The sun will not beat upon them, nor any scorching heat.
> For the Lamb at the center of the throne will be their shepherd; he will lead them to springs of living water, and God will wipe away every tear from their eyes. (Rev 7:15–17)

God will be forever with us and be our God (Rev 21:3).

References Cited

Abernathy, Barbara E. 2008. "Who Am I Now? Helping Trauma Clients Find Meaning, Wisdom, and a Renewed Sense of Self." *Vistas 2008*, from the Counseling Outfitters website. Available at http://counselingoutfitters.com/vistas/vistas08/Abernathy_Article_19.pdf (accessed August 5, 2012).

---

23 The Greek word for "lost" as presented in Luke 19:10 means those who were damaged or marred. The ministry of reconciliation includes serving those who have been wounded by trauma.

24 Some examples include Joni Eareckson Tada, Cori Ten Boom, Brother Yun, and Nelson Mandela.

Adsit, Chris. 2008. *The Combat Trauma Healing Manual: Christ-Centered Solutions for Combat Trauma*. Newport News, VA: Military Ministry Press.

American College of Gastroenterology. 2011. "Psychological Traumas Experienced over Lifetime Linked to Adult Irritable Bowel Syndrome." Paper presented at the American College of Gastroenterology's (ACG) 76th Annual Scientific meeting in Washington, DC, October 31, 2011. Available at http://www.newswise.com/articles/Psychological-physical-traumas-experienced-over-lifetime-linked-to-adult-irritable-bowel-syndrome-stress-associated-with-grief-natural-disasters-and-emotional-abuse-plays-ongoing-role-in-ibs (accessed September 15, 2012).

Anderson, Neil T. 1990. *Victory over the Darkness: Realizing the Power of Your Identity in Christ*. Ventura, CA: Regal.

BBC News. 2009a. "Gaza Looks Like Earthquake Zone." Last updated January 20, 2009. http://news.bbc.co.uk/2/hi/middle_east/7838618.stm.

———. 2009b. "Gaza: Humanitarian Situation." Last updated January 30, 2009. http://news.bbc.co.uk/2/hi/middle_east/7845428.stm.

Brennan, James. 2001. "Adjustment to Cancer—Coping or Personal Transition?" *Psycho-oncology* 10 (1): 1–18.

Breslau, N., H. Chilcoat, R. Kessler, E. Peterson, and V. Lucia. 1999. "Vulnerability to Assaultive Violence: Further Specification of the Sex Difference in Posttraumatic Stress Disorder." *Psychological Medicine* 29 (4): 813–21.

Briere, J., and J. Spinazzola. 2005. "Phenomenology and Psychological Assessment of Complex Posttraumatic States." *Journal of Traumatic Stress* 18 (5): 401–12.

The Center for Mind-Body Medicine. "Healing Haiti." http://www.cmbm.org/global-trauma-relief/healing-haiti/ (accessed August 3, 2012).

Charmaz, Kathy. 1993. *Good Days, Bad Days: The Self in Chronic Illness and Time*. New Brunswick, NJ: Rutgers University Press.

Chassman, Janet. 2012. "Promoting Healing from Trauma." Webinar presentation for the New York State Office of Mental Health (September 5).

Clifford, Cassandra. 2008. "Rape as a Weapon of War and Its Long-Term Effects on Victims and Society." Paper presented at the 7th Global Conference on Violence and the Contexts of Hostility, Budapest, Hungary, May 5–7, 2008. Available at http://www.peacewomen.org/portal_resources_resource.php?id=664.

Cloud, Henry. [2012]. "If Jesus Was Never Sexually Abused as a Child, How Can He Know My Pain of Being Sexually Abused as a Child?" Video on the Cloud-Townsend Resources website, Spiritual Life Channel. http://www.cloudtownsend.com/video-advice/channel/Spiritual%20 Life/cloudA1520/ (accessed September 21, 2012).

Collins, Kathryn, Kay Connors, Sara Davis, April Donohue, Sarah Gardner, Erica Goldblatt, Anna Hayward, Laurel Kiser, Fred Strieder, and Elizabeth Thompson. 2010. *Understanding the Impact of Trauma and Urban Poverty on Family Systems: Risks, Resilience, and Interventions.* Baltimore, MD: Family Informed Trauma Treatment Center. Available from the National Child Traumatic Stress Network website, http://nctsn.org/nccts/nav.do?pid=ctr_rsch_prod_ar or from http:// fittcenter.umaryland.edu/WhitePaper.aspx.

Cooper-Patrick, L., J. Gallo, N. Powe, D. Steinwachs, W. Easton, and D. Ford. 1999. "Mental Health Service Utilization by African Americans and Whites: The Baltimore Epidemiologic Catchment Area Follow-Up." *Medical Care* 37 (10): 1034–45.

Felitti, Vincent J., and Robert Anda. 2010. "The Relationship of Adverse Childhood Experiences to Adult Medical Disease, Psychiatric Disorders and Sexual Behavior: Implications for Healthcare." In *The Impact of Early Life Trauma on Health and Disease: The Hidden Epidemic*, edited by Ruth A. Lanius, Eric Vermetten, and Clare Pain, 77–87. Cambridge: Cambridge University Press.

Felitti, Vincent J., R. F. Anda, D. Nordenberg, D. F. Williamson, A. M. Spitz, V. Edwards, M. P. Koss, and J. S. Mark. 1998. "The Relationship of Adult Health Status to Childhood Abuse and Household Dysfunction." *American Journal of Preventive Medicine* 14: 245–58.

Gergen, Kenneth, and M. Gergen. 1988. "Narrative and the Self as Relationship." In *Advances in Experimental Social Psychology*, edited by L. Berkowitz, 17–56. San Diego, CA: Academic Press.

Goodman, Lisa, S. Rosenberg, K. Mueser, and R. Drake. 1997. "Physical and Sexual Assault History in Women with Serious Mental Illness: Prevalence, Correlates, Treatment, and Future Research Directions." *Schizophrenia Bulletin* 23 (4): 685–96.

Gouge, Bryan. 2012. *Global Trauma and Scripture Engagement.* Global Scripture Impact, May 2012 (American Bible Society), edited by Mark Forshaw and Rhoda Gathoga. Available from http://sister.americanbible.org/ sites/default/files/resources/2012-06-Global-Trauma-and-Scripture- Engagement-SR.pdf (accessed February 5, 2015).

Herman, Judith. 1992. *Trauma and Recovery: The Aftermath of Violence—From Domestic Abuse to Political Terror*. New York: Basic Books.

Hicks, Peter. 2006. *The Message of Evil & Suffering: Light into Darkness*. Edited by Derek Tidball. Downers Grove, IL: InterVarsity Press.

Hill, Harriet, and Peter Edman. 2012. "Discovering Job: Scripture Ministry that Speaks to Trauma." *Record*, Summer (July 5), 23. Available at http://news.americanbible.org/article/scripture-ministry-that-speaks-to-trauma.

Hill, Margaret, Harriet Hill, Richard Bagge, and Pat Miersma. 2009. *Healing the Wounds of Trauma: How the Church Can Help*. Kenya: Paulines.

Hoge, Elizabeth, Eloise Austin, and Mark Pollack. 2007. "Resilience: Research Evidence and Conceptual Considerations for Post-Traumatic Stress Disorder." *Depression and Anxiety* 24: 139–52.

HumanTrafficking.org, A Web Resource for Combating Human Trafficking in the East Asia Pacific Region. http://www.humantrafficking.org (accessed August 2, 2012).

International Organization for Migration (IOM). 2009. "IOM Appeal for Gaza Focuses on Health and Recovery." January 30. http://www.iom.int/cms/en/sites/iom/home/news-and-views/press-briefing-notes/pbn-2009/pbn-listing/iom-appeal-for-gaza-focuses-on-health-an.html.

Isaza, Heidi. 2010. "Trauma Recovery Center Brings New Life to Trafficked Girl." World Vision. Janoff-Bulman, Ronnie. 1992. *Shattered Assumptions: Toward a New Psychology of Trauma*. New York: Free Press.

Jennings, Ann. 2004. "The Damaging Consequences of Violence and Trauma: Facts, Discussion Points, and Recommendations for Behavioral Health Systems." Report for National Technical Assistance Center for State Mental Health Planning (NTAC), National Association of State Mental Health Program Directors (NASMHPD), and under contract with the Center for Mental Health Services (CMHS), Substance Abuse and Mental Health Services Administration (SAMHSA), U.S. Department of Health and Human Services (HHS), 2004. Available at http://www.theannainstitute.org/Damaging%20Consequences.pdf (accessed August 4, 2012).

———. 2011. "The Impact of Trauma on Wellness: Implications for Comprehensive Systems Change." Presentation at the Substance Abuse and Mental Health Services Administration (SAMHSA) 10x10 Wellness Campaign. Available at http://www.promoteacceptance.samhsa.gov/10by10/presentations/ImpactOfTrauma.pdf.

Jeter, Stan. 2010. "Daughters of Cambodia Leave Sex Trade for Christ." CBN News World website. Available at http://www.cbn.com/cbnnews/world/2010/August/Daughters-of-Cambodia-Leave-Sex-Trade-for-Christ/ (accessed August 3, 2012).

Johnson, Darrell. 2004. *Discipleship on the Edge: An Expository Journey through the Book of Revelation.* Vancouver: Regent College.

Karabat, Ankara Avse. 2010. "Trauma Expert Wentz: Systematic Dehumanization in Gaza is Unique." *Today's Zaman.* Available at http://www.todayszaman.com/newsDetail_getNewsById.action;jsessionid=EB630EEF0A7073A9D111038B464DDAAB?newsId=209723.

Kessler, R., S. Zhao, S. Katz, A. Kouzis, R. Frank, M. Edlund, and P. Leaf. 1999. "Past Year Use of Outpatient Services for Psychiatric Problems in the National Comorbidity Survey." *American Journal of Psychiatry* 156 (1): 115–23.

Lazarus, Richard, and Susan Folkman. 1984. *Stress, Appraisal, and Coping.* New York: Springer.

Leger, Donna. 2012. "Cholera Cripples Haiti, Two Years after Quake." *USA Today.* Available at http://www.usatoday.com/news/world/story/2012-01-05/haiti-cholera-outbreak/52419464/1.

Leppaniemi, Ari K. 2004. "Global Trends in Trauma." *Trauma* 6 (3): 193–203. doi:10.1191/1460408604ta314oa.

———. 2009. "Update on Global Trends in Trauma." *Trauma* 11 (1): 37–47. doi:10.1177/1460408608100461.

Meger, S. 2010. "Rape of the Congo: Understanding Sexual Violence in the Conflict in the Democratic Republic of Congo." *Journal of Contemporary African Studies* 28 (2): 119–35.

McAdams, Dan P. 1993. *The Stories We Live By: Personal Myths and the Making of the Self.* New York: William Morrow.

Mollica, Richard. 2011a. "Demystifying Trauma: Sharing Pathways to Healing and Wellness." Teleconference presented for the Substance Abuse & Mental Health Services Administration, September 26, 2011. Available from http://promoteacceptance.samhsa.gov/teleconferences/archive/training/teleconference09262011.aspx.

———. 2011b. *Textbook of Global Mental Health: Trauma and Recovery; A Companion Guide for Field and Clinical Care of Traumatized People Worldwide.* Cambridge, MA: Harvard Program in Refugee Trauma.

———, K. Donelan, T. Svang, J. Lavelle, C. Elias, M. Frankel, and R. Blendon. 1993. "The Effect of Trauma and Confinement on Functional Health and Mental Health Status of Cambodians Living in Thailand-Cambodia Border Camps." *Journal of the American Medical Association* 270 (5): 581–86. doi:10.1001/jama.1993.03510050047025.

———, K. McInnes, N. Sarajlie, J. Lavelle, I. Sarajlie, and M. Massagli. 2009. "Disability Associated with Psychiatric Comorbidity and Health Status in Bosnian Refugees Living in Croatia." *Journal of the American Medical Association* 281 (5): 433–39. doi:10.1001/jama.282.5.433.

Mueser, Kim, Lisa Goodman, Susan Trubetta, Stanley Rosenberg, Fred Osher, Robert Vidaver, Patricia Auciello, and David Foy. 1998. "Trauma and Posttraumatic Stress Disorder in Severe Mental Illness." *Journal of Consulting and Clinical Psychology* 66 (3): 493–99.

———, M. Salyers, S. Rosenberg, L. Goodman, S. Essock, F. Osher, M. Swartz, M. Butterfield, and the 5 Site Health and Risk Study Research Committee. 2004. "Interpersonal Trauma and Posttraumatic Stress Disorder in Patients with Severe Mental Illness: Demographic, Clinical, and Health Correlates." *Schizophrenia Bulletin* 30 (1): 45–57.

Myers, Bryant L. 2011. *Walking with the Poor: Principles and Practices of Transformational Development.* Revised and updated ed. Maryknoll, NY: Orbis.

National Association of State Mental Health Program Directors / National Technical Assistance Center. 2006. *Personalized Safety Plan: Seclusion and Restraint/Trauma Informed Care Curriculum.* Alexandria, VA: National Association of State Mental Health Program Directors.

Norris, F. H., and L. Slone. 2007. "The Epidemiology of Trauma and PTSD." In *Handbook of PTSD: Science and Practice,* edited by M. J. Friedman, T. M. Keane, and P. A. Resick, 78–98. New York: Guilford Press.

Oram, Sian, Heidi Stockl, Joanna Busza, Louise M. Howard, and Cathy Zimmerman. 2012. "Prevalence and Risk of Violence and the Physical, Mental, and Sexual Health Problems Associated with Human Trafficking: Systematic Review." *PLOS Medicine* (May). doi:10.1371/journal.pmed.1001224.

Peterman, Amber, T. Palermo, and C. Bredenkamp. 2011. "Estimates and Determinants of Sexual Violence against Women in the Democratic Republic of Congo." *American Journal of Public Health* 101 (6): 1060–67. doi:10.2105/AJPH.2010.300070.

Pham, P. N., P. Vinck, D. Kinkodi, H. Weinstein. 2010. "Sense of Coherence and Its Association with Exposure to Traumatic Events, Post-Traumatic Stress Disorder, and Depression in Eastern Democratic Republic of Congo." *Journal of Traumatic Stress* 23 (3): 313–21.

"Psychosomatics: Depression, Trauma, Stress Linked to Physical Complaints."
2003. *Health & Medicine Week* (2003): 694. Available from http://
search.proquest.com/docview/206849565?accountid=14585.

Raphael, Beverley. 1986. *When Disaster Strikes: How Individuals and
Communities Cope with Catastrophe*. New York: Basic Books.

———, John Wilson, Lenore Meldrum, and Alexander McFarlane. 1996.
"Acute Preventive Interventions." In *Traumatic Stress: The Effects of
Overwhelming Experience on Mind, Body, and Society*, edited by Bessel
A. van der Kolk, A. McFarlane, and L. Weisaeth, 463–79. New York:
Guilford Press.

Ray, Susan L. 2008. "Trauma from a Global Perspective." *Issues in Mental
Health Nursing* 29 (1): 63–72. doi:10.1080/01612840701748821.

Reiker, P., and E. Carmen. 1986. "The Victim-to-Patient Process: The
Disconfirmation and Transformation of Abuse." *American Journal of
OrthoPsychiatry* 56: 360–70.

Richardson, Jerry. 2011. "Management of Depression and Anxiety." Presentation
on MedicalMissions.com Patient Care Podcast. December 19. http://
www.medicalmissions.com/learn/podcast/academic-areas/patient-
care.

Roberts, Bayard, E. Y. Damundu, O. Lomoro, and E. Sondorp. 2009. "Post-
Conflict Mental Health Needs: A Cross-Sectional Survey of Trauma,
Depression and Associated Factors in Juba, Southern Sudan." *BMC
Psychiatry* 9: 7. doi:10.1186/1471-244X/9/7.

Rosenthal, Michele. "PTSD Statistics." [2012]. On Heal My PTSD website.
http://healmyptsd.com/education/post-traumatic-stress-disorder-
statistics (accessed August 3, 2012).

Sontag, Deborah. 2010. "In Haiti, Mental Health System Is in Collapse." *New
York Times*, March 20. http://www.nytimes.com/2010/03/20/world/
americas/20haiti.html?_r=1.

Stearns, Jamon. 2011. *Dancing in the Glory of Monsters: The Collapse of the
Congo and the Great War of Africa*. New York: Public Affairs Books.

Steel, Zachary, T. Chey, D. Silove, C. Marnane, R. Bryant, and M. van
Ommeren. 2009. "Association of Torture and Other Potentially
Traumatic Events with Mental Health Outcomes among Populations
Exposed to Mass Conflict and Displacement: A Systematic Review
and Meta-analysis." *Journal of the American Medical Association* 302
(5): 537–49. doi:10.1001/jama.2009.1132.

Taylor, Shelley. 1983. "Adjustment to Threatening Events: A Theory of Cognitive
Adaptation." *American Psychologist* 38 (11): 1161–73.

Thabet, A. 2010. "Trauma, Grief, and PTSD in Palestinian Children Victims of War on Gaza." CanPalNet: Canada–Palestine Support Network. Available at http://www.canpalnet.ca/mambo/index.php?option=com_content&task=view&id=442&Itemid=1 (accessed August 3, 2012).

Thoits, Peggy. 2003. "Personal Agency in the Accumulation of Multiple Role-Identities." In *Advances in Identity Theory and Research*, edited by Peter J. Burke et al., 179–94. New York: Kluwer Academic/Plenum.

Trenholm, Jill, P. Olsson, and B. Ahlberg. 2011. "Battles on Women's Bodies: War, Rape, and Traumatization in Eastern Democratic Republic of Congo." *Global Public Health* 6 (2): 139–52.

Van der Kolk, Bessel A., A. McFarlane, and O. Van der Hart. 1996. "A General Approach to Treatment of Posttraumatic Stress Disorder." In *Traumatic Stress: The Effects of Overwhelming Experience on Mind, Body, and Society*, edited by Bessel A. van der Kolk, A. McFarlane, and L. Weisaeth, 417–40. New York: Guilford Press.

Wadsworth, M. E., and C. Santiago. 2008. "Risk and Resiliency Processes in Ethnically Diverse Families in Poverty." *Journal of Family Psychology* 22 (3): 399–410.

Wolterstorff, Nicholas. 1983. *Until Justice and Peace Embrace*. Grand Rapids, MI: Eerdmans.

World Food Programme (WFP). 2009. "WFP Launches Emergency Food Distribution to Families in Gaza." January 4. http://www.wfp.org/content/wfp-launches-emergency-food-distributions-families-gaza.

Yassen, Janet, and Mary R. Harvey. 1998. "Crisis Assessment and Interventions with Victims of Violence." In *Emergencies in Mental Health Practice: Evaluation and Management*, edited by Phillip M. Kleespies, 117–44. New York: Guilford Press.

Zimmerman, Barry, and Timothy Cleary. 2006. "Adolescents' Development of Personal Agency: The Role of Self-Efficacy Beliefs and Self-Regulatory Skills." In *Self-Efficacy Beliefs of Adolescents*, edited by Frank Pajares and Timothy Urdan, 45–69. Charlotte, NC: Information Age.

Shalom and Accompaniment for People Living with HIV and AIDS
The Continuing Challenge

W. Meredith Long, DrPH, and
Debbie Dortzbach, MN, MPH

I (Debbie) ducked to enter the hut as my eyes adjusted to the shift from the dazzling noon sun to the dark shadows of the tiny mud-walled room on the outskirts of Maputo, Mozambique. Slowly, rumpled forms shifted in the bed in front of us. Peering closely, I realized a man, a woman, and an infant were in the bed together. Pastora Joaquina shared the story of the home.

"This is Mary," she said, pointing to a pencil-thin woman seated at a small wooden table. "She is a member of our church and she has AIDS. Although she is sick herself, she is caring for those too sick to get out of bed—her husband, his girlfriend, and their baby. All of them are sick with AIDS. Someone from our church visits regularly, as often as every day to help Mary." We greeted each person, talked with Mary, and prayed together.

"Lord, give strength. Give them nutritious food. Keep away the fevers and allow them to feel better today. Help them get the medicines they need. Keep your presence and peace here."

I felt angry and overwhelmed. It was so unfair and wrong. Mary was one of millions of wives whose only risk of infection had been her fidelity to an unfaithful husband. The tiny infant would soon die. His crime was being born. What about his girlfriend? She looked terribly young. I knew that she had her own story of brokenness.

How could Mary still love and care for her unfaithful husband, his girlfriend, and the child they had conceived? Did they deserve her love?

So I asked her, "Mary, how can you keep going—caring for your husband, his girlfriend and baby, even when you yourself are sick?"

Her reply was simple and penetrating: "Because Jesus loves me, I can love them."

As I have pondered Mary's response in the years since then, I have realized her answer and actions distilled the essence of shalom. Though Mary faced imminent death as a result of her husband's betrayal, she knew the peace of Christ. From that place of peace, she gracefully walked in love beside the very ones who violated her body and heart. As Mary walked beside them—preparing food, washing diarrhea-soaked bodies and bed clothing, comforting and cradling her husband's dying child—she invited them into the healing of reconciliation. Freed from the power and bitterness of broken relationships, Mary responded by inviting the very ones who took life from her into her own peace.

Mary lived the gospel clearly articulated in Galatians 2:20. "I have been crucified with Christ. It is no longer I who live, but Christ who lives in me. And the life I now live in the flesh I live by faith in the Son of God, who loved me and gave himself for me."

HIV and AIDS: Ministry as Accompaniment

Our mental model cannot be that HIV and AIDS is a problem to solve; once one has the virus, the impact is lifelong. Walking with those impacted by HIV and AIDS is a hard and long journey that touches many relationships. This demands that we understand and address HIV and AIDS in the context of relationships—broken, restored, and redeemed. Restoring relationships is the work of shalom. In her own struggle with AIDS, and as she accompanied those responsible for her own journey with the disease, Mary experienced healing from Jesus and extended the hope of that healing to those Jesus had given her to love.

> The practice of accompaniment is highly personal and deeply relational. Accompaniment of the lonely poor involves walking with—not beside or in front of—a real

> person on his or her particular journey in his or her own
> particular place in time, at his or her particular pace. . . .
> It often means being present to terrible suffering, being
> thrown into chaotic circumstances, encountering un-
> expected problems and difficult situations with no easy
> solutions. (Griffin and Block 2013, introduction)

Each of our journeys shapes itself to its own time. But each time is shaped
by the times that came before. Those who are infected or affected, those
at risk from HIV and AIDS, and those who make it their Christian ministry to accompany them become part of a journey that has been shaped
by earlier responses to HIV and AIDS. Because of improved access to effective treatment worldwide, it has become a journey of greater hope for
millions, but suffering and deep inequities are still part of the journey.

HIV and AIDS: An Update

Much has changed since Debbie and I (Meredith) first encountered
people with HIV and AIDS. There is still no cure or effective vaccine to prevent HIV infection. Early in the epidemic, there was also
no treatment that addressed the virus itself. It was not until the 1990s
that effective multi-drug therapy gave hope of an extended lifespan to
those infected with HIV. But this hope was only for the richer countries at first. In 2005, of 24.5 million HIV-infected men and women in
sub-Saharan Africa, only 800,000 were receiving antiretroviral (ARV)
treatment (IRIN 2005). In 2012, of the 35.3 million HIV-infected men
and women in Africa, 9.7 million or 61 percent of those who were clini-
cally eligible for treatment were receiving it (UNAIDS 2012a). While
remarkable progress has been made, much work remains. Though WHO
has changed eligibility guidelines to include early, more effective treatment, only 34 percent of the world's total HIV-positive individuals are
receiving treatment.

The prevention of new infections in the absence of an effective
vaccine has not progressed at the same rate as treatment. In 2012,

2.3 million people were newly infected with HIV. The good news is that new infections are falling, and since 2001 they have dropped by 33 percent. Sadly, however, for groups at highest risk—men who have sex with men, those who pay for sex, and drug users infected through dirty needles—the rate of new infections has remained stable over the last ten years or actually increased (UNAIDS 2012b, 36–40).

Eliminating the transmission of the virus from a mother to her infant is a major global effort. Today no baby should be born with HIV and no mother should live without lifelong treatment for HIV. Together we are working to accomplish an AIDS-free generation (UNICEF 2013).

AIDS spreads from one person to another by transforming pathways of life—blood, sex, birth, and a mother's milk—into channels of death. It destroys life by attacking the very defenses that God created to protect life.

No Simple Solutions

Without an effective vaccination, preventing the spread of HIV becomes an extraordinarily difficult problem. Preventing HIV infection requires much more than a single, isolated decision to receive an immunization. Instead, it requires repeated decisions by multiple actors over a lifetime, from the time a child is in the womb of his or her mother. HIV is spread through bodily fluids, blood, sexual fluids, and breast milk. Globally, HIV is most often transmitted sexually between men and women and between men and men. Avoiding the risk of sexual transmission requires a lifetime of abstinence and then mutual faithfulness among sexual partners. If the risk cannot be avoided, it must be lowered. Lowering the risk of infection requires physical protection for every sexual act, usually a man taking time to put on a condom. Effective prevention, then, requires not just one or two decisions but a lifetime of decisions to control a strong desire that God hardwired into who we are. And, tragically, even that effort can be erased through an act of sexual violence.

Improved and expanded treatment also lowers transmission rates, because the viral load in the blood and sexual fluids decreases. The cost of the first line of treatment has decreased substantially, but it is still expensive. Faced with growing costs as more and more people require different and more expensive therapies across a lifespan, policymakers often choose the least difficult of the solutions—limiting treatment options to those who have the resources to pay.

Before 2003 there was virtually no treatment available to the world's poor, even though the first ARV drug effective in extending life was available as early as 1987 and the multi-drug Highly Active ARV Therapy (HAART) had been available since 1996 (Bartlett 2006). For over fifteen years the vast majority of those infected with HIV faced global neglect. This was driven at least in part by the extremely high cost of the medicines, inadequate medical and drug oversight, and the lack of systems to administer and evaluate drug use, as well as disputes over intellectual property rights that restricted the sale of generic medicines. With little sense of urgency, millions died. Thankfully, the cost of treatment has been dramatically reduced.

The worldwide effort to extend treatment has brought new hope to millions and changed the nature of their journey. But for millions of people, almost all in sub-Saharan Africa, who still cannot access effective treatment or who are not yet tested, the journey is still very much like Mary's.

HIV and AIDS and Broken Relationships

Early in the epidemic we called together our African staff to help us find a cultural bridge to explain a disease that, at that time, was inevitably fatal but did not reveal its existence for months or years while the carrier infected others. The only parallel they could find was a curse. A curse begins with the betrayal of a relationship, kills people in the prime of life, affects those closely related to the targeted person, and is rarely discovered until the accursed is very sick or near death. HIV infection is not a curse; it is a disease. But it is a deeply disturbing disease in that, while caused by a virus and debilitating to the body, its impact is primarily relational. To confront the prevention and treatment of HIV infection means that we will confront broken relationships, both personal and structural.

Infection multiplies through betrayal. Spouses or lovers are betrayed by one another. Commercial sex workers and IV drug users are betrayed by business owners, who see them only as expendable commodities in the pursuit of money. Those who are infected or die early are betrayed by tainted blood transfusions, inadequate medical precautions, and the denial of treatment by their own governments and medical institutions.

BROKEN RELATIONSHIPS WITHIN ONE'S SELF

People living with HIV and AIDS struggle with guilt, regret, helplessness, and loss because their personal choices have brought harm to themselves and those they love. Often this struggle is rooted in a conflict between self-expression and self-control. We too readily accept the lie that self-expression brings fullness of life, a fullness that is diminished by self-denial. Living out this belief is dangerous. We may forfeit the gifts that God wishes to give us through our sexuality—personal intimacy, belonging, meaning, and a legacy of children. In return we discover that we have received only a shadow of our deepest desires, a shadow that retains some goodness but is intrinsically laced with sin.

This temptation to seek self-expression has consequences when it comes to the spread of HIV and AIDS. Men and boys, who have been shaped to believe that being a man requires multiple partners, are unlikely to have only one married partner for life. It's not what men do. Young women and girls, who have been reared to please and submit to men, especially to their elders, find it hard to refuse a male school teacher who asks for sex. It's not what women do.

When sexual preference or practice becomes the primary factor in a person's identity, he or she is more likely to resist messages to change behaviors that they believe are essential extensions of who they believe themselves to be. Gay men who regard high-risk sexual practices as an expression of who they are, or women whose self-esteem is rooted in the response of men to their sexuality, are less likely to modify their risk behavior than those for whom sexual practice is less central to their self-concept.

All of this can lead to a sense of inevitability. When a sense of help-lessness—*This is just the way things are*—roots itself in how we perceive ourselves, the risk of HIV infection and the destructive impact of the virus once infected are both increased. Knowledge of what we *should* do and even the desire to do it often cannot overcome rooted helplessness. Helplessness finds its expression in guilt, regret, resignation, hardness, and bitterness.

Guilt—I'm so, so sorry. I hate myself. Most people with HIV and AIDS struggle with guilt and self-blame. Sometimes the guilt is authen-tic (the husband or wife who brings AIDS to the family because of his or her behavior) and sometimes false (the wife who blames her spouse's unfaithfulness wholly on her own failure). Unresolved and/or unforgiven guilt destroys from within. We avoid people toward whom we feel guilty. Unresolved or unforgiven guilt toward a loved person who has shared our life removes us from the intimacy of a relationship that is essential to our peace. Failure to forgive one who has harmed us destroys both the offended and the offender. The offended person in the relationship pas-sively or aggressively adds to the burden of guilt the offender feels. The offender either withdraws or strikes out. Neither lives at peace, and both feel trapped in the relationship's downward spiral.

Regret—If only I had . . . Regret can paralyze, embitter, or em-power. The pregnant woman who feared an HIV test and then passed the infection to her child, the man who neglected to use condoms with his partners, or even the person who just didn't know his behavior was risky—all suffer regret. When regret is accompanied by helplessness it results in resignation, hardness, or self-blame.

Regret accompanied by hope, however, empowers engagement. Freed from centering inward in anger or self-blame, many people who regret what has happened in their lives focus on keeping others from repeating their experience.

Resignation—I give up; there is nothing I can do. Resignation both embraces and is driven by helplessness. People become paralyzed and are unable to take steps that would change their situation. Resignation becomes fatalism. They no longer attempt to control their behavior or to take precautions to lower their risk. Those who are already infected quickly give up in their pursuit of life and may even lose the perseverance or energy to pursue treatment.

Hardness—I am who I am and I'll do what I want while I still can. I just don't care anymore. Hardness embraces and justifies resentment. It is aggressive helplessness. HIV-infected people who act out their resentment and anger become a danger to themselves and others. They have accepted defeat but are helpless to channel their anger into pathways that effectively fight against the disease or protect others.

BROKEN RELATIONSHIPS WITH OTHERS

The stigma ascribed to people living with HIV and AIDS is still very real. Many people living with AIDS internalize that stigma. In Rwanda, 65 percent of those responding to the People Living with HIV and AIDS Stigma Index reported that they had either lost their jobs or suffered a significant loss of income; 28 percent of those in urban Zambia said that they were excluded from family events; 3 out of 4 in China reported suffering shame or loss of self-esteem; and 22–25 percent of people living with HIV or AIDS in Myanmar, Paraguay, rural Zambia, and the United Kingdom had considered ending their lives (UNAIDS 2012b, 69).

Stigma and the failure of governments to protect basic human rights also hinder prevention and treatment. People at risk of infection or living with HIV and AIDS will choose not to go for testing or treatment if they feel their status will be disclosed publically and result in the loss of their jobs or alienation from their family and community. When World Concern ran a service center for people living with AIDS in Haiti, offering a menu of helpful services, many of the people living with HIV and AIDS near the center would take half a day to travel to another center across town. They did not want their neighbors to see them going into the building.

The brokenness of gender relationships is both a cause and an effect of HIV and AIDS. Women comprise 60 percent of those infected by HIV in sub-Saharan Africa, and among all those 15–24 years old, the number of HIV-infected young women is double to triple the number of HIV-infected men in most countries. This imbalance is driven by the early sexual debut of young women, early marriage, and sexual violence (UNAIDS 2012b, 70). The root causes of this epidemic, then, lie in the deeply rooted brokenness of relationships between men and women.

Wherever women are not intrinsically valued as highly as men, at least some of the following things will likely be true. All raise a woman's or girl's risk of HIV infection:

- Women will be ruled by men who regard it as their right to use them as they please.
- The woman's value will depend upon her husband's position, the number of children, especially sons, she bears, and her ability to work.
- Women and girls who are economically dependent upon men will marry early, remain in abusive relationships, and have sex in return for protection, money, or goods.
- Women will not confront men over their behavior.
- Women will not be protected from sexual violence.
- Domestic violence will be accepted as a norm by both men and women and perhaps as the right of the husband.
- Men will be more likely to take multiple partners, but women who are unfaithful or perhaps even raped may be punished, abandoned, and sometimes killed.

In many parts of the world, women and children who are infected with HIV through sexual violence and even gang rape have found that police and courts might not respond at all, or respond against the woman making the complaint. Failure to protect orphaned children, especially girls, puts them at high risk of sexual violence or exploitation as well as IV drug use.

BROKEN RELATIONSHIPS WITH GOD AND THE CHURCH

Many people living with HIV and AIDS also accept the belief that AIDS is a curse or punishment from God. Their natural response is to flee from God, not to draw near. When churches reflect the condemnation that many of these people already attribute to God, they are left with no place to find the peace they long for.

In the early part of the AIDS pandemic in Africa, many churches failed to stand with those living with HIV and AIDS, spouting words of condemnation rather than peace. The good news is that many churches have repented of their self-righteousness and condemnation. As far back as April 1994, African church leaders from across the continent met in Kampala, Uganda, and drafted the following statement.

> We speak out not because of the good things we have
> done, but because of the work of Christ and from our one-
> ness with all humanity. We confess that we have not said
> or done all we could have. We have been given the pro-
> phetic voice of a watchman to speak as God does against
> sin, but sometimes our call to holy living has sounded as
> if we were blameless. We are not. . . . Jesus meets us in our
> need even when we are in rebellion and reconciles us to
> God. We ought to have been more like Jesus in the midst
> of the life and death struggle of those affected by AIDS,
> but we have not. (MAP Int'l 1996, ii)

If those who are affected by HIV and AIDS are to be reconciled toward God, the most compelling invitation comes when we as followers of Jesus gracefully and humbly accompany them in their journey.

This early negative response to the AIDS pandemic was not just a problem for people in Africa:

> At the beginning of the AIDS epidemic, many Americans had little sympathy for people with AIDS. The feeling was that somehow people from certain groups "deserved" their illness. Let us put those feelings behind us. We are fighting a disease, not people. We must prevent the spread of AIDS while at the same time preserving our humanity and intimacy. (Koop 1986, 6)

We still face the echo of these negative and judgmental feelings identified so early in the epidemic. As we accompany those affected by HIV and AIDS, we need to own our own brokenness. It is too easy to unwittingly divide those infected with HIV into "innocent victims" in contrast to those who brought it on themselves. While we may be willing to walk beside the "innocent victims," we pull away from or are less compassionate to those who we believe "earned" their illness. We've not yet learned the hard lessons of grace and holiness that Jesus modeled for us.

When the Pharisees brought the woman caught in adultery to Jesus, they asked him to choose either the punishment of the Law or the life of the woman cowering before them. Jesus rejected their either/or option. By refusing to condemn the woman, he chose grace and saved her life. But in commanding her to change her behavior, he also chose holiness. In ministering to the wide diversity of those affected by HIV and AIDS, we will repeatedly face this struggle. Knowing the right answer or even having a sincere calling will not sustain us.

One last caution. The victims of HIV and AIDS can also disappoint us and our expectations. After Meredith's wife, Kendra, had completed a spiritual formation workshop among Christians working among Haiti's poor, one young American missionary came to her after her session. "My husband and I came to Haiti because we felt we were called to serve the poor. But then we found that the poor are detestable. But God said to me, 'Look at me. I'm the one who called you here in love. And your calling is to love me as I love the poor.'"

This young woman shared a struggle that many of us feel, but few share openly. We often try to validate our calling by the response of those to whom we are called. They rarely respond as we hope. So we either condemn them or condemn ourselves. If we are to walk authentically alongside people with HIV and AIDS, our calling cannot be contingent on their response. It is not a matter of success or failure. We can never persevere in loving anyone when our love is contingent upon their response to us. We are only able to accompany others in love when we permit Jesus to accompany us in his love.

The Many Dimensions of Accompaniment toward Shalom

SANCTUARY

When the Pharisees brought the woman caught in adultery to Jesus for judgment, they did not really care if she lived or died. They only sought to trap Jesus. Jesus was the only one who really saw the woman herself—her fear, vulnerability, and guilt. By taking the woman to the only person in Jerusalem who truly had the moral authority to condemn her, the Pharisees had unwittingly placed her before the only person in the city who could offer her safety.

We cannot accompany people with HIV and AIDS if they feel unsafe. I (Meredith) was visiting a group of Vietnamese women living with HIV and AIDS. Our Vietnamese staff had sought out and then accompanied these women individually and as a group over the past two years. They had shaped a support group around their own deep caring. As I listened to the women share their joys, sorrows, problems, and fears, I realized that this was probably the only group in which they felt safe. Those who were employed carefully guarded the secret of their infection for fear of losing their jobs. Many of them, who struggled with the side effects of their medication or with family relationships, would have struggled alone if it had not been for this sanctuary. Where stigmatization is high, people are less likely to be tested, to access and adhere to treatment, and to protect their newborn children from mother-to-child transmission. It even reduces the quality of care by family and friends (UNAIDS 2012b, 68).

In responding to the genuine moral issues surrounding the transmission of HIV, the people of God struggle to figure out the relationship between holiness and grace. During that struggle, we become dangerous company for those affected by HIV and AIDS, for we are tempted to try and change people before we know them. When our loudest messages reverberate around the behaviors that "they" must change, condemnation echoes in our minds and reverberates in our churches. Only when we become a community of grace—where all are safe to come—do care, correction, challenge, repentance, and forgiveness also make their home with us. As we walk beside those with HIV and AIDS, we discover that they also walk with us and challenge and teach us. In the context of our relationship to them, we find that the deep, hidden attitudes that separate us from God and others are brought into the light by those we accompany and are transformed into expressions of God's love.

IDENTITY

To accompany others, we must rest in our identity as children of our loving Father, followers of Jesus, and heirs of God's kingdom. Like Jesus, we must know that we have "come from God and [are] returning to God" (John 13:3) before we can show others the full extent of God's love. If our identity rests in the responses of those we are called to walk beside, we place a burden on both them and ourselves that neither is able to bear. It is only when we are secure in our identity in Christ that we can effectively invite those we walk beside into their identities as men, women, and children created by a loving God, bearers of his image and recipients of his grace and sacrificial love.

Our lives of shalom-seeking and shalom-giving must rest upon the love of God for human beings and thus the inestimable value of human life, a far more fundamental starting place than the Western understanding of human rights. When we accompany those living with HIV and AIDS, we soon begin to share their sense of injustice and consequent loss. We know that each person in our lives uniquely and beautifully comes from God. We hunger for their rights to be met and struggle to make it so. But for Christians this struggle around rights has an important limit.

The value God places upon each person prompts us not to demand our rights, but rather to so delight in the love of the God who treasures us that we are willing to yield our rights if God so demands. Our lives are secure in Christ because he loves us. There is nothing greater that we can claim, own, or grasp. The struggle for justice and the reconciliation of wrongs, both societal and individual, often requires the freedom that comes from the willingness to sacrifice our own rights. We fully identify with Christ when we are crucified with him, nailing our claim to our rights on the cross so that we may become the advocates for others.

JUSTICE

We cannot walk beside others on their journey without becoming aware of how they are affected by injustice. Throughout this chapter, we have seen many of the ways that systemic and personal injustice infects the global response to people living with HIV and AIDS:

- Gender and domestic violence
- Denial of access to treatment
- The failure of testing and treatment centers to maintain confidentiality
- The government's failure to protect people living with HIV and AIDS from losing their jobs
- More recently, renewed efforts to criminalize men who have sex with men
- Extortion or overcharging for access to treatment
- Fraud and theft of personal assets
- Unequal access of their children to schools, and many more abuses

More recently, we have witnessed renewed efforts to criminalize men who have sex with men. This criminalization decreases the likelihood that men who have sex with men will risk seeking out testing and care. It will also endanger those who accompany them on their journey, regardless of their sexual orientation, and increase the stigmatization of all people infected by HIV and AIDS in their countries.

When followers of Christ integrate a prophetic call for justice with the grace to love and value those who perpetuate injustice, healing can follow. The US proposal for the President's Emergency Plan for AIDS Relief (PEPFAR) and Congress's willingness to continue funding for the program were both catalyzed and sustained by important voices advocating for those who were dying. But it was also the result of the quieter voices of those who transcended political differences, business interests, and the powerful forces of condemnation and apathy because they shared the graceful and persevering strength of Christ's love.

The fight against the spread of HIV and AIDS is now sustained by an increasingly fragile international commitment. While the gay community in a few countries commands the political power to speak effectively for themselves, the vast majority of those at risk of HIV and AIDS, including people who inject drugs and men who have sex with men in the Global South, still depend upon the strong prophetic voice for justice and the quiet persuasion of grace in maintaining preventive and treatment services. Jesus is still the only man who fully expresses grace and truth. We who are yoked with him in his kingdom are best equipped to proclaim without hypocrisy God's justice for those who have no voice and also to gently build and heal community with the humility that comes from the grace of forgiveness, repentance, and restoration that we have received.

CARING

After facing their own failures to respond to the AIDS epidemic in the mid-1990s, church leaders in Africa committed to becoming "watchmen standing in the gap" and stewards of the hope of God offered in Christ. These "watchmen standing in the gap" witnessed the suffering in their

congregations and communities. Rwandan churches, deeply moved by
the tragedies of the genocide and the rapid spread of HIV, met together
in November 1997 and jointly signed a declaration: "We acknowledge
that we have the belief system, moral authority, and local presence necessary to be effective in AIDS prevention and care. However, we need
training, guidance, and advocacy to change belief to action and apathy
to compassion" (World Relief Rwanda 2004).

They drafted a plan, based on the principles in the Beatitudes of
Matthew 5:

- Blessed are the meek—those who serve others out of a pure
  motive.
- Blessed are those who hunger and thirst after righteous-
  ness—those no longer boasting in self-righteousness and
  stigma against those with AIDS.
- Blessed are the merciful—those who dare to take the first
  steps of service to others, overcoming cultural fears and
  high-risk norms.
- Blessed are those who comfort others—those who accompany the dying and care for the widows and orphans left
  behind.
- Blessed are the peacemakers—those who are not satisfied
  until relationships are healed, even if the body is not.

In Cambodia, the Way of Hope Church, largely comprised of new believers who are poor, felt compelled by Jesus' love for them to care for
persons living with AIDS in their community. People living with AIDS
in Cambodia are deeply stigmatized and believed to be cursed. As a
courtesy to neighbors and family, it is not unusual for a sign of death
such as the skull and crossbones to be drawn with chalk on the wooden
siding or front door, warning anyone who might try to come in that they
are vulnerable to the curse themselves.

Just as Jesus transformed the cross from a symbol of death to a symbol of life, the church members in Cambodia determined to change the
sign of death on the doorposts of houses of people living with AIDS into

a symbol of new life in Christ. They sought out the homes marked with death to begin accompanying members of the household in a journey toward life.

They trained their members to train and assist the people of the household to care for those with HIV and AIDS in their home. The community members responded with shocked wonder when Christian volunteers from Way of Hope Church defied cultural norms, dismissed fears, and boldly entered homes. They not only sat with ill persons, but also bathed them, prepared food for them, sang for them, and read Scripture to them. Among them was Chrub, a young woman dying of AIDS. Pale, stretched skin draped her bones like sheer curtains. She spoke her last words to the Christian volunteer who had journeyed with her to the end. Chrub described her fear of dying alone. "You aren't alone," her friend replied. "We love you. Jesus is with you. We are with you." Chrub simply passed from the embrace of her Christian friend to the joy of Jesus' arms. Her cremation, hours later, was preceded with the church youth dancing and a clear gospel and health message about HIV. As her body rolled into the crematorium, her grandmother, an hour-old new believer, yelled to her, "I'll see you again, Chrub!"

In many parts of the world, the very nature of care is transformed by those who eat with, bathe, and gently and appropriately touch those living with HIV and AIDS. These acts of compassion become a deeper and intuitive symbol of belonging. In many ways care without belonging becomes only treatment. We treat people at an emotional and often physical distance; we care for people only when we are near.

OBEDIENCE

> If anyone loves me, he will obey my teaching. My Father will love him, and we will come to him and make our home with him. He who does not love me will not obey my teaching. (John 14:23,24)

When we think of accompaniment, anything that links love and obedience together seems suspect. In the world, the connection seems to be, "If you obey me, then I will love you." But this is the reverse of the gospel message. The gospel logic is the other way around: "If you love me, then you will obey me." The missionary woman from Haiti found obedience impossible when her calling was focused on the poor. When she understood her calling as loving Jesus in response to his love for her she was better able to walk beside the poor without judgment. We obey him because we love him because he loves us. If we hope to successfully challenge and correct the behavior of those whom we accompany, we must first know them and love them. As we love those we accompany, the Holy Spirit will create times for correction and invitations to change.

A deeper challenge is figuring out how we can continue to obey Christ when we accompany not only those who are grateful, but also those who are so bitter, resigned, angry, or outright hostile that we want to fight or run away. Accountability and social support are essential. Though Mary willingly served her husband and his girlfriend and child, it was not easy. Mary had role models and peers who supported and encouraged her. Her pastor, Pastora Joaquina, and church volunteers visited her regularly—to check up on her, provide tangible items she needed such as food or firewood, share God's truth and promises with her, and arm her for the spiritual battle ahead by praying for her.

Mary recognized that the struggle was not only against the physical things she could see, but against the deep desires of her heart, which were divided. On the one hand, she had been stirred into action by the love of Jesus, while on the other hand, she wrestled with the forces of evil intent and selfish desire. She understood the reality of Romans 7:21–25:

> When I want to do good, evil is right there with me. For in my inner being I delight in God's law; but I see another law at work in the members of my body, waging war against the law of my mind and making me a prisoner of the law of sin at work within my members. What a wretched person I am! Who will rescue me from this body of death? Thanks be to God—through Jesus Christ our Lord!

Mary practiced what she believed. Mary persevered because Jesus and her church walked beside her, loving and directing her. She persevered because she recognized God's love in the daily assistance, gifts, and energy she witnessed many times a day. Her grace and perseverance in ministry became indelibly imprinted on the lives of those she walked beside and also on those who observed her. She challenged and equipped them not only to face their own struggles but also to accompany others.

HEALING AND RECONCILIATION

While there is no cure for AIDS, there can be reconciliation, the mending of relationships and restoration of shalom. In his reflection on his ministry to the poor, Gutiérrez poses this foundational question for any follower of Christ: "How do you say to the poor, 'God loves you'?" (Gutiérrez 2013, 27).

As we accompany people infected and affected by HIV and AIDS, the same question applies. How do we say to people living with HIV and AIDS, "God loves you?" We return to the question that Debbie posed to Mary at the beginning of this chapter: "Mary, how can you keep going—caring for your husband, his girlfriend and baby, even when you yourself are sick?" Mary answers with the foundational response to Gutiérrez's question: "Because Jesus loves me, I can love them."

The difference between helping people living with AIDS and healing the broken relationships that fuel and result from the epidemic is the love of Jesus. Jesus first reconciles them and us to God through his death. Then, because of his love for us, we accompany those living with AIDS on their journey, which now also defines our journey, making the message of reconciliation real to them in both word and deed.

References Cited

Bartlett, John G. 2006. "Ten Years of HAART: Foundation for the Future." Paper presented at the 13th Conference on Retroviruses and Opportunistic Infections, Denver, CO, February 5–8.

Griffin, Michael, and Jennie Weiss Block. 2013. *In the Company of the Poor: Conversations between Dr. Paul Farmer and Fr. Gustavo Gutiérrez*. Maryknoll, NY: Orbis.

Gutiérrez, Gustavo. 2013. "Saying and Showing to the Poor: 'God Loves You.'" In *In the Company of the Poor: Conversations with Dr. Paul Farmer and Fr. Gustavo Gutiérrez*, edited by Michael Griffin and Jennie Block, 27–34. Maryknoll, NY: Orbis.

IRIN News. 2005. "Africa: A Short History of Antiretrovirals." August 2005 In-Depth Report: "Lazarus Drug": ARVs in the Treatment Era. http://www.irinnews.org/InDepthMain.aspx?InDepthId=12&ReportId=56080 (accessed June 25, 2014).

Koop, C. E. 1986. "Surgeon General's Report on Acquired Immune Deficiency Syndrome." Public Health Report 1987, January-February, 102 (1): 1–3. U.S. Public Health Service. Available at http://www.ncbi.nlm.nih.gov/pmc/articles/PMC1477712/.

MAP International. 1996. "Declaration from the All Africa Church and AIDS Consultation, AIDS in Africa: The Church's Opportunity." Nairobi.

UNAIDS. 2012a. "Global Fact Sheet." http://www.unaids.org/sites/default/files/en/media/unaids/contentassets/documents/epidemiology/2012/gr2012/20121120_FactSheet_Global_en.pdf (accessed February 6, 2015).

———. 2012b. *Together We Will End AIDS*. July 18. http://www.unaids.org/en/media/unaids/contentassets/documents/epidemiology/2012/JC2296_UNAIDS_TogetherReport_2012_en_em.pdf (accessed February 6, 2015).

UNICEF. 2013. *Towards an AIDS-Free Generation: Children and AIDS; Sixth Stocktaking Report, 2013*. Available at http://www.unicef.org/publications/index_70986.html (accessed February 6, 2015).

World Relief Rwanda. 2004. *Blessing: The Story of Rwandan Churches Challenging the AIDS Crisis*. Available at http://worldrelief.org/page.aspx?pid=1796 (accessed June 25, 2014).

CHAPTER 9

Shalom and Short-Term Medical Missions
Avoiding a *Step Backward*

Michael J. Soderling, MD, MBA

It is not surprising that the Christian church has been involved in ministries of health and healing since its beginning. Christ's ministries of preaching, teaching, and healing were directed at restoring healthy relationships with God, with each other, and with God's creation. Jesus' ministry of reconciliation provides us with the standard by which all our ministry efforts should be measured. Christ's disciples and the early church simply emulated their Lord. Two thousand years later, Christ's call to his church is unchanged. Those who are called to ministries that address the physical needs of sick and suffering people are called to conduct their work in ways that promote this uniquely biblical concept of shalom.

In this chapter I will use a story from my own experience in cross-cultural ministry to highlight some shortcomings I have noticed in the short-term medical missions movement as I have seen it played out in Central America. In parallel, I will briefly explore how the modern dualistic (material/spiritual) worldview arose and is affecting healthcare missions and short-term missions in particular. Finally, I will propose measures essential to altering this modern paradigm, which shapes the majority of their efforts in ministries of health and healing.

A Birth and Its Tragic Aftermath

I had just zipped up my sleeping bag after a long day of seeing patients in a very rural village in Guatemala. It had been a typical day of long lines of patients with a variety of physical complaints. My American training as an obstetrician/gynecologist had not prepared me to diagnose and treat the majority of patient illnesses that typically present themselves during a short-term medical mission trip. But I was prepared for what followed.

The gentle knock on my door happened at 10:30 p.m. when the clinic was quiet, except for the barking dogs and still crowing roosters. I was informed that a young lady and her husband (I'll call them Alicia and Juan) had been in labor for over a day and their baby had still not delivered. Finally a challenge I knew something about. As is usually the case, this young lady had had no prenatal care. We assembled the team and brought Alicia and Juan into what normally functioned as the minor procedure room. Surrounding the delivery table were five other US-trained physicians. Their specialties included ER medicine, pediatrics, family medicine, and ENT.

With encouragement, patience, and some more time, a 5.5 pound baby with a good cry was delivered into this world. What we didn't know until I checked for the placenta was that there would soon be a second baby making an appearance! Needless to say the twins were a big surprise to this subsistence farmer and his wife. There was much joy as we congratulated the new parents.

We were stunned to learn a year later at our next visit that one of the twins had died some months after birth, likely from severe malnutrition, and the other one was also suffering from severe malnutrition. What was the breakdown that opened the door for such a tragedy? Our team had been unable to coordinate with local healthcare providers to discuss future threats to the twins and appropriate aftercare. Why? We were a short-term missions team, and that meant we had limited time in country. Furthermore, most of the local healthcare workers had taken advantage of our presence by going on leave while we were there.

Before I address the implications of a story like this for short-term medical missions, I need to bring a second but related problem into view—the differing worldviews of Western-trained medical personnel and those we seek to serve in other cultures.

A Change in Worldview

Little exists to illuminate how the early church and the church after the apostolic age integrated the teaching, preaching, and healing ministries. But we do know that the worldview behind Christian ministries of healing and accompanying the dying reflected a holistic worldview in which the material and spiritual were inseparably intertwined. "The Western mind was above all else theistic. Virtually without question, all life and nature were assumed to be under the supervision of a personal God whose intentions toward humans were perfect and whose power was unlimited" (Hiebert 2008, 141).

During the ensuing 1,500 years or so this view of human beings and their world slowly changed. What had been a traditional holistic understanding of the world and daily life gave way to a dualistic view that separated the material from the spiritual, that separated a human being into a body and a soul. Hiebert asserts that the rise of this material-spiritual dualism in the modern worldview was a result of the reintroduction of the ideas of Aristotle, Plato, and Ptolemy to Europe in the thirteenth century with the return of pilgrims from the Crusades (Hiebert 2008, 143). The result of this sacred-secular dualism was the subdivision of our understandings of human beings and human life. Sadly, this new worldview took up residence within the Western church and its theology. The material world was the world of empirical science, while the spiritual world was set aside as the domain of the church. Science and doctors attended to the material part of human beings. Our inner beliefs, especially about things spiritual, were left to the church and Sunday morning. Our religion and spirituality had little to do with how we lived our professional lives during the week.

This change in worldview is important to the topic of short-term medical missions. Western-trained professionals, including Christians, are thoroughly infected with this dualistic frame. Yet this worldview does not reflect the daily lives or beliefs of most of the world's poor. In traditional cultures, people still see life as an integrated interaction between the material (seen) and the unseen spiritual world (Hiebert 1982, 35ff.). The bottom line is that we and they see health and healing in very different ways.

The Short-Term Missions Tsunami

In the last quarter century, a new missions trend has developed that is impacting the way healthcare professionals are involved in cross-cultural health-related ministry. I refer to it as the "short-term missions tsunami."

> The number of lay people in the United States involved in short-term missions grew from an estimated 540 in 1965 to 22,000 in 1979. By 1989 it had grown to an estimated 120,000 and three years later the figure had doubled to 250,000. It is now estimated that there were at least one million short-termers in 2003. (B. Smith 2006)

Sadly, no research exists that allows a firm count of how many of these short-term missions folk are healthcare professionals going to examine and treat sick people. This author estimates that figure to be at least 10 percent or more, or in excess of 100,000. The overall investment in time, money, and material resources is surely well into the hundreds of millions of dollars.

Furthermore, the very important unanswered question for these well-meaning Christian health workers is what the kingdom of God is receiving in return for this immense expenditure of God's people and their resources. Is short-term medical missions promoting a biblical model of health as shalom, or is it promoting something more secular? If it is not promoting health as shalom, is there anything we can do to correct this failing?

The situation is something like this: Churches, with many faithful members and a commitment to missions, are zealous to do "good" anywhere in the world. These dedicated individuals are often highly trained and very skilled at what they do, especially when it comes to volunteers who are medical professionals. But more often than not their worldview reflects the modernist worldview just described. This is exacerbated by the fact that the people they seek to care for function with a worldview that is much more integrated and holistic than their own (Hiebert 2008, chaps. 5 and 6).

Why do I think this point is important to make? Because it matters how the Western-trained healthcare professional is viewed by those who are involved in cross-cultural healthcare ministries. These highly educated and technically very savvy professionals carry immense influence. To many they seem godlike. Unknown to them, this influence may well determine who or what gets the glory from the effectiveness of our health and healing efforts. Jayakumar Christian states, "Whatever we put at the center of the program during its lifetime will tend to be what the community worships in the end" (quoted in Myers 2011, 313).

Our Western reductionist approach to patient care, with its strong emphasis on curative care using medications, high-tech imaging techniques, and surgical procedures, ends up presenting those tools and the "gods" who know how to use them as the explanation for our healing efforts. Our professionalism and the perceived power of our tools get the praise, as God is no longer necessary to explain why and how healing took place. Furthermore, there is no narrative that gives God the glory for having provided these tools in the first place. (See chap. 3 in this book.)

Setting a New Standard

I propose that the following elements are necessary as we strive to overcome old paradigms in order to achieve health as shalom in our short-term healthcare ministry work.

A DEEPER UNDERSTANDING OF HEALTH

First and foremost, we who seek to live out this concept of health as shalom must develop a more biblically based understanding of what a genuinely Christian view of health and healing might look like. Our best source for this is God's word, and we would do well to make every effort to understand health as God has revealed it to us in Scripture, apart from our cultural biases. This is most effectively done in a cross-cultural group context and with someone well versed in interpreting Scripture. The contents of this book on health missions are a good place to start.

Another good resource for this type of study can be found at the Summer Medical Institute website, which has posted an excellent Bible study tool on the subject (www.mcophilly.org; see under Resources > Written Studies). This more comprehensive understanding of health as shalom must become a more central part of all of the church's teaching, working at the level of the family, church, university, or seminary/medical school.

HEALTH AS SHALOM THROUGH WHOLE-PERSON CARE

Once we have a deeper, more biblical understanding of health, we must learn to apply this knowledge to caring for the whole person. Dan Fountain addresses this issue in his chapter on putting the whole person back together (see also chap. 1 in this book; Fountain 1989). In the West there has been a progressive, though as yet incomplete, movement away from a strictly biophysical model of patient care to a bio-psycho-social model and now even to a bio-psycho-spiritual model (King 2000, 6). This is a welcome change that offers the church an excellent opportunity to demonstrate once again the type of shalom-promoting health care that Jesus modeled for us during his ministry. But the unanswered and often unasked question is whether or not this biblical holism is something that can effectively be promoted within current short-term medical missions practice. This question has not yet been addressed, let alone answered.

HEALTH AS SHALOM THROUGH KINGDOM PARTNERSHIPS

Next, I believe we can promote the concept of health as shalom in the partnerships we form cross-culturally. For some this may be the only true form of experiencing shalom with a person of another culture. Most healthcare professionals involved in cross-cultural healthcare missions do not have the tools (sufficient grasp of the local language and local cultural practices) to effectively form long-term relationships with the patients they are treating, nor do they have the time necessary to do so. We saw this in the case that began this chapter. But in our global partnerships between short-term mission teams and healthcare professionals on the ground, we must seek this level of mutual understanding, trust, and accountability. This requires partnerships built on a sense of mutuality that avoids paternalism, unhealthy dependency, and one-sidedness.

> You North Americans love to talk about accountability and always want to see the books to make sure every penny is accounted for. But if we are going to be in true partnership shouldn't we from the underdeveloped nation partner have the right then to come to the US to examine your books to see how your church is using the money the Lord has given you? (Pastor from Mexico at a mission conference at Trinity Evangelical Divinity School)

My countless conversations over the eleven years I served in Central America confirmed that this is how most partners in underdeveloped nations feel.

Phil Butler, in his important work *Well Connected: Releasing Power, Restoring Hope through Kingdom Partnerships,* when outlining true partnership principles, states,

> Trust, openness, and mutual concern are vital ingredients. Partnerships are more than coordination, planning, strategies, and tactics. The heart of the gospel is restored relationships. God longs for Jesus' finished work to be demonstrated in our relationships. Investing time in

getting to know, understand, and genuinely appreciate
each other isn't optional. (2006, 16)

True partnership should be a reflection of our unity as brothers and sisters in Christ. Unity in Christ is what God desires to see happening between God's people. This is not an optional element of our cross-cultural work in health-related ministry. After all, Jesus gave us this vision:

I do not ask for these only, but also for those who will believe in me through their word, that they may all be one, just as you, Father, are in me, and I in you, that they also may be in us, so that the world may believe that you have sent me. The glory that you have given me I have given to them, that they may be one even as we are one, I in them and you in me, that they may become perfectly one, so that the world may know that you sent me and loved them even as you loved me. (John 17:20–23 ESV)

One of the major weaknesses I have seen during my experience in cross-cultural ministry is a lack of strategic thinking and a severe lack of understanding of the complexity of the situations we put our healthcare professionals into. Satan is extremely opportunistic in his efforts to derail any kingdom initiative and uses all the tools at his disposal to do so. We must be equally strategic—something done most effectively in true partnership.

Those with whom we are working in an underdeveloped part of the world will know far more about the most effective strategies to overcome local challenges than those who come from outside that context. But are those from a Western setting, highly trained and technically very savvy, ready to humble themselves to the point of being used by the local partner in the way the local partner sees as most strategic? I am not saying the outsiders have nothing to offer, but rather that they need to honor local knowledge and listen as well as talk.

A final point to be made regarding partnerships is that this should be the central way in which knowledge sharing occurs. It is truly tragic that too often hubris and/or lack of time in a country means that too many healthcare professionals work in underdeveloped countries without ever attempting to share their knowledge with local healthcare providers. Programs such as CMDA's Medical Education International are an excellent example of how this can be made a reality.

HEALTH AS SHALOM BY AVOIDING HARM

One of the best-known mantras of the medical profession is "First, do no harm" (C. Smith 2005, 371–72). Christian healthcare workers, especially when working in another country and a different culture, must consider the possible harm that any intervention might cause.

In their very popular work, *When Helping Hurts,* Corbett and Fikkert (2009) use the following formula to illustrate how well-intended development efforts may nonetheless cause harm (see fig. 9.1). A solely material understanding of poverty joins feelings of superiority on the part of the non-poor, which in turn reinforces feelings of inferiority on the part of the poor—all of which can result in "good deeds" that may unintentionally create harm.

Figure 9.1: A formula for unintended harm
(Corbett and Fikkert 2009, 67)

I would propose a similar warning to those of us in short-term healthcare missions. I suggest that a modern/secular definition of health that is joined to a bias or firm belief in Western biomedical solutions can collide unhelpfully with the more holistic worldviews of traditional cultures in ways that do more harm than good (fig. 9.2). This is a very simple way of explaining the major reason why our efforts at helping people suffering

with illnesses have so often failed to create the transformation we desire
to see in the lives and communities in which we serve.

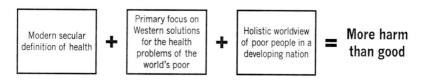

Figure 9.2: A formula for more harm than good

HEALTH AS SHALOM THROUGH EXCELLENCE

The final point I will make relates to the dedication we must show
towards excellence in all we do in our cross-cultural health-related missions efforts. During my medical training, dedication to excellence was
drilled into us from the very beginning, though perhaps not in direct
terms: During Friday morning grand rounds, the presenter was faced
with humiliation if she or he could not explain, usually under withering
questioning from professors, why the avenue of treatment they chose was
the best option for their patient. The implication was that if you chose,
in their opinion, the wrong option, you may have caused more harm
than good and you may not be worthy of the title of medical doctor. In
private practice we are constantly being asked to account for our actions
in the form of monthly departmental meetings where we must explain
such things as our C-section rates and the rate at which our patients had
to return to the OR within twenty-four hours after surgery. Do we take
this same sense of expecting excellence in our efforts and doing no harm
into the cross-cultural health-related ministry setting? Can true shalom
occur if we are not doing our best? "So, whether you eat or drink, or
whatever you do, do all to the glory of God" (1 Cor 10:31 ESV).

When we combine this dedication to excellence with a deep understanding of health as shalom and a team-based whole-person approach to
addressing the needs of the sick through true kingdom partnerships, we

have an incredibly powerful means by which to witness to the kingdom of God on this earth.

Summing Up

In this chapter I provided an explanation of the much more holistic nature of health as seen from a biblical viewpoint than from that of Western medicine. This can best be understood as we study the Hebrew concept of shalom, as Bryant Myers has done in the opening chapters of this book.

I also attempted to give the reader an understanding of the roots of the short-term "medical missions" movement and how it became infected with the dualism that has led to serious problems in cross-cultural health-related missions. I have made suggestions about how to overcome our shortcomings in order to promote and conduct health-related missions activities that have at the center of all our efforts the shalom that Christ brings.

References Cited

Butler, Phill. 2006. *Well Connected: Releasing Power, Restoring Hope through Kingdom Partnerships*. Waynesboro, GA: Authentic.

Corbett, Steve, and Brian Fikkert. 2009. *When Helping Hurts: How to Alleviate Poverty without Hurting the Poor . . . and Yourself.* Chicago: Moody.

Fountain, Daniel E. 1989. *Health, the Bible and the Church*. BGC Monograph. Wheaton, IL: Billy Graham Center.

Hiebert, Paul G. 1982. "The Flaw of the Excluded Middle." *Missiology: An International Review* 10 (1): 35–47.

———. 2008. *Transforming Worldviews: An Anthropological Understanding of How People Change*. Grand Rapids, MI: Baker Academic.

King, Dana E. 2000. *Faith, Spirituality, and Medicine: Toward the Making of the Healing Practitioner*. Binghamton, NY: Haworth Pastoral Press.

Myers, Bryant L. 2011. *Walking with the Poor: Principles and Practices of Transformational Development*. Revised and updated ed. Maryknoll, NY: Orbis.

Smith, Brittany. 2006. "Short-Term Mission Trip or Donor-Paid Vacation?" *Evangelical Press News Service*, October 19.

Smith, Cedric. 2005. "Origin and Uses of *Primum Non Nocere*—Above All, Do No Harm!" *Journal of Clinical Pharmacology* 45: 371–77.

CHAPTER 10

Seeking Shalom at the End of Life
Cooperating with God's Magnificent Design

Rebecca Gagne Henderson,
APRN, ACHPN

A good scientist understands three things—what we know, what we don't know, what we believe.
OTIS BRAWLEY

Can faith-based medicine also be evidenced-based medicine? This is a question posed by Otis Brawley (2012), the chief medical and scientific officer and executive vice president of the American Cancer Society. My answer to this is, emphatically, yes. It could be argued that every medical text, every medical discovery, and every successful medical intervention is evidence of God's existence. Science is the study of God's handiwork. Indeed, the human body has been fearfully and wonderfully made:

For you created my inmost being;
you knit me together in my mother's womb.
I praise you because I am fearfully and wonderfully made;
your works are wonderful,
I know that full well.
My frame was not hidden from you
when I was made in the secret place,
when I was woven together in the depths of the earth.
Your eyes saw my unformed body;
All the days ordained for me were written in your book
before one of them came to be. (Ps 139:13–16)

God has a plan for his people, even for those who are suffering. Consider this famous text addressed to Israel in exile: "'For I know the plans I have for you,' declares the Lord, 'plans to prosper you and not to harm you, plans to give you hope and a future'" (Jer 29:11). The Hebrew word here often translated "prosper" is *shalom*, the deep peace and well-being God desires for us even amidst challenges and pain. While there are a great many verses that illustrate similar promises, these two examples point to God's involvement in the great and small events of our lives. He has planned for all things concerning us. We readily accept God's involvement and design for our births; why would there be less involvement when we walk in the "shadow of death"? God does have a plan for everything. These two texts of Scripture offer an insight into how God's promise of providence is present in our lives throughout all phases of life. And as the Creator, he never abandons us.

Yet healthcare providers in the mission field or in any healthcare setting—chaplain, nurse, physician, psychologist, or social worker—may find it difficult to watch helplessly as our patients die. We sometimes writhe in our inability to rob death of the end to "this mortal coil," as Hamlet puts it. Each member of the healthcare team is subject to doubt, sadness, and fear, as it is painful to see families' grief (Tillich 2000, 168). End-of-life situations may lead us to question our clinical skills and our place in God's plan for shalom in such spaces. But if we are open to it, the end of life provides one of many times when health care and soul care can overlap and promote others' well-being as God intended.

Instead of seeing ourselves as hopeless in the face of death, we can learn from the physiology of our death and see how it provides a window into the intricacies of God's work. Even here we are never alone or forsaken; God keeps his promises. It is lamentable that in our training as providers and clinicians we are not taught the processes of death but rather only how to thwart these processes.

For example, controversy abounds regarding the ethical aspects of the decision to withhold or withdraw artificial nutrition and hydration

(ANH) for the seriously ill and dying patient. While many medical ethicists have concluded that the withdrawal/withholding of ANH can be moral, the Catholic document Ethical and Religious Directives for Catholic Health Care Services (ERD) remains ambiguous: while futile care should not be employed, removal of technology should not directly cause death (USCCB 2009). Debate over such treatment has been smoldering since the Kathleen Quinlan case in the 1970s and blew open again in 2004 with the Terri Schiavo case (Emanuel 1991). However, an understanding of the correlation between how our bodies die and God's mercy helps us navigate these difficult decisions. This appreciation for God's design can lead to patient and family acceptance of the loss of a loved one while offering meaning and purpose to physical death (Ps 145:8–10).

This chapter explores the recent history of this controversy of ANH during end-of-life care; the physiology of death, dehydration, and starvation; scriptural evidence that such physiology exhibits God's mercy toward humanity; and a comparison between Judeo-Christian and secular worldviews regarding this phenomenon. In conclusion, the chapter suggests how this knowledge provides an opportunity to witness to those we serve and how this understanding can be a source of shalom to patients and families while giving the glory to God.

Background

The discussion surrounding the withholding and withdrawal of ANH weaves sociocultural, religious, ethical, and political concerns into a complex web. Discussions tend to polarize, making reasoned debate challenging and indulgence in emotional diatribes tempting for many.

The Schiavo case vividly displayed this. In 2004 and 2005 the television news was fraught with the polemics over a young woman named Terri Schiavo who was in a permanent vegetative state (PVS) (Goodman 2010). The controversy lay in the decision by her next of kin, husband Michael Schiavo, to withdraw ANH from his wife after seven years of being in a PVS. Having been without oxygen after collapsing in her home, Terri Schiavo suffered irreversible anoxic brain injury. She received a formal diagnosis of PVS. In her case, she eventually displayed a "wakeful state of unconsciousness" in which she was awake (i.e., her eyes were open) yet was unaware of her surroundings and lacked conscious or voluntary reactions. A patient in this state of "wakeful unconsciousness" for more than one year is referred to as being in a "persistent vegetative" or "minimally conscious" state.

Ignoring the titillating and melodramatic gossip surrounding the case, what is particularly important for the purposes of this chapter is the arguments put forward by people of great national influence and admiration in the Christian community, intelligent men and women of God. Many of them claimed that withdrawal of ANH would result in Ms. Schiavo's torturous and cruel death, leaving her to a fate of forced starvation. Confoundingly, many asserted and were looked to for leadership while actually being ill informed; they displayed medical and spiritual ignorance about the nuances of this case but felt compelled to offer opinions and exert pressure through mass media. This case became the first such ANH controversy to be influenced by social media, including a blog kept in Terri's name (Malkin 2005). Between posts, cable and broadcast news, iconic television hosts, and bombastic radio talk show personalities, the message was inescapable: Many called for the government to intervene to order continued ANH for Schiavo. In counterpoint, others offered an equally polarizing viewpoint, framing the case as a "right to die." Between these two polarizing options lay an important if obscured truth about the dying process and how God's mercy can be embedded in natural processes.

Scripture and Science

In biblical times, and until the last century's discovery of antibiotics and other medical advances, a person's loss of ability to swallow, defecate, or breathe well served as evidence that this was his time to die. An obvious

Scripture speaking about such attentiveness to a time for death is Ecclesiastes 3:1,2: "There is a time for everything, and a season for every activity under the heavens: a time to be born and a time to die, a time to plant and a time to uproot." Similarly, the scientific mind recognizes this; one need not go further than a high school human biology text to understand that physiologic mechanisms are required to sustain life. With the cessation of any one of these processes, our life ceases.

As people of faith we are blessed to know Scripture as a source of strength; even in this most difficult season we are able to trust God and his word. "Are not five sparrows sold for two pennies? Yet not one of them is forgotten by God. Indeed, the very hairs of your head are all numbered. Don't be afraid; you are worth more than many sparrows" (Luke 12:6,7). When we call out for mercy, God answers us (e.g., Matt 7:7). So as we consider withdrawal or withholding of treatment at this stage of life, we must also seek to cooperate with our God of mercy as healthcare providers, pastors, and counselors.

Risks and Benefits of ANH

We find ourselves in the twenty-first century with an accumulation of incredible technologies. We are able to sustain the oxygenation of human tissue—whether it be skeletal, cardiac, or brain tissue—with the assistance of ventilators, CPR, and (in very late heart disease) ventricular assistance devices. We can divert human waste from the bowel through a stoma into a collection bag that lies between the patient and her clothing. We can simulate the work of the kidneys with continuous renal replacement therapy to provide ongoing renal dialysis. We are often able to impede the inevitability of physical death indeterminately.

For those unable to ingest food on their own, we can place a temporary nasogastric tube through the nose and into the stomach (NGT) or a permanent percutaneous endogastric tube (PEG) by incising a hole through the abdominal wall and threading a tube somewhere along the gastrointestinal tract and suturing the tube into place. We are then able to implement ANH through the tube. For patients with reversible conditions, this is an incredible blessing. However, this is not the case for those who have irreversible conditions. In the case of frail elderly people with dementia—a progressive condition that affects the ability to absorb nutrients—ANH becomes the means by which a patient will most likely experience recurrent episodes of aspiration pneumonia or other infections. These can lead to multiple hospitalizations, pressure ulcers, fluid overload, and the prospect of a prolonged death. One study found that of those to whom ANH was given in order to control various common symptoms, 75 percent of the patients perceived that this procedure failed to benefit them (Raijmakers 2011).

When patients begin to die, the gastrointestinal system along with other body systems begins to fail. One of the first signals of this is often an inability to swallow. Patients with end-stage dementia, or sometimes the old and/or those with other illnesses (e.g., chronic obstructive pulmonary disease [COPD], heart disease, or cancer), become very weak and unable to eat. This usually indicates that the person is nearing death (Coakley and Ellershaw 2007). In such circumstances the feeding tube will not change the disease outcome and offers no meaningful contribution to comfort (Sullivan 2007).

For patients who are alert and able to participate in regular activities but have lost the ability to swallow and eat, a feeding tube may be a helpful way for them to continue to be nourished. Patients who fall into this category include those with ALS (Lou Gehrig's disease), multiple sclerosis, and some kinds of cancer. While these diseases may eventually result in the patient's loss of life, a feeding tube may extend the time a patient has some quality of life.

Normally the procedure for placing the feeding tube itself is not medically complicated; it is widely believed by families and some doctors that these tubes can prevent pneumonia. However, this belief is false. Rather, patients with feeding tubes have no decreased risk of pneumonia and may even be at increased risk for it (Sullivan 2007; Finucane,

Christmas, and Travis 1999). In addition, the tube can foster other problems such as bleeding at the tube site in the abdomen, infection at the site, oozing and leakage, diarrhea, abdominal pain, vomiting, and nausea (CCCC 2012).

While it may seem that concerns about such interventions might not apply in contexts with few supplies or little access to technology, I am unfortunately aware of the ingenuity of many medical missionaries and aid workers. I once knew a secular physician who specialized in tropical medicine who described to me how he treated a man in the bush with advanced cancer and a urinary blockage. He used a coke bottle and some sort of tubing, performed surgery, and inserted a supra-pubic catheter (a tube that goes directly into the bladder for drainage). While an imaginative apparatus in the moment, we can easily imagine what kind of witness this was to the patient and locals once the team left: the tubing would inevitably become clogged or infected, leaving the patient to die in a horrible way that would probably be attributed to the "humanitarian" mission team. We are a creative lot. However, we need to temper our creativity and ingenuity with wisdom. This physician had nothing but good intentions, yet he failed to consider the possible difficulties he was leaving in his wake. As this story illustrates, we must always align end-of-life medical care with the natural processes of dying so that the patient experiences shalom and wholeness as much as possible.

The Physiology of Dehydration and Starvation

It is the most natural thing in the world for all of us—families and clinicians alike—to want to feed and hydrate the patient. Food and water hold a great deal of meaning to all cultures. The meaning of food includes nurturing, love, fun, sustenance, and life itself. To withhold nutrition feels counterintuitive to the way we as humans understand caring for those we love or who are in our charge. However, even those who are not medical professionals need to understand the sometimes difficult reality of how our bodies die and specifically how food and water can actually cause harm at the end of life. With such knowledge, we can come alongside the dying so that we not only intend to care, but also actually cooperate with bodily processes as much as possible to offer comfort and healing at the end of life.

THE PHYSIOLOGY OF STARVATION

First, it is important to address the misconceptions that accompany the withdrawal or withholding of ANH. Probably the one most commonly encountered is, "You are going to starve the patient to death." Actually, starvation is a long physiological course that can take up to three months to occur in the healthy individual. For those with end-stage cancer and other terminal illnesses, starvation may already be occurring by the time ANH becomes a concern due to the natural course of the disease (Saudek and Felig 1976). Understanding starvation and its relationship to hydration helps us understand how to care for patients and accurately assess how our actions regarding ANH affect a dying patient. Starvation occurs in three stages.

Post-absorptive stage. After not consuming nutrition for a day or two, our liver begins to release stored glycogen to sustain us, as this is then readily converted to glucose. The liver has a limited supply of glycogen, lasting only a couple of days. As the stores of glycogen are depleted, a process known as glyconeolysis concurrently begins (Nillson and Hultman 1973). This stage occurs in the 3–5 days after the last consumption of nutrition (Goldblatt 1925). Once the liver is completely depleted of glycogen, the body continues in the post-absorptive stage through converting fat and protein to glycerol and producing ketones as a byproduct. Ketones sustain our brain and, very interestingly, also give us a sense of satiation (Johnstone et al. 2008).

Sustained starvation. This period occurs for up to 5–7 weeks after ceasing nutrition intake and is marked by the onset of gluconeogenesis. Gluconeogenesis is a remarkably complex process in which the kidneys and liver utilize protein and fat broken down from the muscle and organs that are catabolized to be used as energy to continue nourishing the body.

Prolonged and terminal starvation. During this period gluconeogenesis slows and the body is left to sustain itself solely on ketones. Death occurs as late as 3 months after the complete absence of nutrition.

While this process may be difficult to consider, it is important for us to examine where God is in all of this. You will recall that earlier we discussed how ketones provide the sensation of satiation. It is heartening to know that as ketones are produced, simultaneously dynorphins are produced through the breakdown of proteins. These dynorphins are a type of endogenous opiate that is 6–10 times more potent than morphine and also provides an analgesic and anesthetic action (they are known as kappa agonists). An anesthetic effect is different from an analgesic effect (pain relief). Anesthesia blunts feeling and causes drowsiness and apathy. This drowsiness and apathy allow for relaxation and an indifference to what is happening. To a healthy person this is distressing to imagine, but it comforts an individual at the end of the long process of starvation. God has a plan for everything. Also note that when we withdraw or withhold ANH from a patient, the starvation process does not cause the patient's death unless he is already near starvation due to being in the late stages of the disease process.

DEHYDRATION

The patient who has ANH withheld or withdrawn will die not of starvation but rather usually of dehydration. Typically, these are patients who have end-stage dementia or have suffered catastrophic strokes. Particularly painful or contentious might be the decision to withdraw ANH after it has been provided, as was the case for Terri Schiavo. Difficulties arise when well-meaning clinicians recommend ANH to the dying patient or the family but do so without a full understanding of the physiology of dehydration. The failure to appropriately recognize and diagnose the patient as dying obviously contributes to this difficulty.

This proves much easier in a patient's home or in a clinic, but it is less clear and sometimes confounded in a hospital setting in which the "curative" model prevails (Coakley and Ellershaw 2007). As with the accusation that we are starving a dying patient if we withdraw or withhold ANH, another common misunderstanding is that such a patient will be thirsty and experience pain during the dehydration process. This is a biologically complex process and will be simplified here for our purposes, as the intricacies of dehydration go beyond the scope of this chapter.

When we are no longer able to swallow and do not consume food or fluids, our kidneys continue to function and produce urine—a process that requires enough blood volume to create pressure against the kidneys to filter waste from our blood. When the kidneys continue to produce urine without fluid replacement, the blood volume decreases and thus our blood pressure decreases (Guyton and Hall 2011).

At this point the compensatory mechanisms of dehydration begin. With the depletion of blood volume, baroreceptors (receptors that detect when blood pressure is low) recognize the need to increase the pressure. They signal the brain to release vasopressin, a hormone that causes the blood vessels to constrict and thus work to increase our blood pressure. As vasopressin is released from the pituitary gland, endorphin is also released from the pituitary (Guyton and Hall 2011; Beurers, Hertting, and Knepel 1982). Endorphins are similar to dynorphins as endogenous opiates (Guyton and Hall 2011; Beurers, Hertting, and Knepel 1982). As our body attempts to regulate its homeostasis, these endorphins provide analgesia and euphoria; when vasopressin is released, a closely related hormone known as oxytocin is co-expressed from the pituitary. As dehydration progresses, our body increases the release of these three hormones. Meanwhile, the kidneys begin a process leading to the release of a stronger vasopressor known as angiotensin II (Guyton and Hall 2011). The additional angiotensin II causes increased release of vasopressin and oxytocin (Kadekaro et al. 2001).

As this process continues and one's blood pressure decreases, compensatory mechanisms begin to fail and the heart and respiratory rates increase, which increases CO_2 levels. These CO_2 levels further promote release of endorphins. Inexorably, the respiratory rate slows and the heart stops, resulting in death. Like the more commonly known depressive effect of morphine upon respiration, the release of endorphins and dynorphins correlates with the decrease in respiratory rate (Moss and Scarpelli 1981; Gamble and Milne 1990).

All three of the substances—endorphins, oxytocin, and vasopressin—arise from the hypothalamus and are released from the pituitary (Guyton and Hall 2011). We have already discussed the comforting actions of endorphins, but what about oxytocin?

Oxytocin is sometimes referred to as the "love hormone," and it is released in numerous situations, such as during labor and immediately following childbirth. When a woman breastfeeds, her body releases oxytocin, which provides a feeling of love and well-being to the mother, but it is also passed through the milk to the baby and promotes bonding. Our bodies also release oxytocin at orgasm, and it is responsible for what is colloquially known in sex as the "afterglow" (Carmichael et al. 1987). It can also be released when we have a good, cathartic cry (Sullivan et al. 2002, 314), sometimes resulting in what we know as "crying ourselves to sleep." And this hormone is released at the hour of our death. Again, God has a plan.

The Role of the Caregiver

"For I was hungry and you gave me something to eat, I was thirsty and you gave me something to drink, I was a stranger and you invited me in" (Matt 25:35). After having exhausted the technology available to prolong life, I often hear providers say to families and patients, "There is nothing more that we can do." This could not be further from the truth.

Christ calls us to comfort and minister to one another, whether family or stranger. First, as a caregiver, the greatest gift at the end of life is, by your presence, to bear witness and affirm life through love and compassion. We are not so much actively doing something as we are being present as a caregiver (Howarth and Leaman 2001). We can hold the patient's hand, wipe her brow, and bear witness to her pain and suffering and thus love her. We have the extraordinary yet simple opportunity to exemplify God's promise by not leaving her to die alone. Notably, oxytocin is also released through touch, so that the simple gesture of holding someone's hand or rubbing her back can be a source of comfort to both the caregiver and the patient (Morhenn et al. 2008).

As we provide care for the dying patient, simple and basic "nursing" tasks remain, including offering water and food, as he is able and willing to tolerate them. This addresses another misunderstanding regarding withdrawal/withholding of ANH—that the patient is denied food and water. In hospice and palliative care generally, patients who desire them and are alert and able to swallow can take small amounts of water or food at the end of life (ELNC 2012; Ferrell and Coyle 2010). If the patient is not, the caregiver can provide oral care, keeping the mouth moist with a water-soaked swab or cloth. This is important, as it keeps the mucosa moist and keeps the lips from cracking and chafing. During this time, many wonder whether the patient experiences thirst. There is evidence that as dehydration progresses, the patient exhibits a "thirst deficit," which often is more pronounced in the elderly. One study found that the relief of thirst was obtained by moistening of the oral cavity (Phillips et al. 1984). In my own professional practice over the course of eighteen years, I have found that the first day or two when offered fluids with a swab, the patient will suck the water off of the swab, but by the end of the second day the patient will resist the swab even for moistening the mucosa.

Beyond this, other basic care includes keeping the patient clean and warm (or cool) and repositioning the patient to prevent wounds and alleviate pain from lying in the same position for long periods of time (Ferrell 2010; ELNC 2012). Common symptoms at the end of life include pain, anxiety/agitation, shortness of breath, constipation, nausea and vomiting, and fever (Ferrell 2010). For these and other symptoms, care providers can administer a wide variety of basic medications, such as morphine, Ativan, Compazine, Tylenol, and Senna.

Trust God

Medicine has traditionally understood anxiety as a medical or psychological problem. Wisely, this tendency is diminishing with the realization that anxiety is also a spiritual crisis. Paul Tillich discusses humankind's anxiety and fear of death, noting that the healing of anxiety and fear in the spiritual domain is equally important as (and in my opinion, more important than) the cure (Tillich 2000). Healing is what God promises us, and I have witnessed incredible and miraculous spiritual healing in my practice. In cooperating with God, we need to distinguish between curing and healing, as well as between life and living.

As noted by the ecological pioneer Charles Elton and others, one of the processes required to sustain life is symbiosis, or "interaction with other organisms." Obvious to those who study them, these communal interactions of organisms are necessary for life and survival. As scientists, we know what these interactions look like in a Petri dish or under a photon microscope, yet we may not acknowledge this at the macro-level and sometimes forget that we are organisms. We observe it in the rutting of bucks in the forest during spring, the spawning of fish in a stream, but it also happens when putting your toddler's shoes and socks on, making a cup of tea for someone you love, holding the hand of your mother in her sickness, and your mother's gaze into your eyes before she dies. Once these interactions have ceased, so has life.

In nursing school, I recall being taught not to tell patients "everything will be alright." I was told that this wasn't true and gave people false hope. With experience I have learned that this advice was false. Rather, whatever happens to us, everything *will* be all right. But this is not because we will be cured; rather, it is because we are never alone or forsaken (Heb 13:5).

Participating in God's Mercy at the End of Life

A secular worldview tells us that we are born in order to perpetuate the species. As offspring grow, the only reason our parents protect us is that our species has been programmed to protect our young, so that they too may fulfill their purpose of perpetuating the next generation. We are designed to fight, struggle, and compete for survival. Once our time to die comes, we hopefully have fulfilled this mission. Our purpose served, we then continue to be useful by providing nutrients to the earth as our bodies decompose. We might be tempted to assume this merely natural mindset, even if only unconsciously, when we come alongside others at the end of life.

But if we assume the Christian vision of a God who desires shalom and makes our participation in this possible, then we need not adopt the stance that our actions must serve some evolutionary or utilitarian purpose. As we have seen, there are also mechanisms in the natural order that testify to God's mercy and steadfast love for his children—every one of us, regardless of gender, status, race, culture, or religion. In addition to the Christian hope for eternal life, this mechanism points to our loving Creator, who cares deeply for his creation. We can find solace in this realization during these very trying times, and embrace death not merely as difficult but also as a season that reveals God's magnanimous design.

Despite our best intentions, in our very human and fallen way we sometimes block these mechanisms and thwart God's provision in creation at the end of our earthly existence (Rom 8:28). Armed with knowledge, a missionary in the field can share this understanding with patients as they search for hope and make medical decisions amidst the dying process. We can welcome this season as an opportunity to share another dimension of God's love, offering a source of shalom by cooperating with the holistic care of God provided to us even at the end of life.

References Cited

Beurers, U., G. Hertting, and W. Knepel. 1982. "Release of P-Lipotropin and P-Endorphin-Like Material Induced by Angiotensin in the Conscious Rat." *British Journal of Pharmacology* 76: 579–85.

Brawley, O. 2012. "Prostate Cancer Screening: What We Know, Don't Know, and Believe." *The Annals of Internal Medicine* 157 (2): 135–36.

Carmichael, M. S., R. Humbert, J. Dixen, G. Palmisano, W. Greenleaf, and J. M. Davidson. 1987. "Plasma Oxytocin Increases in the Human Sexual Response." *The Journal of Clinical Endocrinology and Metabolism* 64 (1): 27–31.

Coakley, A., and J. Ellershaw. 2007. "The Terminal Phase." *Medicine* 36 (2): 105–8.

Coalition for Compassionate Care in California (CCCC). 2012. "Tube Feeding: A Guide for Decision Making."

Emanuel, Ezekiel J. 1991. *The Ends of Human Life: Medical Ethics in a Liberal Polity.* Cambridge, MA: Harvard University Press.

End of Life Nursing Consortium (ELNC). 2012. "Advancing End of Life Nursing Care." City of Hope National Medical Center and American Association of Colleges of Nursing.

Ferrell, B., and N. Coyle. 2010. *Oxford Textbook of Palliative Nursing.* 3rd ed. Oxford: Oxford University Press.

Finucane, T. E., C. Christmas, and K. Travis. 1999. "Tube Feeding in Patients with Advanced Dementia: A Review of the Evidence." *Journal of the American Medical Association* 282 (14): 1365–70.

Gamble, G. D., and R. J. Milne. 1990. "Hypercapnia Depresses Nociception: Endogenous Opioids Implicated." *Brain Research* 514 (2): 198–205.

Goldblatt, M. W. 1925. "CXXXIX. Observations on the Effect of Various Carbohydrates on the Ketosis of Starvation in Human Subjects." From the Medical Unit Laboratories, St Thomas's Hospital, London. *Biochemical Journal* 19 (6): 948–57.

Goodman, Kenneth W., ed. 2010. *The Case of Terri Schiavo: Ethics, Politics, and Death in the 21st Century.* Oxford: Oxford University Press.

Guyton, A. C., and J. E. Hall. 2011. *Textbook of Medical Physiology.* 12th ed. Philadelphia: Saunders, Elsevier.

Howarth, G., and O. Leaman, eds. 2001. *Encyclopedia of Death and Dying.* London: Routledge.

Johnstone, A. M., G. W. Horgan, S. D. Murison, D. M. Brenner, and G. E. Lobley. 2008. "Effects of a High-Protein Ketogenic Diet on Hunger, Appetite, and Weight Loss on Obese Men Fed Ad Libitum." *American Journal of American Clinical Nutrition* 87 (1): 44–55.

Kadekaro, M., M. L. Terrell, V. Bui, and J. Y. Summy-Long. 2001. "Central Interactions between Angiotensin II and PGD(2) in the Regulation of Vasopressin and Oxytocin Secretion in Dehydrated Rats." *Brain Research* 889 (1–2): 84–88.

Malkin, Michelle. 2005. "The Schiavo Autopsy: A Sober Look." Michelle Malkin website (June 16). http://michellemalkin.com/2005/06/16/the-schiavo-autopsy-a-sober-look/.

Morhenn, V. B., J. W. Park, E. Piper, and P. J. Zak. 2008. "Monetary Sacrifice among Strangers is Mediated by Endogenous Oxytocin Release After Physical Contact." *Evolution and Human Behavior* 29 (6): 375–83.

Moss, I. R., and E. M. Scarpelli. 1981. "Beta-Endorphin Central Depression Respiration and Circulation." *Journal of Applied Physiology: Respiratory, Environmental and Exercise Physiology* 50 (5): 1011–16.

Naim, T., and R. Hammel. 2009. "Compassionate Choices Statement." *The Catholic Health Association* (December).

Nilsson, L. H., and E. Hultman. 1973. "Liver Glycogen in Man—The Effect of Total Starvation or a Carbohydrate-Poor Diet Followed by Carbohydrate Refeeding." *Scandinavian Journal of Clinical and Laboratory Investigation* 32 (4): 325–30.

Phillips, P. A., et al. 1984. "Reduced Thirst after Water Deprivation in Healthy Elderly Men." *The New England Journal of Medicine* 311 (12): 753–59.

Pool, R. 2004. "You're Not Going to Dehydrate Mom, Are You? Euthanasia, *Versterving,* and Good Death in the Netherlands." *Social Science and Medicine* 58 (5): 955–66.

Raijmakers, N., S. Fradsham, L. van Zuylen, C. Mayland, J. Ellershaw, and A. van der Heide. 2011. "Variation in Attitudes towards Artificial Hydration at the End of Life: A Systematic Literature Review." *Current Opinion in Supportive and Palliative Care* 5 (3): 265–72. doi:10.1097/SPC.0b013e3283492ae0.

Robert M. Veatch. 2009. "The Evolution of Death and Dying Controversies." *The Hastings Center Report* 39 (3): 16–19.

Saudek, C. D., and P. Felig. 1976. "The Metabolic Events of Starvation." *The American Journal of Medicine* 60: 117–26.

Smith, S. A., and M. Andrews. 2000. "Artificial Nutrition and Hydration at the End of Life." *Medsurg Nursing* 9 (5): 233–47.

Sullivan, P., P. Mulani, M. Fishman, and D. Sleep. 2007. "Quality of Life Findings from a Multicenter, Multinational, Observational Study of Patients with Metastatic Hormone-Refractory Prostate Cancer." *Quality of Life Research: An International Journal of Quality of Life Aspects of Treatment, Care and Rehabilitation* 16 (4): 571–75.

Sullivan, D. A., M. E. Stern, K. Tsubota, D. A. Dartt, R. M. Sullivan, and B. B. Bromberg, eds. 2002. *Lacrimal Gland, Tear Film, and Dry Eye Syndromes 3: Basic Science and Clinical Relevance Part A*. Advances in Experimental Medicine and Biology 8. New York: Kluwer Academic.

Summy-Long, J. Y., L. M. Rosella-Dampman, G. L. McLemore, and E. Koehler. 1990. "Kappa Opiate Receptors Inhibit Oxytocin from the Magnocellular System During Dehydration." *Neuroendocrinology* 51 (4): 376–84.

Tillich, Paul. 2000. *The Courage to Be*. 2nd ed. New Haven: Yale University Press.

Tucker, Todd. 2007. *The Great Starvation Experiment: Ancel Keys and the Men Who Starved for Science*. Minneapolis: University of Minnesota Press.

United States Conference of Catholic Bishops (USCCB). 2009. "Ethical and Religious Directives for Catholic Health Care Services, Fifth Edition." November 17.

CHAPTER 11

"Jesus Wept"
Why Healing and Hope Require Practices of Lament

Erin Dufault-Hunter, PhD

Introduction

As creative pieces go, the assignment probably didn't classify as "high art," but it was quite striking and beautiful. The triptych (a three-paneled altar piece) was simple in construction and style, but the images were arresting and unexpected. On the left panel was a woman in scrubs. In the middle was a loving Madonna, Mary the mother of Jesus, holding a baby. As I recall, the panel on the right depicted a hospital bed with a female figure lying in it. Upon looking closely, one could see that the figures were made up of tiny pieces of paper with words on them that had been torn, applied to the panels, and then painted. In front of the triptych, the student placed a single votive candle.

As the final project for a medical ethics course, I invite students to respond to the material we have covered either in an academic paper or in a creative art project. This particular student was a nurse in a Neonatal Intensive Care Unit. While often a joyful job, she told the class about how she had to approach the mothers whose babies had just died with clipboard in hand, filling out personal information, line by agonizing line. She recalled how she loathed this cold task, how she couldn't respond to their shock and sorrow. It was those forms, torn into small bits, that supplied the material of the triptych. "I never had the time to mourn for those mothers' losses, never had the time or space to feel their sadness. I had to get on with my job."

In her willingness to be vulnerable, she taught me much about the unique burden healthcare professionals bear as they tend to the needs of patients and bear witness to their pain. She also underscored the need for all Christians to engage in the ancient practice of lament before God.

Healthcare providers must enact Christian hope as they work and care for others. They must also lament the brokenness and pain they regularly experience. If they do not hold both of these elements together, they fail to fully image the one who invites them into his ministry of shalom. To understand how these elements come together in health care, we will first turn to Jesus. He modeled a hope that entails both compassionate action toward a broken world and vulnerable mourning of sin's lingering effects. We will then consider how biblical lament violates the supposed need for healthcare workers to be "professionally detached" from their patients. Lastly, I will propose that biblical lament sustains Christian healthcare workers in faith, hope, and love.

"Jesus Wept": The Model for Best Practice of Christian Hope

Lament is a much-neglected Christian practice. Ellen Davis points out that while the majority of the Psalms could be characterized as laments, our worship services seldom utilize them, preferring the upbeat language of praise and thanksgiving. Ancient Israel, however, "believed that the kind of prayer in which we most need fluency is the loud groan" (Davis 2001, 15; see, e.g., Ps 6).

When I was a child, we were sometimes asked to quote the shortest sentence in the Bible: "Jesus wept." This line appears in John 11, amidst the fantastic story of the raising of Lazarus from the dead. In a quick reading of the passage, one might focus on the triumphant language of Jesus: "I am the resurrection and the life. The one who believes in me will live, even though they die; and whoever lives by believing in me will never die" (John 11:25,26). This wondrous claim becomes reality when Jesus stands before the tomb—from which the stench of decay already seeps—and dramatically commands, "Come out!" Yet there it is, sandwiched between assurances of miracle and the unstoppable power of God: "Jesus wept."

Why? Why would the Christ, the Lord of life and death who is utterly confident of God's victory, become "greatly disturbed in spirit and moved" and break down, crying, even as he is about to perform one of his most spectacular miracles? Verse 33 notes that he sees Mary weeping as well as those Jews who were with her. He responds by "groaning" in his spirit (KJV).

Some assert that Jesus is grieved at the disbelief of the people. Such a myopic interpretation does not account for his attention to his close friend Mary's distress, nor for the fact that some—such as Martha—clearly believe that Jesus is the Messiah who has come into the world (v. 27). In the shedding of tears, we have Jesus responding as the Fully Human One, as the one who perfectly enacts faithfulness to God. In this situation, such faith means shamelessly acknowledging the reality of losing someone to death. He admits by his weeping that he loves this world into which he has come, and love for another necessarily links us together in their pain. Jesus responds unflinchingly to this aspect of human life: he sheds tears of embodied grief.

Christ's response to Lazarus's death reveals how we too must respond. We must proclaim God's triumph over disease and death, yet also openly acknowledge that before the kingdom comes fully, there is suffering and agony. If hope is to be thoroughly Christian, both the readiness to act for others' healing and the willingness to lament sin's real effects must be present.

Jesus' actions in John 11 hold together the tension inherent in Christian hope. Although we might expect him to proclaim in word and deed only the triumph of God over disease and death, we are surprised that he offers himself to grief. In his ministry, Jesus spends himself, using time to speak and act in God's power, sure of his conquest of death by the force of God's love. But Christ also seemingly wastes his tears, displaying the weight of sorrow not only over a fallen world but also over the very particular sadness of a close friend's passing.

Why "Professional Detachment" Is a Bad Idea for Christians

Undertaker and poet Thomas Lynch said, "Grief is the tax we pay on our attachments." Yet this seems to fly in the face of the oft-repeated mantra "Medical professionals need to maintain a professional distance from their patients." How does such detachment square with my insistence that lament must be an aspect of Christian care?

Attachments seem to get in the way. Who wants an ER nurse so distraught over the mangling of a child in a car accident that he can no longer perform life-saving techniques? Or a missionary doctor immobilized by the meagerness of her aid compared with the massive needs of a disease-ridden community? We have all heard the assertion that healthcare workers must maintain professional detachment; it seems self-evident.

I assert that this is a false portrayal of what we want from healthcare workers; we actually need them to be attached to us. Detachment might well prevent them from making the connection to patients that fosters healing—and it places the providers themselves at greater risk for exhaustive burnout.

The commitment to caring focuses the provider so that he can attend to a patient rightly, mercifully. Consider again Jesus the Great Physician, who like any good doctor regularly had to bracket his physical repulsion to decay, disease, and death. Caregivers work for healing despite how bad it all looks, smells, and feels. Love means digging in and treating the patient—sometimes even when the physical signals tell us it is a long shot. Just as Christ's response at the tomb of Lazarus was far from "disinterested," so too the Christian healthcare provider sets aside their sensory responses to act in mercy toward the patient.

If we joke that some healthcare workers have a "God complex"— aloofness combined with a blithe confidence in their powers—then the god being imitated is not that of John's Gospel. We need doctors and caregivers who do what Jesus does in John: the ones who will confidently act, trusting God's healing power made present through them, but will also lament that suffering remains.

Mourning as Hopeful Practice: Why Christians Must Grieve

This world is filled with complex and devastating illnesses such as cancer or AIDS in which we make great strides but then also seem to suffer setbacks. We continue to battle obesity, cholera, or malaria; we watch as pollution, corrupt governments, and greed suck medical resources or mangle healthcare delivery for those desperate for aid. In response, some become embittered; others hide from such unpleasantness or, finally, despair.

As Christians, we need not shy away from such realities, for we know that this world is still being rescued. We know the end of the story, that heaven will one day fully invade the earth (e.g., "Thy kingdom come on earth as it is in heaven"). But that kingdom is here-but-not-yet.

When we mourn, we do so as a sign and witness that this world is not the way our Lord intends. When our responses to disease and death are positive platitudes such as "It's all good" or its Christianized equivalents, "It's all for the best" or "She's in a better place now," we reveal an unwillingness to be vulnerable to others' pain. As evangelicals (and unlike the psalmists), we sometimes seek to excuse God for the trauma of human life. We might think, "He's going to make it all OK, so I'd better not be moved by disease and death so I let people know I'm not losing my faith."

Jesus does not seem to need an excuse to weep about losing a friend. He feels more than "Hey, great, another opportunity for the kingdom." He also feels, "Dear God, this world is one of tremendous sorrow, too great to bear at times."

In a culture drowning in ads for things that will make us feel better (by rendering us more sexually appealing, smarter, healthier, hipper, etc.), there are people who wonder, "Are we all on the same planet? I am sad: about my illness, my divorce, my unfulfilled dreams, my family's ugly past, the millions of AIDS orphans in Africa. Is there something other than the victory of decay and violence?" Healthcare workers can ill afford a superficial faith that denies or avoids such suffering.

Again, we see this in Christ, particularly in the Gospel of John. We know by looking at Jesus what it means to be a person of mercy and truth. He models for us a willingness to be vulnerable to others' suffering. In the Lazarus story, we witness something we do not expect from the God-Man: grief. In the weeping Christ, we glimpse the surprising God who created the universe but also takes humanity's plight on himself.

But this vulnerability is not mere sadness at the human condition. Jesus offers himself to grief knowing that such hope relies on God's power to redeem misery, to raise the dead; don't forget those exultant phrases in John 11 about life! So when we participate in others' sufferings through lament, we also proclaim the resurrection in small ways—with one foot in eternity with Christ and in his victory over death.

Lament as Disciplined Remembering

The regular practice of mourning works against burnout. If others' sadnesses have no place to go—if they are not rightly placed in God's hands as the psalmist models—then we risk two equally dangerous outcomes. We might shut out others' pain, becoming bitter, failing to see our patients as persons and resenting their agony or discomfort. Alternatively, we might become overwhelmed by such sorrows. We may well crack under such a false sense of importance, failing to tend to our own health or to other relationships that sustain us. We may become depressed or manic, tempted to use pleasures or people as a means to hide or disguise our pain.

When I speak about the need for healthcare workers to lament, there is the obvious focus of patients' illness and pain. Beyond that, we also mourn for our own human limitations, failures, or mistakes. We further regret the fractures of systems and institutions that do not serve patients effectively. With too many patients and too little time and resources, there's no shortage of areas in health care that contain shadows.

I encourage healthcare workers—from doctors to nurses to administrators and chaplains—to integrate lament into personal as well as communal practices. The psalms offer pre-phrased prayers as well as models for how to lament (and rage) before God. Sometimes we pray them on our own behalf and sometimes for others.

Such mourning can also be done communally when possible in churches, small groups, or even work places. One of my students served as a nurse in an overseas women's hospital. Because the death of their children was relatively common, mothers placed amulets around their necks to ward off evil. Those who lost children often resisted shedding tears; their culture encouraged them to ignore their feelings and move on. As Christians who instinctively understood the dual nature of hope, the staff gently encouraged the women to grieve for their babies and offered to say prayers or simply sit with them while they cried or held their child.

Conclusion

It is through embodied practice of these two aspects of hope—compassionate action and active lament—that all of us proclaim the gospel, but healthcare workers do this in a unique way and with a sustained attentiveness few other jobs require. In this, they imitate the one who was full of mercy and truth, the Great Physician who entrusts to us his ministry of healing and hope, until his kingdom of shalom comes fully, and every tear is finally wiped away by his hand (Rev 7:17 and 21:4).[25]

---

25 Resources for further reading: Walter Brueggemann (1986), "The Costly Loss of Lament," *Journal for the Study of the Old Testament* 36 (October): 57–71; Ellen F. Davis (2001), *Getting Involved with God: Rediscovering the Old Testament* (Lanham, MD Cowley); Stanley Hauerwas (2012), "Salvation and Health: Why Medicine Needs the Church," reprinted in *On Moral Medicine: Theological Perspectives in Medical Ethics,* ed. M. T. Lysaught et al., 3rd ed., 43–51 (Grand Rapids, MI: Eerdmans); John Swinton (2007), *Raging with Compassion: Pastoral Responses to the Problem of Evil* (Grand Rapids, MI: Eerdmans).

CHAPTER 12

Caring for Practitioners
Relationships, Burnout, and Sustainability

Cynthia Eriksson, PhD,
Ashley Wilkins, MA,
and Judith M. Tiersma Watson, PhD

Let's start with a question. Before you begin reading this chapter, take a minute to stop and reflect. In your work and ministry, what is it that you seek for those you are serving? What is the healing or wholeness that you desire for the people to whom you minister? Write those thoughts down.

Cynthia recently asked a group of urban ministry workers that question, and their answers reflected a desire for holistic wellness in the communities they served. They said that they wanted the kids and families to know how much God loves them, to see all of the skills and gifts that they had been given, to be able to live in such a way that they have physical health and loving relationships with others, to be transformed and healed from the losses and traumas they had experienced. They desired joy and healing. What is included in your list for wholeness: health, contentment, love?

Now, consider that list for yourself. How does your life reflect that place of wholeness? God desires that you also live in a way that is connected intimately with the knowledge of who you were created to be, that you know how much God loves you, and that you are transformed and healed! God wants you to have a ministry plan that can sustain you. Is that the plan you follow?

Introduction

Ministry with shalom at its center is a mutually transforming ministry. As we pursue a life of service that seeks to live out shalom for others, God seeks to transform us so that we live in dynamic relationship with our self, God, our loved ones, and our community. Our participation in ministry is then a reciprocal involvement in redemption and restoration; we are restored as we participate in the restoration of others.

Yet how often does the work of ministry, health care, or psychotherapy lead to the experience of exhaustion, disillusionment, or despair? It is not uncommon to hear colleagues say that they are "burned out," or even if one is not flirting with the edge of burnout, we feel we are not "working hard enough" or truly "sacrificing." Is this what you desire for the people you are serving? Is your goal for them to be so invested in their work and ministry that they do not have time to pause and rest? How can this be what God desires for you?

In this chapter we will explore the association between burnout and shalom, and the ways that human relationship to God, self, others, and community are interwoven in these experiences of wholeness and brokenness. We assert that it is within the transformative power of relationship that we move toward shalom, and when we break down in our authentic connection to God, self, and others we are prone to burnout. In fact, we do violence to others and ourselves, and we violate God's plan for shalom when we do not value the authentic needs of self and of others.

Myers's framework of shalom in chapter 2 identifies the foundational need for whole relationships with God, self, others, and community.

> Our identity and vocation are embedded and expressed most fully in a family of relationships—our relationship with God, with each other, with those we call Other, with the natural world where we live, and within ourselves. Emulating the triune God, our relationally embedded selves were intended to embody and express love, justice, and peace.

Myers notes that the effects of broken or unjust relationship with others and community are "domination" and "oppression" and the consequences of an unjust or broken relationship with self is "psychopathology, disease, [and] marred identity—poverty of being and vocation" (2011, 172). It is not a stretch to consider the experience of burnout as a "poverty of being and vocation." The healthcare or ministry worker experiencing burnout has been expended beyond capacity. She may even begin to doubt her call; or she may question whether her work makes any difference in the community. The broken relationship in the community might be represented in an agency culture that encourages or allows staff to overextend or sacrifice without rest. Ultimately, a burned-out worker enacts a subtle oppression of disregard by treating people like numbers or reacting cynically to the needs they confront.

What Does Psychology Say about Burnout?

Social psychologist Christina Maslach in her early research and writing on burnout emphasized that "what is unique about burnout is that the stress arises from the *social* interaction between helper and recipient" (1982, 3; emphasis in the original). Burnout is relational; it is in the context of relationships that the stress develops. By connecting with others in need and experiencing the emotional burden of another's pain and suffering, the caregiver is required to give of herself emotionally to create an opportunity for healing—for shalom. The experience of burnout is also relational as it is connected to one's sense of relationship to self, which is influenced by one's relationships with colleagues and leaders within the ministry or care setting. This primary relational context joins our understanding of ministry burnout to the concept of shalom.

Maslach's theory includes three components of burnout: "emotional exhaustion, depersonalization, and reduced personal accomplishment" (1982, 3). The theory suggests an interactive relationship between these three components. The emotional demands of serving people in healing or helping roles can cause workers to extend themselves beyond their capacities. Needs may feel urgent and ever-present, and the worker can begin to feel "used up," that there is "nothing left" and no source for gaining energy for the work. When *emotional exhaustion* sets in, one possible way to try to conserve energy is to not extend oneself as much to the relationships. This can move the worker to a place of distancing from or *depersonalizing* those whom he/she is caring for. While a certain balanced amount of detachment may be a necessary boundary in emotionally charged work, a worker who is burning out becomes emotionally cold and unfeeling or cynical about the needs of the client. Finally, these experiences of distance and exhaustion can be exacerbated by a sense of *limited personal accomplishment,* and perhaps even self-recrimination that they have "failed" or "become like the other burned out workers" (Maslach 1982, 3ff.; Maslach, Schaufeli, and Leiter 2001, 399).

The impact of burnout moves beyond these internal experiences of exhaustion and lack of accomplishment. Research suggests that burnout is associated with lower work productivity, lessened commitment or loyalty to an organization, more sick days, more stress-related illness, and finally, attrition (Maslach et al. 2001, 406). There is more than simply risk of personal misery when a health professional experiences burnout; it ripples outward and affects ministry relationships, organizational culture, and morale.

Maslach and her colleagues have identified six specific areas within the work setting that contribute to the risk of developing burnout: "workload, community, values, personal control, reward, and fairness" (2008, 500ff.). We will briefly describe these constructs and connect them with the overall framework of relationship. As might be expected, *workload* is a critical factor in burnout, particularly with respect to emotional exhaustion. When the work demand is beyond one's capacity, and when there are not seasons of lessened work to allow for recovery, exhaustion can develop (Maslach and Leiter 2008, 500). *Community* is the general quality of relationships within the workplace or organization. Support from peers can increase one's sense of accomplishment and effectiveness in work, while support from supervisors can buffer against exhaustion.

Personal control in work is exemplified in the ability to contribute to organizational decisions and having clarity and limited conflict in job roles; more control is associated with less burnout. While there may be limits to the ability to control outside circumstances or resources, the ability to participate in decisions and problem solving may help to buffer the impact of these limitations. The importance of *reward* is also associated with burnout—not only financial compensation, but also recognition for work accomplished. *Fairness* in the job setting is the perception that decisions are equitable, processes of decision-making are unbiased, and one's efforts, time investment, and skills are justly acknowledged and compensated. In a longitudinal study, Maslach and Leiter found that for those already at risk of burnout, unfairness was a key predictor for them actually experiencing burnout a year later (2008, 500ff.). Finally, we consider worker *values.* These ideals and principles bring people to a particular job, motivate them for their work, and set expectations for what they want to accomplish. When these personal values align with organizational values, burnout is less likely (Maslach and Leiter 2008, 500). This requires us to be able to reflect and identify what our personal values and motivations for ministry truly are.

Relationships and Burnout

Because relational stress in work correlates to burnout, an important antidote against it is supportive work relationships. Humans turn to relationships when stressed, and social support as a psychological construct represents both the experience of being emotionally and practically supported ourselves and doing this for others (Cutrona and Russell 1987).

Psychological literature identifies four main sources of social support that mitigate burnout: *professional, personal, organizational, and church-based. Professional* support comes from supervisors, colleagues, and patients (Prins et al. 2007, 5). Family and friends provide *personal* life social support (Ross, Altmaier, and Russell 1989, 466). *Organizations*, through policy and other structures, institute supportive environments. Two examples of organizational support include predictable workloads and employee input in policy (Killian 2008, 42). *Churches* not only offer emotional support through clergy and members but also provide avenues of encouragement to maintain, deepen, and integrate faith with daily life (Krause et al. 2001, 642).

The presence of social support can both prevent and buffer against the effects of burnout, as "social support not only reduces the likelihood of strain, but social support is mobilized as a coping mechanism when strain does occur" (Halbesleben 2006, 1140). Research with samples of healthcare workers, first responders, psychologists, caregivers of patients with advanced cancer, and counseling center staff supports the conclusion that higher levels of burnout occur when there are low, insufficient, or dissatisfying levels of social support. Perceptions of low social support also contribute to burnout (Gustafsson et al. 2010, 34; Prati and Pietrantoni 2010, 411; Daly et al. 2009, 294; Ross, Altmaier, and Russell 1989, 469). In one example, Dutch medical residents' dissatisfaction with social support provided by supervisors was associated with higher levels of emotional exhaustion (Prins et al. 2007, 5). In humanitarian aid workers, social support was significantly related to less emotional exhaustion and more personal accomplishment, and organizational support (indicated by a feeling of being supported by the agency, as well as the perception of supportive policies) correlates to lower levels of emotional exhaustion and depersonalization (Eriksson et al. 2009, 675ff.).

Shalom and Burnout

How can whole, shalom-oriented relationships contribute to a work or ministry model that can move past burnout into a sustainable ministry? Clearly shalom cannot be attained by addressing only one aspect of our lives or work but rather requires a dynamic understanding of our relationships. Realistically, even when we desire to embody a reciprocal transformative model of ministry, there may be seasons in which we are overextended. However, attending to the warning signs of these seasons of stress allows ministry workers to create time for continued refinement and transformation. Facing burnout remains an opportunity to grow in understanding more about ourselves as well as others. In order to more deeply explore this interaction, we begin with a model of human relationship.

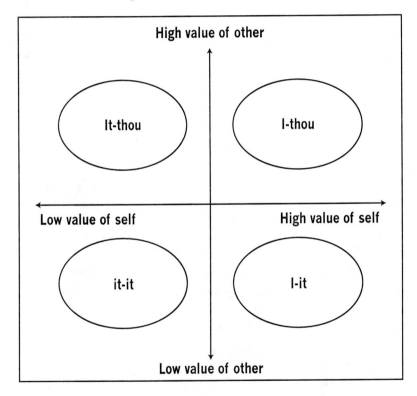

Figure 12.1: I-Thou quadrant
Taken from *The Reciprocating Self* by Jack O. Balswick, Pamela Ebstyne King, and Kevin S. Reimer. Copyright © 2005 by Jack O. Balswick, Pamela Ebstyne King, and Kevin S. Reimer. Used by permission of InterVarsity Press, P.O. Box 1400, Downers Grove, IL 60515, USA. www.ivpress.com.

Martin Buber offers a theological framework for humanness that reflects the relational image of God and the value of persons. In a simple way, his

"I-Thou" understanding of personhood reflects the fact that we are a true self only within relationship; the self is known only in relation to another. The relationship with another—"I-Thou"—reflects the sacred space that is formed when we are in authentic relationship; Buber contrasted this with having an "experience" of a person, rather than authentic connection, represented as "I-It" (Buber 1970, 53ff.). Balswick, King, and Reimer expound on Buber's theological anthropology to present a model of relatedness with four quadrants, based on the framework of an x-axis that represents value of self (from low, insecure sense of self, "It," to high, a secure sense of self, "I") and a y-axis to identify the value of the other (from low recognition of the unique humanness of the other, "It," to a high regard for the other, "Thou") (2005, 41ff.). This model then identifies four quadrants or types of relations depending upon the location on the axes: I-Thou (upper right quadrant), I-It (lower right), It-Thou (upper left), and It-It (lower left).

The I-Thou relationship is then the best description of a whole and healthy relationship with self and with other. God's intention is that we be fully ourselves and fully acknowledge the uniqueness of another in relationship. Shalom is based on an I-Thou model, a developing self that is secure in an understanding of her/his particular identity and value, in relation with Thou (an Other with unique being and identity). Burnout as just described is represented in the quadrants where either the "I" or the "Thou" has become an "It." When we live out of a place of limited self-awareness and self-identity, our own needs and values can become subsumed in the caring relationship, demonstrated, for example, when it feels impossible to say "no." When we thus become exhausted by the emotional demands of those in need, the other may become an "It" in an effort for the "I" to survive. We may feel it is too much to relate to the unique value of each person in need and may disconnect from our ministry relationships.

We enact I-Thou or I-It relationships within our ministry cultures, so we must seek to reinforce the value of self and value of other within them. An organization that esteems its own workers (or its ministry identity) over recipients often lacks sensitivity to the unique needs of the community and cultural context; it also fails to embody mutuality and the reciprocal nature of all ministry. Organizational cultures that value the recipient over the worker oppress their own workers and impede their health and transformation. This is clearly not participation in God's shalom.

Implementing Practices for Shalom

How might Buber's I-Thou model enrich our understanding of shalom? We consider the personal, social, and organizational impacts of this model. First, within the mutual transformation model of ministry, each self is of value; we must commit to the challenging work of authentically regarding both self (I) and other (Thou). Transformational ministry also recognizes the ongoing mutual healing of both the caregiver and the care-receiver. Finally, institutions bear responsibility for creating an organizational culture of shalom, places that encourage and reward relationships of mutual enrichment rather than burnout and oppression.

PERSONAL IMPACT OF THE ABSENCE OF SHALOM

A dynamic model of shalom reminds us that we are in the midst of transformation, and we each bear a personal responsibility to pursue well-being and spiritual maturity. We have already argued *against* the idea that burnout is merely a matter of personal weakness. Nonetheless, we do participate in our transformation. In this regard, Miner and colleagues have identified an "internalized orientation to ministry" that serves as a buffer to burnout in clergy. They define this orientation as

> a sense of spiritual relatedness, a sense of ministry competence based on training and ministry skills, and a perceived capacity to function in ministry in the absence of direct congregational support indicative of personal autonomy. (Miner et al. 2010, 169)

This emphasis on an internal sense of identity, role, and competence highlights the importance of a secure sense of ministry self—an "I" as ministry worker, not an "It."

Having a secure ministry identity challenges the temptation to a messiah complex. A messiah complex springs from an overactive sense of agency in which we consider our role to be greater than it actually is. We are not truly connected to our own unique gifts and needs; in surprising ways we may be treating ourselves as an "It." Of course, caregivers do not wake up in the morning and decide that today they will become the messiah to those for whom they care. Rather, this savior complex subtly (or not so subtly) enters in when caregivers find it difficult to let God be God and thus take on more than they intend. At this point we are not participating with God but rather have taken on God's role as well as our own (Tiersma 2009, 15). When we are *unable* to stop or say no to the requests of others, we may be acting as rescuers rather than as coworkers with the one true Savior who redeems us for shalom. The messiah complex prevents us from realizing our own need for transformation, instead seeing transformation as something that needs to be accomplished "out there" and not "in here."

The principle of Sabbath is one way to regain perspective on our identity and role in our work. Sabbath means not only resting but ceasing, including ceasing to try to be God. On the Sabbath, "we do nothing to create our own way. We abstain from work, from our incessant need to produce and accomplish. . . . The result is that we can let God be God in our lives" (Dawn 1989, 29). When we remember who God is in our lives, we are reminded of our role and God's role; we can refrain from the temptation to be God in the lives of those for whom we feel responsible.

Father Greg Boyle, founder of Homeboy Industries, is known for his decades-long work among gang youth in Los Angeles. He acknowledges that in his early days, his life was out of whack. "G-dog," as the homeboys call him, was available 24/7 to put out fires in his efforts to save the gang youth he loved. "It was crazy-making, and I came close to the sun, the immolation that comes from burning out completely in the delusion of actually 'saving' people" (Boyle 2010, 125). As a Jesuit, he was required to take a sabbatical. In the still place of meditation and surrender, perspective returned to his life. He recounts drawing consolation from a story that is told of Pope John XXIII. Every night the Pope would pray that he had done everything he could for the church. But it is God's church, and each night he would give the work to God and go to bed in peace.

Sabbath creates a time and space in which shalom relationships are lived out and marred relationships are made whole. The accurate "I" view of the self is deepened as we experience God in the keeping of the Sabbath and Sabbath rest. Exhaustion is not the mark of spirituality. Sabbath is not only about personal time with God, or a personal time of rest, but also the place in which social support can be encouraged; Sabbath is a communal event that is best and most fully shared with others. Once Sabbath thus alters our orientation, it is not so much an isolated day as an atmosphere, a climate in which we live all our days (Heschel 1951, 21). Importantly, Sabbath offers a foretaste of what is to come, when all will live in shalom. Messianic rabbi Stuart Dauermann writes,

> In fact, the standard Jewish salutation at the end of conversations or letters during the week as the sabbath approaches is "*Shabbat* shalom" wishing someone "Sabbath wellness/wholeness/restoration as an anticipation of that Day when all is altogether shalom." (Personal communication with Rabbi Stuart Dauermann, August 14, 2012)

Caring for ourselves and living out Sabbath rest in community impacts how able we are to truly care for our team, our family, and those we seek to serve. Through the ongoing transformation of a commitment to pursue shalom, we maintain an accurate sense of self.

The psychological literature we reviewed emphasizes the importance of authentic, supportive relationships with colleagues, peers, and supervisors as protective against burnout. We need to foster relationships in the care-giving context with others who are walking on a similar journey. If we have begun to disconnect from others or are treating others as "It" objects, we both lose our opportunity to experience support within that relationship and limit our ability to support or care for others. In this sense, attempts to protect or conserve our resources can limit our opportunity to experience positive care or reinforcement (Hobfoll 1989, 515).

SHALOM IN ORGANIZATIONS

The call to shalom and healthy community relationships requires a countercultural perspective. Cultural values of progress and productivity directly threaten healthy relationships; Sabbath counteracts this. Health care or any ministry that rigidly follows managerial culture by primarily valuing numerical growth or monetary cost runs the risk of treating others as "It"—one more cancer patient, one more family in economic need. What happens when the cancer patient does not get better? What is felt when the economic needs become more complex? We are not advocating an unreal or idealistic perspective on the vast needs of ministry and healthcare settings, but we are asking for an organizational commitment to eschewing an orientation that considers progress or productivity the ultimate goal of service.

Organizational leaders seeking shalom recognize that viewing progress and productivity as their highest values *will not* create an organizational culture that supports workers' choices for margin, rest, and restoration (Swenson 2004, 39). In a shalom-oriented organization, leaders model keeping the Sabbath; they encourage staff to take their vacation time. Leaders need to uphold a high view of the value of each worker as well as each person they serve while themselves exemplifying healthy "I-Thou" relationships. Mutual transformation can then occur at all levels of the agency.

Conclusions and Implications

We violate God's plan for shalom when we do violence to ourselves and others through burnout. While this statement may seem extreme, we would contend that the experience of burnout represents a violence of self-deception and expectations of others that extend beyond capacity for health. Here we offer practical suggestions for overcoming burnout and maintaining wholeness and health in relationships.

SUGGESTIONS FOR SELF

One should begin with a reflection on the commitment to healthy relationship with self. Borrowing Buber's language, how do you remain an "I" and not become an "It" in relation to others? This model of shalom grounds healthy relationships in the love and grace of Christ. Solitude and reflection facilitate and maintain our connection to self and God; decisions and cares about work and the suffering of others can be carried with the wisdom of the Holy Spirit. Consider these practical suggestions for maintaining an authentic view of one's self:

- Maintain a time of Sabbath in your week.
- Practice spiritual disciplines that value reflection and growth (e.g., the Ignatian Examen prayer; fulleryouthinstitute.org/2010/08/ignatian-examen/).
- Reflect on your personal and professional goals and expectations and discuss them with a trusted advisor or mentor.
- If there are times that you carry burdens that God does not intend for you to carry, at night, ask God for the grace to let God be God, and give those burdens into his hands.
- Reflect on your skills, values, and temperament. Consider the ways that who God has made you are consistent with your ministry organization and role.
- Learn to say no when needed.
- Create and follow a plan for maintaining physical health.

SUGGESTIONS FOR PEERS AND COMMUNITY

In relationships with the other, it is important to consider how one might maintain an "I-Thou" approach. In demanding ministry settings, leaders and health workers need to know how to avoid creating the "I-It" experience that can dehumanize and oppress those who need care. In addition to creating a foundation for personal wellness and secure sense of self, committing to a healthy community or healthy work relationships deepens our resources. First, consider the need for sharing your load. Jesus sent his disciples out in pairs (Mark 6:7); we do not work alone. Establish relationships with peers that allow for positive feedback and affirmation as well as pragmatic support through advice and problem solving. In addition, mutual "I-Thou" relationships with peers can provide healthy accountability. Sharing stories can normalize our feelings of stress, but we must also be open to others' encouragement to rest or retreat. The following practices may be helpful in promoting such relationships:

- At least weekly, schedule times for peer support, prayer, and problem solving in ministry teams.
- Deal with team conflicts; do not let them fester or grow.
- Let a teammate know what the signs are that you are stressed and moving to burnout; give that person (or persons) permission to confront you when they see them.
- Consider a team approach for tasks or responsibilities; no one is indispensable.

SUGGESTIONS FOR ORGANIZATIONS

Finally, the challenge to ministry institutions and organizations is to resist the cultural norm of overwork and progress that creates a mindset that treats staff and volunteers as "It" and not "Thou." Realistic workload assignments, policies regarding rest and Sabbath, respect for the input of colleagues, and appropriate reward for work accomplished are the result of a healthy attention to relationships within a leadership level. Consider these practical suggestions:

- Plan a regular time within team meetings that gives positive but not comparative feedback on workers' strengths and growth.
- Create intentional reviews between supervisors and workers to assess workload, resources, and goals.
- Review your organization's mission statement. Assess whether policies (e.g., human resources or other organizational procedures and systems) reflect values that are consistent with that mission. Advocate for changes when there are inconsistencies.
- Do not reward workaholism. Reward Sabbath-keeping and the maintaining of healthy margins of time, energy, and finance.

Shalom is a model that embeds the value of relationship and the call to mutual transformation within the center of ministry and health care. By adopting a perspective of ministry as shalom, we move away from burnout and sustain healthy persons in organizations that in turn offer others this health and wholeness.

References Cited

Boyle, Gregory. 2010. *Tattoos on the Heart: The Power of Boundless Compassion.* New York: Free Press.

Buber, Martin. 1970. *I and Thou: A New Translation, with a Prologue and Notes by Walter Kaufmann.* New York: Charles Scribner's Sons.

Balswick, Jack O., Pamela Ebstyne King, and Kevin S. Reimer. 2005. *The Reciprocating Self: Human Development in Theological Perspective.* Downers Grove, IL: InterVarsity Press.

Cutrona, Carolyn E., and Daniel W. Russell. 1987. "The Provisions of Social Relationships and Adaptation to Stress." In *Advances in Personal Relationships,* edited by W. H. Jones and D. Perlman, 1:37–67. Greenwich, CT: JAI Press.

Daly, Barbara J., Sara Douglas, Amy Lipson, and Helen Foley. 2009. "Needs of Older Caregivers of Patients with Advanced Cancer." *Journal of the American Geriatric Society 57* Suppl 2: S293–95.

Dawn, Marva. 1989. *Keeping the Sabbath Wholly: Ceasing, Resting, Embracing, Feasting.* Grand Rapids, MI: Eerdmans.

Eriksson, Cynthia B., Jeff P. Bjorck, Linnea C. Larson, Sherry M. Walling, Gary A. Trice, John Fawcett, Alexis D. Abernethy, and David W. Foy. 2009. "Social Support, Organisational Support, and Religious Support in Relation to Burnout in Expatriate Humanitarian Aid Workers." *Mental Health, Religion & Culture* 12 (7): 671–86.

Gustafsson, G., S. Eriksson, G. Strandberg, and A. Norberg. 2010. "Burnout and Perceptions of Conscience among Healthcare Personnel: A Pilot Study." *Nursing Ethics* 17 (1): 23–38. doi:10.1177/0969733009351950.

Halbesleben, Jonathon B. 2006. "Sources of Social Support and Burnout: A Meta-Analytic Test of the Conservation of Resources Model." *Journal Of Applied Psychology* 91 (5): 1134–45. doi:10.1037/0021-9010.91.5.1134.

Heschel, Abraham. 1951. *The Sabbath.* New York: Farrar, Straus & Giroux.

Hobfoll, Stephen E. 1989. "Conservation of Resources: A New Attempt at Conceptualizing Stress." *American Psychologist* 44 (3): 513–24.

Killian, Kyle D. 2008. "Helping Till it Hurts? A Multimethod Study of Compassion Fatigue, Burnout, and Self-care in Clinicians Working with Trauma Survivors." *Traumatology* 14(2): 32–44.

Krause, Neal, Christopher G. Ellison, Benjamin A. Shaw, John P. Marcum, and Jason D. Boardman. 2001. "Church-Based Social Support and Religious Coping." *Journal for the Scientific Study of Religion* 40 (4): 637–56. doi:10.1111/0021-8294.00082.

Maslach, Christina. 1982. *Burnout: The Cost of Caring.* Englewood Cliffs, NJ: Prentice-Hall.

––––––, and Michael P. Leiter. 2008. "Early Predictors of Job Burnout and Engagement." *Journal of Applied Psychology* 93 (3): 498–512.

Maslach, Christina, Wilmar B. Schaufeli, and Michael P. Leiter. 2001. "Job Burnout." *Annual Review of Psychology* 52 (1): 397–422.

Miner, Maureen H., Martin Dowson, and Sam Sterland. 2010. "Ministry Orientation and Ministry Outcomes: Evaluation of a New Multidimensional Model of Clergy Burnout and Job Satisfaction." *Journal of Occupational and Organizational Psychology* 83 (1): 167–88. doi:10.1348/096317909X414214.

Myers, Bryant L. 2011. *Walking with the Poor: Principles and Practices of Transformational Development.* Revised and expanded ed. Maryknoll, NY: Orbis.

Prati, Gabriele, and Luca Pietrantoni. 2010. "The Relation of Perceived and Received Social Support to Mental Health among First Responders:

A Meta-Analytic Review." *Journal of Community Psychology* 38 (3): 403–17. doi:10.1002/jcop.20371.

Prins, J. E., H. M. Hoekstra-Weebers, S. M. Gazendam-Donofrio, H. B. Van de Wiel, F. Sprangers, F. C. A. Jaspers, and F. M. Van der Heijden. 2007. "The Role of Social Support in Burnout among Dutch Medical Residents." *Psychology, Health, & Medicine* 12 (1): 1–6. doi:10.1080/13548500600782214.

Ross, Randall R., Elizabeth A. Altmaier, and Daniel W. Russell. 1989. "Job Stress, Social Support, and Burnout among Counseling Center Staff." *Journal of Counseling Psychology* 36 (4): 464–70.

Swenson, Richard A. 2004. *Margin: Restoring Emotional, Physical, Financial, and Time Reserves to Overloaded Lives.* Rev. ed. Colorado Springs, CO: NavPress.

Tiersma, Jude. 2009. "What Does It Mean to Be Incarnational When We Are Not the Messiah?" In *God So Loves the City: Seeking a Theology for Urban Mission,* edited by Charles Van Engen and Jude Tiersma, 7–25. Eugene, OR: Wipf and Stock.

NEW APPROACHES
IN HEALTHCARE
MISSIONS

CHAPTER 13

Overcoming Barriers in the City
Transforming Practices for Health Workers

Anntippia Short, RN, MSN, CNE,
and Isaac B. Voss, MPH

The prophet Jeremiah called for Israel to "seek the peace [shalom] of the city" (Jer 29:7 KJV). This chapter explores five overlapping spiritual practices that lead us toward transformed relationships of shalom within the complex context of the city: hospitality, encounter, compassion, Christian witness, and justice. These practices or disciplines create sacred spaces in which we can notice God and respond to his word to us. Our reflections spring from our particular ministry context in a primary health care clinic in Watts, California.[26]

As we consider these disciplines, keep in mind a few introductory comments. First, although the metaphor of a journey is used, the practices do not represent linear steps in a path toward shalom. Individuals and communities are encouraged to integrate these practices into their journey in a way that complements what God is doing in their unique context. Secondly, the reader is encouraged to move beyond this brief introduction and to explore and integrate Christianity's rich tradition of spiritual practices (Calhoun 2005). In other words, these practices represent just some of the diverse, time-honored tools that are available to Christian health workers in their ministry of healing. Thirdly, the emphasis of this chapter is primarily on the interpersonal level;

---

26 Watts is a neighborhood located ten miles south of downtown Los Angeles, California. The clinic operates as a partnership between a local church, a missions organization (World Impact, Inc.), and a federally qualified health center (Los Angeles Christian Health Centers).

however, there is important work to be done on how the spiritual disciplines can be applied at the communal and structural levels.

Hospitality

It is 6:00 a.m. on a Wednesday morning, and there is already a line formed outside a white, nondescript building in Watts; some have been waiting since 4:30 a.m. Each of them waits patiently for a young man to open the gate and admit them into the clinic. The scene is typical of Wednesday mornings at this building, which houses a church, an elementary school, and a clinic.

In one of the earliest days of the clinic, two of the guests who waited at that gate were Darryl and Marie.[27] They entered with a history of addiction and homelessness. Because Darryl is African American and Marie is Caucasian, they had found it difficult to find a community in Watts in which they both felt a sense of belonging and connectedness. When this couple saw the sign indicating that the clinic was open, they came in for care. Inside the clinic, there was coffee waiting, they were warmly greeted, and their stories were respectfully heard by the volunteer that checked them in.

This couple's experience illustrates the first practice in the journey toward shalom: hospitality. Conde-Frazier sees hospitality as the creation of a place of connectedness—a place in which each individual is respected, including the stranger (2004, 171). In her book on Christian hospitality, Christine Pohl points out that in the strict sense, strangers are those who are disconnected from basic relationships that provide each of us a secure place in the world (Pohl 1999, 13).

The practice of hospitality toward those of a different background has the potential to heal communities and to turn "strangers" into welcomed insiders. In contrast, tendencies such as ethnocentrism lead an individual to hold his or her way of life as superior to others'

---

27   Please note that these are not the real names of the guests.

(Kulwicki 2009, 109). Ethnocentrism is often the basis for prejudices, assumptions, or biases that separate us and render our healthcare practices less effective. When we refuse to value the opinions and innate worth of others, we negate the work of God in their lives. When an individual is guided by hospitality, he or she begins "a journey toward visibility," toward truly seeing the outsider (Pohl 1999, 62).

Ultimately, our hospitality reflects our recognition of God's hospitality to humankind, particularly to those on the margins (Pohl 1999, 172). Hospitality is an act of worship, a welcoming of Jesus himself. In Matthew 25, Christ asserts that the offer of food, shelter, and protection to the vulnerable or "little ones" is an offer to Jesus himself. Luke 14 and the parable of inviting those who cannot repay us to the banqueting table is another image of hospitality (Conde-Frazier 2004, 171). Remarking on these texts and the practice within the Benedictine tradition, Esther de Waal suggests that after all our hospitable activity we are faced with two questions: "Did we see Christ in them? Did they see Christ in us?" (De Waal 1984, 121).

Imagine hospitality in your context by considering the following questions: When have you been welcomed in a way that deeply touched you? When have you been wounded because you were not welcomed? How has the welcome of Jesus touched your life and wounds (Calhoun 2005, 139–40)? Finally, who has modeled hospitality in health care for you?

Encounter

Hospitality opens us to people who are unlike us. When we deeply encounter someone very different from ourselves, there is often a collision in which we uncover differing views on family, communication, value, time, health practices, and more. But encounter is where risk-taking happens, an opening to a creative engagement with another person that opens us to God and new possibilities (Conde-Frazier 2004, 176). Jesus modeled the discipline of encounter in that he "did not consider equality with God something to be used to his own advantage; rather, he made himself nothing by taking the very nature of a servant" (Phil 2:5–8).

Consider the story of the Apostle Peter and the Roman centurion Cornelius. Peter was on a rooftop in prayer when God gave him a vision that convinced him that God's mercy was not limited to the Jews (Acts 10:9–22). Peter then had the opportunity to share the good news of Jesus with Cornelius—a Gentile and a member of the oppressive Roman army. When the opportunity arose and Peter was invited to the home of Cornelius, he went and ate with him. The result of this encounter was that many Gentiles received salvation and the gift of the Holy Spirit.

Note that in this story Cornelius and Peter experience an encounter through something rather ordinary—eating. It is in the acceptance of an invitation that something remarkable happens for Cornelius but also for Peter. Through this encounter both Cornelius and Peter are transformed as they come to see the larger vision to which Peter's dream points—God's mercy extends to the Gentiles. What a powerful result of a risky encounter!

In speaking of cross-cultural health care, Campinha-Bacote offers a framework for care that supports our need for encounter (Campinha-Bacote 2002, 183). She proposes that in order to competently care for those from other cultures, we must first examine the biases, assumptions, and prejudices that arise from our own culture. For example, in our roles in Watts we have seen many volunteers, including ourselves, come with a "professional bias"—an underlying assumption that the communities' challenges should neatly match our area of professional expertise (be it dentistry, diabetes, or construction), rather than listening to what community members identify as important (Sumner 2008, 44). Myers points out that we must increase our awareness of areas in which we suffer from a deformed desire to play God in the lives of others (Myers 2011, 172).

In humility, we must recognize where we need to obtain further information concerning different cultural and ethnic groups so that we can understand how members of a different group may view health, illness, and healing. Once we have taken the time to obtain that knowledge, we must collect relevant cultural data that pertains to the healthcare practices of our client. When people are valued, they are more likely to share their true concerns (Campinha-Bacote 2002, 183).

The medium of storytelling provides a practical means by which we can value and empower the patient. Brazilian educator Paulo Freire comments that the disadvantaged are rarely given opportunities to "speak their world"—to name their experiences in their own words under conditions in which others respectfully listen to them (Freire 1970). By its nature, storytelling requires listeners. Conde-Frazier points out that in an initial encounter, "we can observe, but we cannot decode. We cannot make all the connections between the lived phrases (daily events and routines) of people's lives" (Conde-Frazier 2004, 179). In order to do so, we must carefully listen to others, and this aspect of an encounter may be one of the hardest steps for the health provider who has been trained to tune into and fix medical problems. As we listen carefully, we need to avoid the impulse to arrive quickly at a solution that is determined from within our own set of assumptions. Instead, we tune ourselves to hear commonalities between our worlds that point to common wounds and passions and for the call of God on our patient's life (Conde-Frazier 2004, 181).

In such broader attentiveness to the patient, healthcare providers may at times find themselves in encounters that are conflictual. While it might be easy to avoid an uncomfortable topic with the patient, in the healthcare arena the avoidance of conflict will often lead to potentially life-threatening issues. For example, avoiding a difficult conversation with a patient regarding unhealthy eating habits could lead to increased complications from diabetes. Alternatively, direct feedback and constructive conflict may lead to positive change. Constructive conflict involves focusing on the defined issue, not introducing secondary issues, and making the goal of the conflict cooperative problem solving (Augsburger 1992, 47). In the context of the above example, constructive conflict would involve focusing on the defined issue of eating habits and diabetes. It would also involve guiding the patient back to the primary focus of the conversation if they begin to get sidetracked by unrelated issues.

Finally, encounter necessitates reframing the role of healthcare provider from that of expert to coinvestigator and fellow problem-solver. In this approach, the provider is attentive to that which is of value to the patient. Conde-Frazier describes the process of "listening as attending." In attending, "one shifts from a hierarchical role to one of servant leadership, where one listens for the Lord's presence and assists others in their own attentive response to God's movement in their lives" (2004, 184). Burger explains that "active listening means being attentive to what the client is saying both verbally and nonverbally" (Burger 2009, 352). This approach facilitates meaningful communication between the client and healthcare provider, because it enhances trust and conveys to clients their dignity and worth.

Literature on healthcare communication suggests a direct link between the quality of patient-provider communication and the degree of patient satisfaction, adherence to treatment, and healthy practices, and thus healthy outcomes. Conversely, if providers fail to consider and understand cultural differences as needed, there is a greater chance of poor health outcomes (Smedley 2003, 200).

As Christian healthcare providers we must also recognize our own biases and prejudices. We must take the time to educate ourselves concerning the cultural distinctions between our clients and ourselves and actively pursue therapeutic communication in order to assess and address the needs of our clients. The process of encounter and constructive conflict is usually messy and unpredictable.

Consider the situation of a couple who visited our clinic. The man entered the clinic and was registered; however, the woman was reluctant and appeared angry and distraught. She was undecided about seeking care and remained in the parking lot, visibly upset. She expressed self-destructive thoughts and, at one point, drove away and then returned.

In many contexts, the woman may have been seen as a threat, or at very least unwelcome at the clinic. However, the staff responded by praying for her. When the woman later returned, the staff members and the pastor warmly greeted her. God's presence was in this encounter, because the woman recognized the hospitality that was offered. She was seen by the healthcare provider and over the ensuing months was treated for a serious vision problem and other health issues. She came to her appointments with an optimistic outlook and encouraged those around her. She openly praised God for the work he had done in her life. Although hospitality initially introduced conflict, the staff was able to constructively work with her as they recognized God's presence in the situation.

Though encounter is a necessary step toward shalom, it is not always easy. At times, deep-seated biases result in conflict and misunderstandings. On another busy clinic day, a guest entered the clinic. She had diabetes and was insulin-dependent. She had a history of coming to the clinic only when she had been out of medication for a while. She regularly disregarded needed referrals that had been made for her and showed little respect for the health provider's advice.

On this particular day, the client demanded to be seen, saying that she had been out of her medication for two weeks. The clinic was already full, and the receptionist told her that the staff would do their best to see her but that she would have to wait until the other guests were seen. The woman became angry, began swearing at the receptionist, and threatened to sue the clinic. The situation was aggravated by the client's demeaning references to the ethnicity of the receptionist. Eventually the nurse, who knew the client from previous visits, was able to convince her to come into an office so that they could talk. Listening to the client helped her to calm down and talk reasonably about the need to see all the scheduled clients.

Eventually, the woman received her refill of medications. Although she apologized to the nurse and provider, she did not speak to the receptionist again. In this case, even though hospitality was offered, the encounter did not end peacefully.

While we cannot control others or the outcome of encounter, this practice consistently calls us to move beyond stereotypes in our relationships. Encounter is often risky and uncomfortable. It requires that we take the risk of being misunderstood and rejected. However, we are unable to effectively minister to the "other" if we only allow ourselves to journey with them from a distance. If we desire to be effective in the ministry of health care, then we must be open; we must risk a collision with another in such encounters.

Consider the following questions in applying the practice of encounter to your context: How can you listen to people's stories within the time constraints of your guest encounters? In your encounters, how can you verbally and nonverbally help the underserved discover their identity as loved children of God?

Compassion

By definition, compassion ("suffering with") involves us in others' pain so that, in the midst of hurt, we witness to God's presence and care. In practicing compassion, we make the unbounded kindness of God visible. Jesus consistently demonstrates compassion, as explicitly noted with the leper (Mark 1:41), the people who were like sheep without a shepherd (Mark 6:34), the sight of a harassed and exhausted crowd (Matt 9:36), the two blind men (Matt 20:34), and the widow of Nain grieving for her only son (Luke 7:13).

In Jesus' parable of the Good Samaritan (Luke 10), the Samaritan "was moved by compassion" to sacrificial action. Seeing another in pain and being moved to help are one and the same for him. He stands in contrast to the others on the road who saw the man in pain but chose avoidance. Compassion entails action. Thus compassion moves the Samaritan to sacrificially act in a way that disrupts his plans and costs him time and energy. In contrast to those who passed by on the other side,

God calls us to follow the Samaritan's example and to demonstrate "solidarity through action with the lowly" (Esser 1976, 596).

Not merely approaching from above or beyond, compassion compels us to step into another's world in the way that he or she has experienced it (Conde-Frazier 2004, 195). Nursing literature speaks of empathy as one technique in therapeutic communication. As Burger states, "Empathy is the ability to understand and accept another person's reality, to accurately perceive feelings, and to communicate this understanding to the other" (Burger 2009, 353). Empathetic listening is a first step toward suffering with the other. We consciously put aside our own judgments and biases and listen to our client or colleague from the standpoint of his or her reality. Those things that were once their issues now break our hearts, make us angry, and move us to press for change because we now hold these issues in common (Esser 1976, 600).

When guests walk in the door of the Watts Christian Health Center, the first two staff members they meet are Christian and Julie. Many guests enter the clinic with prior healthcare experiences in which they have been denied services, demeaned, and devalued. As Christian greets the guests he shows a God-given ability to minister God's peace to the people in the waiting area. He offers coffee, listens to people's stories, and checks them in efficiently. He expresses understanding for the frustration and even anger at what some clients experience. The result is that the clients are given a sense of dignity and worth. Julie continues with the check-in process by taking the guest's vital signs and health history. She speaks kindly and listens attentively. She takes the time she needs to understand why the client came to the clinic. Both Christian and Julie are bilingual in Spanish and English, thus putting many of our clients at ease.

What is a particular instance in which someone has been compassionate toward you? Which story of Jesus in the Gospels best communicates his compassion for you? What attitudes or emotions surface when you relate to those in need? Do you tend to try to control

situations of suffering, run away, or practice compassionate lament (see
Dufault-Hunter chapter)?

Christian Witness

Myers points out that the goals of Christian witness are changed people
and changed relationships. Whether it is the poor or the non-poor, we
desire that everyone experiences the freedom that comes from understanding one's true identity as God's child and one's central vocation as
a steward in God's creation (Conde-Frazier 2004, 201–2). At the end of
the day we desire that those whom we serve give praise, not to the competence of a health professional or a new technology, but to the living
God. We have witnessed the powerful effect that this vision of transformation brings to our community in Watts.

For example, when Darryl and Marie entered the clinic, they were
greeted and their stories were heard. The healthcare provider saw them
as persons, and their medical needs were addressed. Because this is a
church-based clinic, the pastor was also in the waiting room and offered
to pray with them. Overall, Darryl and Marie were treated with dignity
and responded well to holistic care.

Darryl, who was diabetic and had many other health needs, was able
to receive excellent and timely health care. Through the ongoing ministry of the clinic staff and the pastor, Darryl and Marie accepted Jesus as
their Savior and Lord and became a part of the partnering church family.
As they had been living together for many years as an unmarried couple,
the pastor invited them to consider marriage. The couple immediately
expressed a desire to be married. A short time later this small church held
a joyous wedding celebration for the couple. Darryl and Marie became
valuable, committed workers in the church and the healthcare clinic.
Their involvement provided the context in which their own sense of self-
worth was transformed.

However, not only Darryl and Marie benefited from this encounter.
Those who offered hospitality also saw the work of God in their lives.

The clinic director recounted that when Darryl and Marie arrived at the clinic, showing hospitality had been especially challenging for him. It was the end of a long day and it was time to close the clinic. He was tired. However, upon entering the facility the distressed couple walked directly to him and asked to be seen at the clinic. As this encounter progressed, the director was amazed at how God changed his superficial view of two additional homeless clients into a transformed relationship with a loved brother and sister in Christ. This is the power of a true encounter—both parties have the opportunity to walk away transformed. Both parties have the opportunity to discover their true identity as loved children of God who are called to serve (Myers 2011, 316).

How has God transformed your identity and sense of vocation? At the end of the day, to whom do your guests/patients give praise? What are practical ways in which you can share the good news with those you serve?

Justice

True transformation involves the restoration of true identities and vocations and the healing of unjust relationships and structures. Justice involves helping others through correcting and redressing wrongs so that others might be treated fairly (Myers 2011, 178), and pursuit of justice usually occurs at multiple levels (Calhoun 2005, 193). First, it can occur within the household. When Darryl and Marie discovered their identity as children of God, they desired to have a committed relationship with each other before God. In addition, Marie was reconciled with her mother and sister, from whom she had been estranged for years.

In a similar way, the anthropologist Elizabeth Brusco has researched the positive effect of the gospel on low-income households in Colombia (Brusco 1986). In her research she found that as men accepted the gospel message it led to the redirection of resources back to the household as the men avoided drinking, smoking, and extramarital sexual relationships. In commenting on this study, Myers notes that when men and women believed the gospel in Colombia it led to the enhancement of the women's status in the community (Myers 2011, 342).

Secondly, the pursuit of justice also occurs at the level of the social system. Martin Luther King Jr. once stated, "Of all forms of inequality, injustice in health care is the most shocking and inhumane" (Diaz 2004, 120). In Los Angeles, the urban underserved have suffered repeated closures of clinics, emergency rooms, and access to urgent care facilities. This tragedy was highlighted when a forty-three-year-old woman in the Watts community suffered in pain for forty-five minutes as she lay on the floor of an emergency room waiting room until she died, having never been seen by a member of the healthcare team (Vara-Orta 2007). Her name was Edith Isabel Rodriguez. At one point, the security camera footage for the waiting room shows the hospital janitor pushing a broom around the suffering woman. This story illustrates how a broken and unjust social system can painfully neglect the poor and disregard the image of God in which they are made.

The tragic death of Edith Rodriguez occurred two blocks from the Watts Christian Health Center. The clinic is an active partnership between a local church, a mission organization, and a nonprofit healthcare organization. When this group of Christ followers heard of Mrs. Rodriguez's death, it evoked sadness, anger, and a renewed sense of passion to work for justice. Together, these organizations are seeking "to do justice, and to love kindness" in Watts (Mic 6:8 ESV).[28]

Have you listened to the voices of the poor? Do you understand the injustices facing those who live in underserved communities in which you serve, as they would articulate them? Are you aware of what God is

---

28   Development theorist Jayakumar Christian has helpfully pointed out that the roots of injustice extend beyond the social system and into the cultural system, where there are inadequacies in worldview, and the spiritual system of principalities and powers. It is beyond the scope of this chapter to explore these dimensions in detail; however, for further study please see Christian's book, *God of the Empty-Handed* (Christian 2011).

passionate about in the neighborhood? Are you stewarding the resources that God has given you toward justice and fairness?

Shalom: Linking the Practices Together

Shalom involves wholeness, health, peace, safety, rest, and the absence of discord. Shalom offers us a glimpse of what God's reign might look like in our present world, even as it will one day be known in fullness. This vision implies reconciliation with God, our community, the other, the environment, and ourselves. It is a "vision of connectedness for an entire community" (Conde-Frazier 2004, 169). In a community that is journeying toward shalom, barriers due to age, ethnicity, gender, socio-economic status, and health practices are being removed. For example, for Darryl and Marie this journey toward wholeness involved Pastor Todd sharing the gospel with them and leading them to discover their transformed identity in Christ. Just as important in witnessing to sha-lom, Christians and others can respond to a tragedy in a local emergency room with increased awareness and concrete change (Vara-Orta 2007).

For Christian health providers, our assurance that the fullness of God's shalom shall come brings us hope. Those of us who work in health care must accept in humility that if the wholeness of the kingdom of God is to be the goal, then we must walk in dependence on the Holy Spirit. We must learn what Jesus meant when he said, "I am the vine; you are the branches. If you remain in me and I in you, you will bear much fruit; apart from me you can do nothing" (John 15:5 NIV).

In light of this vision of transformation, we ask God to teach us what it means to experience shalom in our own lives so that we can share it with those we work with. We pray for the grace to see reality as our clients see it and then to move together toward God's intentions.

Concluding Thoughts

This chapter has explored a framework for creating barrier-crossing relationships that reflect the shalom of the kingdom of God. While the practices of hospitality, encounter, compassion, Christian witness, and justice have been described and grounded in the context of a small health clinic, we encourage you to imagine how these practices might be embodied within the context of your neighborhood, hospital, office, or particular healthcare setting. As we apply these practices, may we know God's guidance and strength, following the one who humbly crossed barriers in order that he might bring life-transforming hope and healing.

References Cited

Augsburger, David W. 1992. *Conflict Mediation across Cultures: Pathways and Patterns*. Louisville: Westminster/John Knox.

Brusco, Elizabeth Ellen. 1986. "The Household Basis of Evangelical Religion and the Reformation of Machismo in Colombia." PhD thesis, City University of New York. Ann Arbor, MI: University Microfilms.

Burger, Jeri. 2009. "Communication." In *Fundamentals of Nursing*, 7th ed., edited by Patricia Ann Potter and Anne Griffin Perry, 339–60. St. Louis, MO: Mosby Elsevier.

Calhoun, Adele Ahlberg. 2005. *Spiritual Disciplines Handbook: Practices that Transform Us*. Downers Grove, IL: InterVarsity Press.

Campinha-Bacote, J. 2002. "The Process of Cultural Competence in the Delivery of Healthcare Services: A Model of Care." *Journal of Transcultural Nursing* 13 (3): 181–84.

Christian, Jayakumar. 2011. *God of the Empty-Handed: Poverty, Power and the Kingdom of God*. Rev. ed. Brunswick East, Australia: Acorn Press.

Conde-Frazier, Elizabeth. 2004. "From Hospitality to Shalom." In *A Many Colored Kingdom: Multicultural Dynamics for Spiritual Formation*, edited by Elizabeth Conde-Frazier, S. Steve Kang, and Gary A. Parrett, 167–210. Grand Rapids, MI: Baker.

De Waal, Esther. 1984. *Seeking God: The Way of St. Benedict*. Collegeville, MI: Liturgical Press.

Diaz, Robyn Whipple. 2004. "Unequal Access: The Crisis of Health Care Inequality for Low-Income African-American Residents of the District of Columbia." *Journal of Health Care Law & Policy* 7 (1): 120–395.

Esser, H. H. 1976. "Mercy." In *The New International Dictionary of New Testament Theology,* edited by Colin Brown. Exeter: Paternoster.

Freire, Paulo. 1970. *Pedagogy of the Oppressed*. Translated by Myra Bergman Ramos. New York: Herder & Herder.

Kulwicki, A. 2009. "Culture and Ethnicity." In *Fundamentals of Nursing*, 7th ed., edited by Patricia Ann Potter and Anne Griffin Perry, 106–20. St. Louis, MO: Mosby/Elsevier.

Myers, Bryant L. 2011. *Walking With the Poor: Principles and Practices of Transformational Development*. Rev. and updated ed. Maryknoll, NY: Orbis.

Pohl, Christine D. 1999. *Making Room: Recovering Hospitality as a Christian Tradition*. Grand Rapids, MI: Eerdmans.

Sumner, Andrew, and Michael Tribe. 2008. *International Development Studies: Theories and Methods in Research and Practice*. Thousand Oaks, CA: Sage.

Vara-Orta, Francisco, and Charles Ornstein. 2007. "Tragic Catch-911 for Dying Woman." *Los Angeles Times,* June 13. Available at http://articles.latimes.com/2007/jun/13/local/me-calls13.

CHAPTER 14

Empowering toward Shalom
The Lay Health Movement

Grace Tazelaar, MS, RN, and
Carolyn "Care" Newhof

In 2008 one of the chapter authors, Grace, made a visit to Uganda. She was apprehensive about what she would find. When she had left in 1991 after serving six years as a missionary nurse, phone service was almost nonexistent, the country was coming back from civil war following the ouster of Idi Amin, and HIV had just been identified as the cause of the pandemic known as AIDS.

"Sister Grace, it is good you have come back," said John Kiyimba, now the project director for Kyetume Community-Based Health Care. John had been one of the medical assistants she trained as a Trainer of Community Health Workers. "Come see the health center we have built." There were several buildings filled with people. They toured the facility, saw the laboratory, and visited the pharmacy filled with antiretroviral drugs for AIDS supplied by PEPFAR (US President's Emergency Plan for AIDS Relief). "We care for about 1,500 HIV/AIDS patients here," John said. "We do this with the help of the AIDS counselors and health workers that we have trained to visit people in their homes." Clearly the community had come behind John and supported the development in the area. Then John said, "It is because of you that we have been able to do these things." "No," Grace said, "You have done this work." "But," said John, "We could not have done it without the training you gave us."

The purpose of this chapter is to explore the background and implications of a church-based lay health movement. Two key questions for this chapter are, (1) What if every church saw health as integral to the gospel? and (2) What if local churches mobilized and equipped community health workers in their communities? To address these questions, we'll first look at the background of the lay health movement. Second, we'll consider key implementation questions in regard to ownership, worldview, teaching methodology, focus, and evaluation. Finally, these issues will be considered and illustrated within the case study of the home visitors program at the Cary Christian Center in Mississippi.

The Lay Health Movement

Throughout history most health care has been given by people who have not been trained professionally in health care. Mothers nursed their children through illnesses, people with knowledge of herbs and plants used them as pharmaceutical agents, and elders were the dispensers of wisdom and the guardians of relationships. In the Bible we see many guidelines for healthcare practices.

As Gorske (chap. 5) and others point out, the church has historically been involved in caring for the sick, dying, and injured. As part of the mission endeavor of bringing the gospel of Christ to foreign lands, healthcare personnel were sent to care for the missionaries. Healthcare missionaries set up hospitals and clinics to care for people where churches and schools were being established (Van Reken 1990). Mission hospitals became the foundation for modern medicine in many developing countries. Initially healthcare institutions had close relationships with the church. A provision was made to care for those who could not pay. But as health care and medicine advanced, the cost of providing care grew, and health care assumed a business model.

The Christian Medical Commission was set up to address concerns regarding the mission hospitals around the world (Swezy 2008). The work of the Christian Medical Commission in collaboration with the World Health Organization (WHO) led to the conference in Alma-Ata (Almaty), Kazakhstan, and the Alma-Ata Declaration in 1978.

The principles established at Alma-Ata legitimized community-based primary health care. The key Alma-Ata principles were as follows:

- Prevention as well as curative clinical care;
- Service at the closest point of contact (in the community, not in a distant hospital);
- Service by the lowest level provider appropriate to the task;
- A tiered system of health care, starting with the family and community at the household level, through the community-based clinic, and on to primary, secondary, and tertiary referral facilities;
- Equity in service provision, with special emphasis on women. (Swezy 2008)

These principles led the Christian healthcare community to include community health development (CHD) work as part of their mission. Early writings such as *Where There Is No Doctor* (Werner 1977) became a resource that many missionaries carried to the field to care for their own health as well as the people they were teaching about Jesus. The training of community health workers (CHWs) was seen as a way to prevent common diseases, provide access to health care for the underserved, and move the responsibility for health care to the closest point of contact. David Werner wrote *Helping Healthcare Workers Learn* (Werner and Bower 1982). Roy Shaffer, working with the African Medical and Relief Foundation (AMREF), published *Beyond the Dispensary* (1984) and began training health workers and trainers throughout East Africa. Anne Hope and Sally Timmel wrote a three-part training manual, *Training for Transformation: A Handbook for Community Workers* (1984), which was based largely on the educational methodology of Paulo Freire. Leaders in CHD believed that achieving success in health would also lead to improving other aspects of people's lives.

Implementation Questions in Community Health Development

Early programs in CHD were excited about the idea of training CHWs to bring appropriate health to people without access. Initial questions centered on what to call them (advisors, workers, promoters?); what qualifications they should have (male or female, level of education); and how they should be selected.

Over time the community health development practitioners learned that other fundamental questions needed to be considered. These questions include

- Ownership—who will ultimately be in charge of the program?
- Worldview—what are the core values and beliefs that determine health behaviors?
- Teaching methodology—how will health information be presented in order to change health behavior?
- Focus—should the CHW focus on prevention or also be taught some curative care measures?
- Evaluation—how will the program be judged a success?

OWNERSHIP

A critical question is who will ultimately own the health program. Purists believe that the community is responsible for its health programming and therefore should be responsible for selecting and overseeing the work done by the CHW and for providing their compensation. However, in an effort to meet funding reporting requirements, many CHD programs have paid some of the project personnel in the community. It is argued here that measures such as this undercut long-term goals of community ownership.

Those who advocate paying CHWs accuse volunteer programs of exploiting poor people for the purpose of the program. Those who advocate volunteer CHWs point to the sustainability of their programs, which often continue after support for the program ceases. It takes a much longer time to build the capacity of a community to own and care for health programming.

If the church embraces the concept of shalom and includes health as part of the gospel message, then ideally the local church should be the owner and encourager of community health programs. However, if the church is organizing the community health program, it needs to include the entire community if it is to impact the health of a community. If only Christians use latrines, that does not keep the water sources from being contaminated by non-Christians. Often it takes an ecumenical effort of multiple churches in a community so that the program is not seen as a program of one particular church.

WORLDVIEW

As Dan Fountain and others have pointed out in this volume, healthcare missionaries often fail to recognize that their understanding of disease and health is rooted in a worldview that differs dramatically from other worldviews. Western medicine sees disease as coming from microorganisms, altered physiology, or environmental factors. Animism often sees disease causation in relational terms—a curse is placed on someone, an ancestor is unhappy, a bride price has gone unpaid. Eastern religions may attribute disease to an imbalance in energies.

In order to change behavior and healthcare practice, a bridge is so often needed between these worldviews. For example, I (Grace) vividly remember the failure of a 1989 project in Uganda due to the lack of such a bridge between worldviews. We worked with a community over a year to protect a spring. The community understood that the source of many of their gastrointestinal problems came from the drinking water they were using; they had seen the improvement in health of nearby villages when they protected their spring. The community would collect the necessary sand and stones and bring them to the spring. The cement and pipe would be bought and brought to the site. But on the day everyone was to assist with digging and mixing the concrete to protect the spring, no one showed up. We later learned that the village elder had told the community that there was a spirit in the spring that took the form of a snake. If the spring was disturbed by being protected, that spirit would take revenge on the village. Sadly, the spring was never protected during our involvement. Changing a person's worldview requires transformation that often depends on the involvement of the Holy Spirit and the provision of a bridge between a Christian worldview and a non-Christian worldview.

TEACHING METHODOLOGY

Foundational to Community Health Development is the community health workers' owning the healthcare message and changing their personal healthcare practice. They can then encourage members of their communities to do the same. The goal of health education is positively changed health practices. It does not necessarily require the health worker to be an expert on the topic.

Using problem-posing, learner-centered, participatory education is the preferred means of developing transformed health practices (Labonte 2010). Using this method is a way to gain a greater appreciation for the operative worldview in the community. Healthcare personnel trained in curative medicine that uses traditional pedagogical methodologies often feel ill prepared to teach health using informal education methodology; just providing knowledge does not always lead to changed behavior. For adults, information is filtered through the experience and beliefs, the worldview, of the learner. The effectiveness of a community-based healthcare program requires that healthcare professionals be competent in adult education methodology.

FOCUS

There has been considerable debate about the place of curative care and the use of pharmaceuticals in health development programs (Farmer 2003). The need for curative care in areas where there is little to none has led some programs to use health workers to treat common illnesses.

Where There Is No Doctor (Werner 1977) frequently becomes a valuable guidebook for these workers.

Compensation derived from the provision of medicine and curative services has been posited as a means for community health workers to be paid and to sustain the program. Leaders in favor of limiting the role of community health workers to preventive healthcare services felt that if these health workers were compensated for curative care, there would be little incentive to prevent disease. For example, when we visited a church clinic in Uganda, we noted that the healthcare provider was treating a lot of gastrointestinal parasites. We discussed this and asked about the water source for the community. It was an unprotected spring. When we suggested that he might work with the community to protect the spring, he responded that he would then be out of a job and a source of income.

If the role of the CHW is determined to include some curative care, the oversight, continuing education, and supply of pharmaceuticals all become programmatic concerns that need to be carefully addressed.

EVALUATION

It has been argued here that the desired outcome of Christian community health development programs is the increased shalom of the community. This can be difficult to measure. Most often, outcome indicators such as infant mortality and malnutrition rates are the gold standard. However, these common indicators are not solely dependent on a community health development program. Outside factors such as droughts or floods, epidemics of new diseases such as HIV/AIDS, and armed conflict may impact these vital statistics.

It is best if communities set their own goals and determine how they will measure their progress. However, funding for healthcare programs often comes from external organizations that are focused on a specific issue (e.g., HIV, diabetes). Smith and Bryant (1988, 909–17) explain how this challenge emerged in response to the growth of primary health care:

As the health needs of developing countries met the reality of inadequate resources to provide health for all, an important dichotomy arose. Many health ministers and program administrators wanted to pursue balanced, carefully allocated, comprehensive primary health care—so-called horizontal programs. Others held out for targeting selective—vertical—programs that focused on achievable program goals. Donors, who had decided that an achievable victory was worth the investment, as well as being politically useful in obtaining additional funds and political credit, often influenced decisions to implement vertical programs.

If both the community and the public health program share a priority, such as immunization, then both are in sync and can forge a helpful partnership. But if the community has a different priority, then conflict can arise. Likewise, communities who look to funding organizations to determine their healthcare priorities may neglect the real community health problems. The following case study explores some of the issues and opportunities that can emerge when community health workers are empowered.

Cary Christian Center Home Visitors: A Case Study

Cary Christian Center (a.k.a. "the Center") began through the work of Dr. Peter Boelens in the early 1970s. Boelens, a missionary to Korea, had returned to the States to earn a degree in public health and to do a residency in pediatrics at the University of Minnesota. There he was challenged with the healthcare needs of the poor in the United States. Ultimately God led him to Cary, Mississippi. At the time this town was located in one of the poorest counties of the state, and this state was the poorest in the country (Boelens 1991).

Boelens began his work in the community as a public health officer for the district. He realized that many of the mothers did not receive adequate prenatal care and needed education in how to care for their children. Clinic nurses organized classes for the new moms. They convinced Boelens that Carolyn "Care" Newhof, a volunteer with a degree in child development, should be brought on board to head a "Parent Child Ministry" that would educate pregnant women and new moms. Care held classes for the moms, who were provided transportation via the Center bus.

Over time, Care noted that some mothers were helping other moms in the class and expressing concern for their children. In 1989, the Center was awarded a five-year grant that allowed Care to train two local women—Barb Williams and Hattie Lewis—to become lay home visitors. The women were taught how to conduct home visits on newborn infants and their mothers. Each mother enrolled in the Parent Child Ministry and was assigned to one of the home visitors. They visited each mother prenatally and within two days of her arrival home from the hospital. They also assisted the director of the Parent Child Ministry in conducting the classes. Each mother and child was visited for the first year of a baby's life.

The fact that the home visitors were trusted women from the community and experienced mothers allowed the new mothers to accept them into their homes and to disclose their concerns confidentially. Home visitors were familiar with the common problems facing mothers and offered practical advice for dealing with them. They were trained to detect problems early and to treat some of the simple common health problems of newborns and infants.

During the fourth year of the project, the increase in enrollment in the Parent Child Ministry, along with the addition of early prenatal classes and the extension of the program to include toddlers, led to adding a third home visitor—Irma Johnson—to the program. Each home visitor was reimbursed mileage for travel and any telephone expenses. They were also given a stipend for each visit. Over the project period the home visitors made a total of 10,937 home visits.

In 1989 the five-year average infant mortality rate for Sharkey county was 20/1000 overall, 27.8 for the white population and 18.3 for the non-white population (Cary Christian Center/Luke Society 1995). In 1995, one year past the completion of the project, the Mississippi State Department of Health reported a five-year average infant mortality rate of 7.2/1000 overall, 17.2 for the white population and 5.2 for the non-white population. This is in contrast to the 1995 state average of 11.2/1000 overall, 7.6 for the white population and 15.1 for the non-white population (Cary Christian Center/Luke Society 1995).

The population numbers for Sharkey County make determining statistical significance difficult. A comparison with nearby Washington County, a more populous county but one that has similar population statistics, shows that the lay home visitor program did make a difference (Boelens et al. 1997). It should be noted that confounding variables in this study were minimal, as the lay home visitor program was the only health program change in the two counties served for the duration of the project.

In 2009, CBS was investigating a rise in infant mortality rates following Mississippi's reduction in Medicaid. They reported that Mississippi's infant mortality rate had leapt to more than 11/1000, and the black population was losing babies at 17/1000. However, there were no deaths in Sharkey County. From 1991 to 2004, Sharkey County's black infant death rate was around 5/1000, beating the overall national average of about 7/1000 (Serrano 2009).

Cary Lay Home Visitors and Shalom

MOTHERS

Many mothers have been helped by the home visitor program. Mary Davis was one of the first mothers whom the health visitors met with. Mary was living in a shack with holes in the floor. Snakes regularly appeared in the house, including in her mattress coils. She was psychologically depressed. With the help of a social worker and the Center, the health visitors helped Mary relocate to a trailer home. The health visitor began reading the Bible with Mary and shared with her how Jesus loved her and cared about her. Mary embraced this new identity as one loved by God. Slowly her life began to change. She began caring for her children better. She was less depressed.

Jennifer was a teen mom who was diagnosed with HIV when she gave birth to her daughter. She had some learning disabilities. She lived with different relatives in the community, as her mother was unable to properly care for her. One of the health visitors, Barb Williams, visited her and helped her learn healthy ways of responding to her HIV status. As her daughter was also diagnosed with HIV, the health visitor also gave her practical instruction on caring for her. Repeated conversations about her life, her health status, and her relationship with God helped Jennifer to understand her situation. Shortly before her death she accepted Christ and asked to be baptized. After her death, relatives cared for her daughter. The home visitors assisted the family with accessing the required antiretroviral therapy and medical care. When the relatives could no longer care for her, she lived for a time with Care until she could move to live with relatives in another state.

HOME VISITORS

The first home visitors have moved on. Irma Johnson is now working with the Delta Infant Mortality Elimination project sponsored by the State Department of Public Health. Irma was hired to follow up on all the premature babies born at the University Medical Center in Jackson, Mississippi. She attends the office visits with the mother and baby, and works with the mother, who is most often unmarried, to set life goals. When others ask her about her commitment, she refers to how Jesus was a servant and that she too is a servant as a follower of Jesus. Irma says, "I've raised six children and I believe that there are things that I can share with others in my community." Currently there are plans to extend the health department visitation program to the mothers of premature babies born at the Regional Health Center in Vicksburg, Mississippi. Irma is working with other public health leaders to help identify and train other home visitors.

The current Family Support Coordinator in the Parent Child Ministry, Marion Tyler, grew up at the Center. When Marion was a teenager she became a mother. Care was her home visitor and "spent unreal time with me teaching me about how to nurture a child." For a time Marion moved to Illinois but found that living there with little support was difficult. She managed to continue her education and is now a licensed social worker. She moved back to the Mississippi Delta and is excited about helping others who are struggling as she has struggled. She tells young moms, "The system keeps you dependent, and the harder you try to get out the less you get. Government assistance should only be used as a bridge, not to build a house."

CARY COMMUNITY

Local leaders have now risen to direct the Center and keep the various programs running. Dorsey Johnson, who was raised in Cary, leads the children's afterschool programs. Dorsey and Care have worked together closely and have worked hard to understand each other's perspective. They have lived in the community for more than thirty years and have each built a home on a street they named "Shalom." Today they serve as the co-directors of the Center, modeling a vision of Christian community by being a black man and a white woman serving God together in the rural South.

In the early years, vandalism of the Center was a regular problem. Recently the community asked if they could use the baseball field that is on the Center's property. When rivalries between teams threatened to become violent and property was damaged, Care and Dorsey met with the responsible parties. They explained that the community needed to see the Center as their property and take responsibility for it.

The community agreed, put up signs prohibiting alcohol, drugs, and cursing, and organized to have police come by regularly.

In many ways Cary typifies the lay healthcare movement. The program was initially owned by the Cary Christian Center and is only now beginning to be an integral part of the community. The clinic has closed due to the high cost of health care. The physician who operated the clinic maintains a private practice in the community. The Center maintains the dental clinic and other programs that contribute to the development of the community. Through the relationships that were formed in the Parent Child Ministry, using adult education methodology, mothers were transformed from dependent care recipients to care providers and community leaders. The impact on the health of the community has been documented by lower infant mortality rates. More importantly, the program is biblically based, holistic, and focuses on relationships.

The Future

According to a spending brief produced by the Altarum Institute, the national expenditure on health care in June 2012 was 15.65 percent of the gross domestic product (Altarum Institute 2012). Economically, increases in healthcare costs will be unsustainable. While emphasis on health promotion and disease prevention is increasing, many health problems, such as substance abuse, obesity, and domestic violence, have their root causes outside the purview of curative medicine. In other words, the brief conversation with the patient in the clinic does not supply all the necessary information to understand the living situations of people whom God is placing in our lives.

The church needs to follow the example of Jesus, who went to the people, had compassion on them, and healed them. We can include health education, health promotion, and health outreach as part of our mission. We can empower Christians to become servants who go into the community to teach others about health practices *and* the gospel.

Returning once again to Uganda, as I (Grace) was saying goodbye to John Kiyimba, he said, "Sister Grace, we need you to come back and teach more of us about community-based healthcare." My response was that I thought there were people like John who could and should teach others. Finding leaders like John and providing minimal education in program development can bring health care and the gospel to people with limited to no access.

In looking toward the future, we ask these two questions: What if every local church saw health as integral to the good news? What if each church mobilized and equipped some of its members to be community health workers in its unique context?

References Cited

Altarum Institute. 2012. *ALTARUM INSTITUTE Spending Brief #12-08: June 2012 Data.* June 2012.

Boelens, Peter. 1991. *Delta Doctor.* Vicksburg, MS: Luke Books.

———, Kurt Kooyer, Andrew George, and Carolyn Newhof. 1997. "An Approach to Reducing Infant Mortality Rate through the Utilization of Lay Home Visitors." *Journal of the Mississippi State Medical Association* 38 (10): 379–83.

Cary Christian Center/Luke Society. 1995. "Sharkey-Issaquena Health Alliance." Final Grant Report for Maternal Child Improvement Projects, Vickburg, MS.

Farmer, Paul. 2003. *Pathologies of Power: Health, Human Rights, and the New War on the Poor.* California Series in Public Anthropology. Los Angeles: University of California Press.

Hope, Anne, and Sally Timmel. 1984. *Training for Transformation: A Handbook for Community Workers,* Parts 1, 2, and 3. Gweru, Zimbabwe: Mambo Press.

Labonte, Ronald. 2010. "Reflections on Stories and a Story/Dialogue Method in Health Research." *International Journal of Social Research Methodology* 14 (2): 153–63.

Serrano, Alfonso. 2009. "Fighting a Rising Infant Mortality Rate." *CBS Evening News,* February 11. http://www.cbsnews.com/stories/2007/06/03/eveningnews/main2879278.shtml?tag=mncol;lst;1.

Shaffer, Roy. 1984. *Beyond the Dispensary.* Nairobi: AMREF.

Smith, D. L., and J. H. Bryant. 1988. "Building the Infrastructure for Primary Health Care: An Overview of Vertical and Integrated Approaches." *Social Science and Medicine* 26 (9): 909–17.

Swezy, Curtiss. 2008. "The Christian Community's Contribution to the Evolution of Community-Based Primary Health Care." Based upon a presentation by Dr. Carl E. Taylor and Dr. John H. Bryant, Christian Connections for International Health (CCIH) 2008 Annual Conference, May 24, Buckeystown, MD. Available at http://www. ccih.org/community-health/Christian-Contribution-to-Evolution-of-CBPHC.pdf.

Van Reken, David. 1990. "Medical Missions and the Development of Health." In *A New Agenda for Medical Missions,* edited by D. Merrill Ewert, 19–31. Brunswick, GA: MAP International.

Werner, David. 1977. *Where There Is No Doctor: A Village Health Care Handbook.* Palo Alto, CA: The Hesperian Foundation.

Werner, David, and Bill Bower. 1982. *Helping Healthcare Workers Learn: A Book of Methods, Aids, and Ideas for Instructors at the Village Level.* Palo Alto, CA: The Hesperian Foundation.

CHAPTER 15

Empowering the Local Church
Community Health Evangelism

Terry Dalrymple, MDiv,
with Jody Collinge, MD

Introduction

There is an urgent need for church-initiated community health programs. Consider the following facts:

- 21,000 children before the age of five die each day, most from preventable or treatable causes (United Nations Children's Fund 2011).780 million people do not have access to clean drinking water (WHO/UNICEF Joint Monitoring Programme [JMP] 2012).
- 2.5 billion people lack access to improved sanitation facilities (WHO Global Health Observatory 2012).

The church is uniquely positioned to respond to these needs. The church in many places is the only institution with the capacity to mobilize enough volunteers to do what is needed in the area of community health. When children are dying from preventable causes and the church has the capacity to prevent those deaths, the church must respond.

Biblical health, or shalom, has been described in previous chapters as harmony with God, self, others, and the environment. Similarly, the World Health Organization (WHO) defines health as "a state of complete physical, mental and social well-being and not merely the absence of disease or infirmity" (WHO 1948). WHO's definition is not far from our definition of shalom, except for the absence of any direct reference to God or spiritual well-being. As Christians, we affirm that there cannot be a state of complete well-being apart from Christ, who forgives our sin, gives us new life, and restores us to right relationship with God. Health from a Christian perspective is a state of complete physical, mental, social, and spiritual well-being.

If the goal of a Christian community health program is harmony with God, self, others, and the environment, then strategies for Christian community health should address the physical, mental, social, and spiritual. In order to achieve this goal, our strategies need to move beyond typical primary care interventions such as growth monitoring, oral rehydration, immunization, breastfeeding, family planning, female education, and food supplementation. These are all good and necessary, but they are inadequate in themselves to bring wholeness.

This inadequate view of wholeness can be illustrated through the story of a man named Mr. Mafu. While the story is fictional, it is representative of the experience of many villagers around the world.

> Mr. Mafu had a nice horse. As he rode to work one day, the horse stepped into a hole. Mr. Mafu fell off and broke his leg. His neighbor, a good friend, took him home and the family called the traditional healer. The traditional healer said the neighbor had "witched" him and brought this evil on him. He also advised him to go to the hospital. At the hospital his leg was put into a cast. In the hospital, Mr. Mafu kept saying, "It shows that you cannot even trust your best friend!" When the cast came off, he was so glad the leg was healed, but he wanted to go and pay back the evil his neighbor had done. He planned his revenge, and started doing wrong things against his neighbor. (Global CHE Network)[29]

Is Mr. Mafu healthy now that his leg is well? The answer is no. Mr. Mafu is not well emotionally, because he is angry and bitter at his neighbor.

---

29   All information about the principles and training materials of Community Health Evangelism (CHE) can be found on the Global CHE Network website. This story comes from the Training of Trainers course, an open source CHE curriculum available to registered members.

He is not well socially, because he is trying to pay back the evil his neighbor has done, and he may be creating clan wars for generations to come. He is not well spiritually, because he is disobeying the Lord's commands to love and forgive. On top of all that, he may be struggling economically because of hospital bills and the loss of a good horse!

People need many things in order to be truly healthy: food, water, sanitation, shelter, work, education, family, friends, purpose, forgiveness, truth, and so much more. Community Health Evangelism (CHE) is a participatory strategy that seeks to empower communities to address the relevant concerns for their context. This chapter will present CHE as a strategy for improving health from a biblical perspective.

Overview of Community Health Evangelism (CHE)

The goal of Community Health Evangelism is the transformation of lives and communities through the power of the gospel. The first CHE programs took place in Uganda under the direction of a missionary with Campus Crusade for Christ (now Cru) named Stan Rowland (Rowland 2011).

Today, CHE is used by hundreds of missionaries, churches, and Christian organizations around the world. CHE integrates Christian discipleship with disease prevention and community-based development. It is a Christ-centered educational program that equips communities to identify issues and mobilize community resources to achieve positive, sustainable change. Lives and communities are transformed as people come to Christ and work together to address local needs.

The authors have been privileged to travel to CHE communities around the world and see firsthand the impact of the ministry.

Here are a few snapshots of community transformation that we have witnessed through implementing the CHE strategy:

- A small town in the Philippines is recognized nationally for their godly leaders, empty jail, clean streets, and healthy homes. A sign at the entrance to their municipality says "Welcome to a Christian Community."

- In the foothills of the Himalayas, a village burned out twice by Maoist rebels has been lifted from the ashes. Their homes and economy are restored. Every family in the village has come to Christ. They have changed the name of their village to "Bethany," named for the place where Jesus raised Lazarus from the dead.

- A village in Africa is committed to caring for their fifty-four AIDS orphans in the name of Christ. The children are all in school, taught the word of God through Tuesday gatherings, and cared for in homes.

- Youth in one of the largest slums in Africa dig their homes out of the rubbish and declare, "God is going to transform this community, and he is going to use us to do it."

- A fishing village in Asia is rid of intestinal worms, scabies, and pervasive domestic violence. The leaders testify that before they came to Christ it was as if everyone in the village had megaphones in their homes from which they would broadcast the shouting and verbal conflict. Now there is peace.

- In the West Pacific, tribal warfare in one district has ceased after sixteen years of fighting. Footpaths have been built and decorated between previously warring communities.

These are just a few stories of the impact of Community Health Evangelism around the world. There have not been many impact studies done on CHE programs, largely because the majority of CHE ministries are carried out by groups of volunteers on a small budget in isolated communities. However, what research has been done demonstrates significant enough impact to commend the strategy and warrant further study.

Dr. James Engel (2002) led a research team investigating thirty CHE communities in the Congo. Their findings appeared in the team's executive summary:

> The evaluation team left the Congo with the united impression that we are seeing firsthand what the kingdom

of God can be when evangelism, nurture, and social change are woven into one coordinated and integrated program. Hundreds have now become believers and are now church members. Church unity is a reality and not a cliché. Community Health has notably improved, and village members are now cooperating in community farming and other ventures, which have all but overcome the problem of hunger and even starvation during the dry season. (Calhoun 2003, 2–3)

Dr. Sam Voorhies, former director of Leadership Development at World Vision International and a coworker with Dr. Engel on this evaluation, concluded, "In over 20 years of two-thirds world ministry, having evaluated dozens of 'wholistic' programs in numerous countries, I have not seen anywhere such dramatic impact for such little cost" (Calhoun 2003, 6).

In the remainder of this chapter, we will explore the principles and practices of Community Health Evangelism. In addition, we will seek to understand why and how these impacts are achieved.

Core Principles of Community Health Evangelism

CHE is built on a set of core values. These values have been articulated by different practitioners in different words throughout the history of the CHE movement, but the basic principles are the same. They might be summarized as follows: (1) development instead of relief, (2) integration or holism, (3) local ownership and initiative, (4) participatory learning and self-discovery, (5) multiplication and movements, and (6) volunteerism.

COMMUNITY HEALTH EVANGELISM CORE PRINCIPLES	
Development instead of Relief	Concentrating efforts on long-term solutions that break the cycle of poverty and disease. Training, equipping, and empowering people to do for themselves. A hand up rather than a hand out.
Integration or Wholism	Complete obedience to all that Jesus commanded, including compassion for the physical needs of people as well as evangelism and discipleship. Seeking the total development of the whole person—physically, intellectualy, socially, and spiritually.

Local Ownership and Initiative	Human beings are made in the image of God as stewards of resources rather than victims of circumstance. Local ownership requires that the people themselves participate in choosing their own priorities, finding their own resources, and managing their own development programs. Sustainable programs are owned by the people and built on local initiative.
Participatory Learning and Self-Discovery	People are active participants rather than passive recipients in the development process. Training methodology must engage participants in a process of reflection and action (self-discovery).
Multiplication and Movements	Multiplication and movement is facilitated by training people to train others using concepts that are transferrable. Use of local resources and appropriate technologies ensure that solutions can be passed along neighbor to neighbor and community to community.
Volunteerism	People with heart and passion, grateful for the changes God is working in their lives, give themselves to bring the truth and touch of Christ to their neighbors and friends.

Table 15.1: Community Health Evangelism core principles

DEVELOPMENT INSTEAD OF RELIEF

Crisis situations require disaster relief. The victims of a disastrous event may have an immediate need for water, food, clothing, medical assistance, shelter, and other forms of aid. These are usually provided by outsiders who resource and direct the relief effort. The duration of relief activities is short term, and the primary objective is to save lives. Relief activities are necessary in a crisis situation, but they are not intended to bring long-term solutions to chronic situations.

Chronic situations such as poverty call for a different kind of response. Those living in chronic poverty need the capacity to create solutions that address the underlying causes of their socioeconomic conditions. This kind of activity is called development. Development is long term, and the primary objective is to improve the quality of life. Good development programs are resourced and controlled by the people themselves and result in sustainable solutions that are not reliant on outside resources or support (Christian 2011).

One of the keys to helping without hurting is to know when to do what (Corbett and Fikkert 2009). If we do development when relief is needed, people may die. If we do relief when development is needed, we create unhealthy dependency and fail to deliver long-term, sustainable solutions.

To illustrate this principle, here is a positive example of a CHE project. CHE trainers had spent months in a community raising awareness and mobilizing the community to work together against its own problems. The community elected leaders to serve on a development committee that was trained by the CHE team to identify needs, choose priorities, gather resources, plan their project, and implement and evaluate it.

Community leaders identified goiter as a priority concern. In their community of 2,000 people, 230 cases of goiter had been reported in the previous six months. The underlying cause for this condition was a lack of iodine in the diet. CHE trainers at work in the community responded by educating the community about goiter and its cause.

After some time, the leaders concluded that the problem was that the salt sold in the community was not iodized. Initially the community did not want to be convinced, because salt without iodine was about half the price of iodized salt. Breakthroughs came when community members began to calculate the real cost of salt without iodine, which included treatment for goiter.

Understanding the cause of the problem, the development committee together with the trainers made a plan to address the problem. The CHE trainers researched and found a simple and inexpensive way to test for iodine in the salt. Armed with this test kit, the community leaders tested the salt being sold in the community and then alerted residents when the salt was not iodized. Vendors with non-iodized salt ran away when they saw the leaders coming. Eventually these same vendors returned with iodized salt. The goiter problem was resolved.

In this story, the people themselves chose the priorities, created the solutions, and carried out the plans. They created a solution that was sustainable and did not depend on external support (Dalrymple 2006). The outsiders in the process were facilitators. They raised awareness, inspired hope and vision, and mobilized people to work together. They responded to this chronic problem with development.

If the facilitators had chosen to respond to this chronic problem with relief, they would have assessed the community's needs themselves, established their priorities, blueprinted a plan, pitched their solution to donors, bought salt in the city, and distributed it to community residents. That solution would have failed to solve the problem over the long term.

INTEGRATION OR WHOLISM

When I (Terry) arrived on the mission field as a young missionary, a veteran pulled me aside with a single word of advice. His advice summarized the philosophy of ministry of my new colleagues: "If you feed somebody today, they will be hungry again tomorrow. If you save their soul today, they will be saved forever." His words were consistent with what the majority of evangelicals at that time believed about the mission of the church. We had come to the Philippines not to care for the physical needs of people but to preach, save souls, and plant churches (Dalrymple 2006).

As a group of missionaries, we thought about our Christian faith almost exclusively in terms of a personal relationship with God and fellowship with his people. Our faith was about receiving forgiveness of sins and a place in heaven. We did not connect our faith with justice and compassion.

The result of this dichotomy between the sacred and the secular was that we planted churches without a social conscience. Our disciples gathered to pray, study their Bibles, and have fellowship, but were not engaged in issues of justice and compassion for the poor. The tragic result was churches that were marginalized and isolated, almost irrelevant in the eyes of the community.

CHE aims for obedience to all that Jesus commanded. This includes compassion for the physical needs of people as well as evangelism and discipleship. This involves seeking the total development of the whole person—physically, intellectually, socially, and spiritually.

LOCAL OWNERSHIP AND INITIATIVE

The biblical basis for the concept of local ownership is the simple fact that human beings are made in the image of God as stewards rather than victims of circumstance. Human development inspires personal responsibility rather than unhealthy dependency.

"Local ownership" is people working together voluntarily to achieve their own initiatives. Projects that are community owned are conceived and controlled by the people themselves. They assess their own needs, choose priorities, set goals, make plans, gather resources, and evaluate. Community-owned projects help the poor to make use of local resources and create solutions that are sustainable and reproducible. Unhealthy dependency disappears, and people recover their God-given vocation as stewards of resources. The outcomes and impact of community-owned projects are often intangible assets such as dignity, hope, vision, and unity; but these intangibles are essential to lasting change.

PARTICIPATORY LEARNING AND SELF-DISCOVERY

CHE facilitators (or trainers) seek to ensure that community members are active participants rather than passive recipients in the development process. Instead of blueprinting solutions and telling the community what to do, CHE facilitators pose problems and, through a process of guided self-discovery, encourage community members to create their own solutions. The result is that community members own the ideas and act upon them voluntarily because they see that action to be in their own best interest.

CHE training is intended to empower individuals and communities as architects of their own development. The CHE trainer does not deliver pre-packaged solutions in a lecture, but facilitates discussions that involve the people themselves in creating their own solutions. The table below compares the two approaches.

Lecture (Traditional Approaches)	Discussion (The CHE Way)
• Content focused	• Learner centered
• Advice giving	• Awareness raising
• People listen	• People create solutions
• Outsiders own the solutions	• Insiders own solutions
• People wait for outsiders to resource the project	• People take action

Table 15.2: Lecture vs. discussion

CHE lessons are formatted to make it easy for the trainer to facilitate discussions and involve the people themselves in analyzing problems, identifying resources, and creating solutions.

MULTIPLICATION AND MOVEMENTS

Jesus set before his disciples a vision that led to a movement that would reach to the very ends of the earth and would transform nations from the inside out. With this vision, each disciple becomes a disciple maker. Followers learn to obey Jesus and to pass that knowledge on to others.

Jesus spoke of his kingdom as something that started small. His kingdom would start small like a mustard seed, but would grow to be a large tree. His kingdom would be like leaven that works itself through the whole lump of dough (Matt 13:31–34). Jesus has not sent us to do small projects but to achieve a large vision. He has not sent us to only make converts, or establish a local congregation, but to catalyze a movement. His vision is broad, extending to the ends of the earth. His vision is deep, transforming lives and nations from the inside out. His vision is long, extending from generation to generation.

While his vision is large, his strategy is simple. He commands his followers to make disciples. The process of making disciples of all nations is one of multiplying followers and influence. The gospel went forth from the city of Jerusalem to the ends of the earth as his followers reproduced their faith in others.

If we view our mission endeavors as projects that we finish and not movements that we are only beginning, then we have lost sight of something fundamental to our calling. Here are some good questions to ask about our mission endeavors:

- Will our efforts contribute to a movement or just small projects?
- Can what we are doing be multiplied by those we are serving, without input from the outside?
- Are we creating dependencies on outside resources that will eventually slow the progress of the gospel, or are we unleashing local resources for the cause of Christ?
- Are we using methods that make people passive recipients, or are they becoming active participants in the cause?

VOLUNTEERISM

Jesus initiated a movement of volunteers when he commissioned his followers to make disciples of all nations. His followers would take up their cross not because they were paid to do it, but because they were compelled by his love. I (Terry) have heard it argued that volunteerism is impossible for those who are struggling from day to day for survival. My experience tells me otherwise.

One hot, dreary Sunday afternoon, I visited a slum in Metro Manila in the Philippines. A patchwork of makeshift shelters made from cardboard, rice sacks, bamboo, and other scavenged materials littered the land. Squatters protected their space in crowded, unsanitary conditions.

About a dozen volunteer Community Health Evangelists (CHEs) gathered to meet me in a small church on the edge of this shantytown. These women had come to the Lord through our ministry and had been trained to set up micro businesses. They were studying the Bible together and were learning the basic principles of health, sanitation, and hygiene. Each woman was assigned a small number of homes to visit regularly in order to share what she was learning with the rest of the community. I listened as each one of them proudly told of the small business enterprises they had undertaken. They walked me to their homes and showed me what they were doing: one lady made dolls, another sold frozen meats, and another sold candy.

Later, they took me to meet a few of the people they were ministering to through home visits. They took me to one home I will not soon forget—a shanty made of cardboard and scraps of bamboo on the edge of a tall cliff. A woman lived there with her eight children. She had nothing in her little home except a small tub of laundry waiting to be washed by hand and malnourished children with runny noses and skin infections. I noticed a hole punched in the bamboo wall at the back of the hut. She told me her story. Her husband was shot and killed by drug addicts, and one of her young children had fallen through the hole in the back wall over the cliff and died.

These volunteers with small microenterprise businesses were taking steps toward health and wholeness, and their success gave hope to the woman with eight children. They were not only taking steps to improve the quality of their own lives, but they were leading others to do the same (Dalrymple 2006).

Outcomes and Indicators

In the previous section, we explored six core principles that are the backbone of CHE work everywhere. In this section we will examine the desired outcomes of CHE work. What is it we are working to achieve?

On a recent trip to a very poor country, we had a few minutes with the country's vice president. We shared with him our plans for leadership development and CHE. He responded by welcoming us, and then he said, "The problem in our country is that our people view development as something outsiders will do for them rather than something they will do for themselves." He then applauded the effort to raise up local leaders among the people who will inspire communities to work together with hope and vision to achieve a better future. His statement highlights an important point about outcomes that lead to long-term impact. Such outcomes are people centered. Our ministries should be more focused on empowering people than on doing projects.

With people-centered outcomes in mind, here is a list of desired outcomes, indicators by which we measure the success of a CHE program (Global CHE Network 2012b):

- Shared Vision: The community sees a better future and has hope that it can be achieved.
- Leadership: Godly Christian leaders are positioned and equipped to lead the community toward the accomplishment of its vision.
- Ownership: People are taking responsibility for their own health and well-being.
- Cooperation: People are united and working together for the common good.
- Volunteers: Significant numbers of people are taking the initiative and acting sacrificially to meet the legitimate needs of others.
- Dignity: People have recovered their identity as made in the image of God and their vocation as stewards of resources.
- Learning, Skill, and Resources: People are equipped to identify needs and resources, put together a plan, and mobilize volunteers to accomplish their vision. People are continually reflecting on what is happening in order to learn how to be more effective.
- Christian Community and Witness: Believers are meeting together for Bible study, prayer, fellowship, and worship. Believers are sharing Christ with their neighbors in word and deed.

The CHE Process

CHE is not a set of steps to implement but a set of principles to apply. CHE principles have been applied on every continent, in every major political and religious environment. As a result, different models have emerged that have demonstrated effectiveness for specific contexts.

There are community-based, church-based, church-initiated, family-based, government-initiated, clinic-based, and school-based models (Rowland 2011). To do CHE effectively, facilitators must internalize the principles of CHE and work them out creatively in the context in which God has called them to serve.

Resources for Starting a CHE Ministry

For those who are interested in learning more, training and curriculum are available from the Global CHE Network. The Global CHE Network is an association of people and organizations using the CHE strategy around the world. The goal of the network is to facilitate collaboration between individuals and organizations for the strengthening of ministry and the expansion of the CHE movement. Network members share useful ideas and best practices, encourage each other, coordinate efforts, and optimize the use of limited resources.

The network provides a large pool of resources from which all members draw. By coordinating our efforts with a determination to build up each other's ministries and expand the CHE movement, members gain access to ideas and resources and create new opportunities to do together what no one could achieve alone.

CHE training is offered through a series of seminars by experienced CHE facilitators. More information and training materials may be found on the Global CHE Network website (www.chenetwork.org). CHE lesson plans enable CHE workers to equip and mobilize communities to solve their own problems using local resources.

The CHE curriculum is a collection of best practices from around the world condensed into simple participatory lesson plans that can be taught in the community. Lesson plans can easily be adapted to the context. The latest lesson plan disk contains more than ten thousand documents including lesson plans, stories, picture books, teaching aids, surveys, and tools for monitoring and evaluation. The material is arranged on the disk to walk step by step through the whole CHE process. CHE training materials are also available as PDF manuals on a wide range of health and development topics (Global CHE Network 2012a).

Conclusion

Community Health Evangelism is a tool for church-initiated community health and development ministry. Our prayer is that CHE might be a tool in the hands of the church that will bring people to faith in Christ, restore broken relationships, promote health, prevent disease and death, and contribute to the well-being of individuals, families, and communities.

References Cited

Calhoun, Paul. 2003. "Executive Summary: Ministry Impact in the Democratic Republic of the Congo." Medical Ambassadors International.

Christian, Jayakumar. 2011. *God of the Empty-Handed: Poverty, Power and the Kingdom of God*. Rev. ed. Brunswick East, VIC 3057, Australia: Acorn Press.

Corbett, Steve, and Brian Fikkert. 2009. *When Helping Hurts: How to Alleviate Poverty Without Hurting the Poor . . . and Yourself*. Chicago: Moody.

Dalrymple, Terry. 2006. "Stories of Transformation: From the Travel Diaries of Terry Dalrymple."

Engel, James. 2002. "Impact Evaluation: Community Health Evangelism Project." The Democratic Republic of the Congo.

Global CHE Network. 2012a. "CHE Lesson Plan Materials," "CHE Training Info," and "Training for Trainers" curriculum. Available at http://www.chenetwork.org/store.php.

———. 2012b."What is CHE?" http://www.chenetwork.org/what.php (accessed February 10, 2015).

Rowland, Stan. 2011. *Multiplying Light and Truth through Community Health Evangelism*. Mumbai: GLS Publishing.

United Nations Children's Fund. 2011. "Child Mortality Report 2011." Estimates developed by the Inter-agency Group for Child Mortality Estimation. Available at http://reliefweb.int/sites/reliefweb.int/files/resources/Child_Mortality_Report_2011_Final.pdf.

World Health Organization (WHO). 1948. Preamble to the Constitution of the World Health Organization as adopted by the International Health Conference, New York, 19–22 June, 1946; signed on 22 July 1946 by the representatives of 61 States (Official Records of the World Health Organization, no. 2, p. 100) and entered into force on 7 April 1948.

WHO/UNICEF Joint Monitoring Programme (JMP) for Water Supply and Sanitation. 2012. "Progress on Drinking Water and Sanitation: 2012 Update." Available at http://www.who.int/water_sanitation_health/publications/2012/jmp_report/en/index.html.

WHO Global Health Observatory Data Repository. 2012. "Population Using Improved Sanitation Facilities." Available at http://www.who.int/water_sanitation_health/publications/2012/jmp_report/en/index.html.

Looking Forward in the Healthcare Missions Movement

Isaac B. Voss, MPH, Erin Dufault-
Hunter, PhD, and Rick Donlon, MD

Having explored the rich history of healthcare missions in this book, we see how the healing ministry of the church finds its roots not in human organizations but rather in participation in God's mission. We recall how the early followers of Christ practiced the ministry of healing and radical hospitality, tending to the vulnerable through hospitals and providing sanctuaries for the mentally impaired and the blind. Turning toward the present, we surveyed the current global reality of healthcare missions through considering such issues as HIV/AIDS, child health, and urban poverty. Finally, we have considered the frontiers of healthcare missions theology and the emerging models and practices of this movement.

We have viewed the past, present, and future of the healthcare missions movement through the lens of relational well-being, or shalom, as understood within the broader biblical narrative of the Creation, Fall, and redemption. This frame has equipped us for an interdisciplinary conversation that draws on insights from such fields as theology, psychology, public health, medicine, nursing, and international development. In this final chapter, we respond to two questions. First, what have we learned from one another? Second, in light of this learning, how can we engage in healthcare missions going forward? We respond to the first by identifying some of the book's central themes. We then envision the future of the Christian healthcare movement through these insights.

Reflecting on this collection, we discern a fourfold call for a healthcare missions movement that is identity-transforming, incarnational, integrative, and innovative. These four marks are by no means the only guides for the future of the healthcare missions movement, nor are they exhaustively representative of the diverse motifs that were explored in this book. However, these themes provide a framework for what has emerged as well as concrete direction for further research, reflection, and action.

An *Identity-Transforming* Healthcare Missions Movement

A recurring theme in this book has been the importance of a transformed identity. A transformed identity involves a movement from a position of marred identity and forgotten vocation to one of security and steward-ship in God's family. The transformation of identity was discussed at both the individual and the communal level. The importance of identity transformation has been highlighted in respect to three groups: Chris-tian health providers, the oppressed, and non-Christians.

THE IDENTITY OF CHRISTIAN HEALTH PROVIDERS

Christian health providers must seek as honestly as they can to recognize who they are and who they are not. They must ground their identities in the image of God, which involves the divine calling of human beings to act as God's representatives (Middleton 2005). One of the first implica-tions of this vocation is that Christian health workers are called to know *whom* they represent.

In knowing God we find the central motivation for the healthcare missions movement: We love because he first loved us. Consider the story that Debbie Dortzbach shares in chapter 8 about Mary, who contracted AIDS from her husband yet then cared for her bedridden husband, her husband's girlfriend, and that couple's child. When asked why she served those who had caused her such emotional, social, and physical pain, she replied, "Because Jesus loves me, I can love them." In their call to walk with those who are oppressed, Long and Dortzbach insightfully point out that we can never persevere in loving anyone when our love is contingent upon their response to us. We only accompany others in love as we permit Jesus to accompany us in his love. The recognition that we are compelled by God's love and not our own liberates us from an unhealthy—and false—expectation that our ministry is ultimately dependent on our own character or willpower. We see this same insight reflected in multiple ways, as in the caution from Eriksson and colleagues that unless we recognize our human finitude as servants and not messiahs, we burn out and may shatter our relationships. At the level of group identity, they also raise some important questions in regard to the types of organizational cultures we create. Do our organizations see themselves as the saviors of the oppressed or do they point to the Savior? How can we create organizations that allow staff members to say no to unhealthy ministry demands without feeling guilty? In our calling to transform the identity of health providers and organizations, we must embody personal and institutional practices that remind us, as well as those we serve, that the love of God is our impetus and participation in his mission is our calling.

THE IDENTITY OF THE OPPRESSED

Those who work in healthcare ministry frequently confront brokenness and suffering. This brokenness is external and internal, individual and systemic. For health professionals animated by Christian hope, such brokenness is neither God's original intention nor our inevitable future. A good God created humankind in his image, and while that royal image is too often obscured by poverty or poor health, the divine imprint remains. This core conviction radically alters how we conceive of our work and how we engage with others. For example, Myers notes in chapter 2 that rediscovery of this image among the oppressed involves both the healing of their marred identity and an invitation to a vocation of purpose and stewardship. Scott points out that the *imago Dei* in children necessitates an appreciation of their sense of dignity and agency.

The seven affirmations he offers provide a pathway for further research with children that turns aside from the predominant yet superficial frame of self-preservation and sentimentality. Finally, consider how Dalrymple and Collinge encourage us to pay attention not only to individual transformation but also to community transformation. By developing participatory methods that respect the collective agency of our communities, we recall that the *imago Dei* is not only a call on individuals but also on diverse communities ("male and female") that come together for the good of all.

AN INVITATION TO CHRISTIAN WITNESS

The pinnacle of the biblical narrative is the person of Christ and the good news of the kingdom of God. As his followers, we are called to live out the gospel as we re-present the risen Christ (Ramachandra 1999, 171). In chapter 3, Myers proposes a framework for understanding Christian witness and encourages health professionals to live in such a way that they provoke questions to which the gospel is the answer. As an example of the power of provoking questions, consider the testimony of Dr. Kent Brantly, a missionary-doctor infected with the Ebola virus in West Africa who stimulated curiosity and puzzlement among non-Christians by sacrificially offering the vaccine to one of his infected coworkers instead of taking it himself. As he put it, "I prayed that in my life or in my death that [God] would glorified" (BBC 2014). Throughout this collection, others have shared creative strategies by which we present the whole gospel in word and deed.

The much-used shorthand phrase "give God the glory" names what we mean by Christian witness: we point to Jesus Christ not only by offering health care but also in *how* we do so. Myriad pressures, such as the push for efficiency, can seem at odds with Christian values—for instance, our conviction that each person deserves attention as God's child. Amidst these tensions, God calls faithful healthcare professionals to enter into this ministry in such a way that those around them might catch a glimpse of the one who makes self-offering, image-affirming care not only possible but also joyful.

An *Incarnational* Healthcare Missions Movement

Central to our faith is the wonderful and surprising declaration that God "became flesh and made his dwelling among us" (John 1:14). Jesus was born among a subjugated people to an unmarried woman who delivered him in a stable. In his three decades, Jesus encountered hunger, exhaustion, and even homelessness. As a man, Jesus endured personal isolation and alienation as well as possible fevers, diarrhea, and other maladies common to humankind. As Hebrews states, "For we do not have a high priest who is unable to sympathize with our weaknesses, but one who in every respect has been tempted as we are" (Heb 4:15). As members of his body, we imitate his willingness to enter into the suffering of others. While this central Christian conviction perhaps obviously impacts many aspects of life and mission, here we suggest implications for the spiritual lives of healthcare workers, for our work in local churches, and for our engagement with the emergent Global South.

Just as Jesus practiced life-giving spiritual disciplines, we have examined how such practices shape healthcare workers. We specifically considered lament (Dufault-Hunter), Sabbath-keeping (Eriksson et al.), incarnational presence (White and Henry), hospitality, and encounter (Short and Voss). If Christ himself models these sustaining disciplines, we too must integrate these into our daily lives and patterns of work. To do otherwise risks not only arrogantly placing ourselves above Christ, but also rejects the implication of the incarnation as a model of how to be fully, deeply human.

A second implication of incarnational healthcare missions is the importance of respecting the embodied expression of Christ—the local church. The centrality of the church in incarnational healthcare missions has been a key theme of this book. The theologian Lesslie Newbigin noted, "The church lives in the midst of history as a sign, instrument and foretaste of the reign of God" (Newbigin 1995, 110). There is much interdisciplinary research and reflection to be done on creative ways in which the local body can be an increasingly effective agent of kingdom healthcare.

Another implication of the incarnation is the recognition of the rise of the church of the Global South. Historian and missiologist Andrew Walls has pointed out that in the incarnation God became human within a particular context and thereby affirmed the value and importance of indigenizing the gospel into particular cultures (Walls 1996). Dan Fountain in his chapter underscores the importance of this message in his experience with the church in the Congo. Fountain notes that there are new questions and answers emerging for those who have eyes to see and ears to hear from the Global South. As the gospel has been translated into the native languages of the Global South, we are witnessing the shift of Christianity from the North to its new homelands of Asia, Latin America, and Africa (Sanneh 2008). As the church of the South continues to grow in influence, it will have a powerful shaping effect on the future healthcare missions movement.

An *Integrative* Healthcare Missions Movement

Enacting God's shalom involves reconciliation and justice. Participating in God's future by anticipating his full reign on earth, we call individuals and communities to move from dis-integration to integration. Integrative healthcare, then, involves a move toward individual and collective wholeness. To do this effectively in our time, we need further research and practical responses in at least three areas: (1) recovery of an integrated worldview among Christian health workers, (2) research on our response to psychological disintegration and trauma, and (3) greater awareness and advocacy for just and peaceful socioeconomic structures.

Regarding the need for an integrated biblical worldview, multiple authors point out the harm caused by modernity's artificial separation between the physical and the spiritual (e.g., Hiebert 2008). Myers argues that this dualism has resulted in the "excluded middle," or the neglect of the spiritual in everyday life. This dichotomy has allowed modern science to concentrate on understanding and treating biochemical and physical abnormalities while ignoring (or paying only lip service to) religion as a private, subjective realm of reality. The health sciences often limit knowledge to those domains that can be objectively measured, thereby providing for individuals and communities a truncated health care that is blind to the spiritual, psychological, and social dimensions of their longings, losses, and needs.

Myers uncovers twin perils associated with this dualism. First, those of us who profess a Christian anthropology are in danger of becoming "functional atheists." Out of fear or ignorance, we may submit ourselves to the limited materialistic model of medicine that rejects the soul and all things supernatural. The second danger arises when we operate as healthcare missionaries in non-Western cultures that assume the reality of unseen spiritual forces. In those settings, we risk deifying medical science and its practitioners, rather than glorifying the God who has created an orderly world that permits observation, experimentation, and curative medicine. When God supernaturally heals our patients physically and/or spiritually and does so seemingly outside of medical therapies, we must readily direct the credit to him.

Based on the depiction of Jesus' activities in the Gospel of Mark, Myers presents a framework that begins with an understanding that Jesus advanced the good news of the kingdom first by his presence (incarnation, again), and then by preaching, healing, and casting out demons. Stated otherwise, Jesus used a combination of words (preaching), deeds (healing), and signs (miracles, spiritual warfare) to call humanity to repentance and reconciliation.

Myers then argues that integrated care delivery must imitate Jesus, including an expectant reliance on God's supernatural intervention. Some of us from noncharismatic backgrounds may pause here, but Myers points out that a miraculous healing or deliverance initiated many of the New Testament's most impressive evangelistic events. When God's extraordinary saving power is demonstrated, people seek answers. I (Rick) confess I'm more open to the miraculous when in Afghanistan or North India than when I am seeing patients in inner-city Memphis.

The widely admired pioneer and eminent champion of integrated healthcare ministry is the late Dan Fountain. For many of the contributors to this volume, the present authors included, Fountain's work has proved deeply influential and central to our understanding of healthcare missions. In his chapter on whole-person care, Fountain assails what he terms "reductionism in medicine," the practice of assuming that all health problems are rooted in physiological processes that can be addressed by medications, surgical procedures, or other treatment modalities. Within this misguided framework, when difficulties are identified that fall outside of empirical medical categories—say, psychological or social needs—patients are prematurely pawned off to professionals in other fields.

After years of frustration with this model, Fountain recalls the simple yet profound impact that Mrs. Masieta's intake question had on his practice. Having widened the avenue through which God could offer healing and help, Fountain noted, "With this approach to the 'cure of the soul,' we were finally seeing the medical view of a human being getting put back together." Alternatively, ministering to discrete body parts while ignoring the reality of humans as embodied spirits yields disappointing results.

Fountain and others have taught us that our physical bodies are highly influenced by our minds and souls, and vice versa. Several other authors illustrate how such reintegration needs to occur in healthcare missions. Gagne Henderson discusses this in the context of the dying process, inviting us to see God's presence and cooperate with the grace evident even in our last days. Soderling highlights the dangers of short-term missions that so myopically focus on Western-style, high-tech medicine as "curative" while missing the opportunities for true partnership and deep healing that evidence a rich sense of God's shalom. In one of the most sobering chapters of this book, Wong-McDonald examines the challenge of profound trauma and violence that shatters the mental health of so many around the world and isolates them from others. Rather than denying this suffering, she turns to the one who also suffered. Jesus comes alongside, making possible the recalling of even horrific experiences in the lives of victims so that these experiences are reintegrated, not only within themselves but also with others in relationship. Wong-McDonald points out that for those who have experienced trauma, the journey of reintegration involves a discovery, or rediscovery, of God's goodness and love for them. The essence of shalom is the ministry of reconciliation, beginning with "God, who reconciled us to himself through Christ and gave us the ministry of reconciliation" (2 Cor 5:18). All these stories invite us as healthcare workers to reimagine how we might participate with God in limitless ways, so that we become open to God's willingness to heal and power to do so in creative, unexpected ways.

Finally, an important area in an integrative health missions movement is the call to transform and reorient disintegrating and unjust structures. Long and Dortzbach note that we cannot walk beside others on their journey without becoming aware of how they are affected by injustice, while Short and Voss poignantly illustrate how our broken healthcare system disregards the dignity of the poor and even allows them to die on the floors of our emergency rooms. The healthcare missions movement must continue to struggle with how we can advocate for socioeconomic structures that enable the integrative flourishing of individuals and communities. Authors in the medical journal *Lancet* argue that "the future of health care generally, and primary care specifically, depends on the integration of personal health care and public health at the level of the local community" (van Weel, De Maeseneer, and Roberts 2008, 871). As Gorske and Myers ask, who "is better placed to help create this connection with the local community than its churches?"

Integrated ministry will invariably result in the creation of church fellowships that foster shalom in the lives of members and in their wider community. Integrated care means bringing all of Jesus to all of our personal, family, and community needs.

An *Innovative* Healthcare Missions Movement

In his discussion on the modern history of the healthcare missions movement, Myers notes that the Christian Medical Commission (CMC) advocated for innovative approaches to health care. More specifically, the CMC was an early pioneer and advocate for the field of primary care and community health. Building on this legacy, Myers calls for a continuing commitment in the healthcare missions movement to extending health services to the poor, wherever they may be. In line with this appeal, Gorske and Myers call for innovative reengagement of Christian healthcare missions with the World Health Organization (WHO). Christian Connections for International Health (CCIH) and other such groups are exploring creative avenues of partnership with agencies such as WHO and the United States Agency for International Development. We believe that the work of CCIH and similar associations is critical, as there is an urgent need for competent Christian leaders in these important policy conversations.

One innovative strategy of engagement involves the empowerment of community health workers. Multiple authors note that the future of health care calls for broader strategies than what our traditional models offer. The next generation of medical missions will include a growing number of nonprofessionals. Tazelaar and Newhof describe the effective deployment of lay health workers among marginalized patient populations in both international and domestic settings. Given proper training and supervision—as was the case with Grace's Ugandan coworker John Kiyimba—local people without formal education can perform many crucial health- and ministry-related functions. This is consistent with principles of the 1978 Alma-Alta Declaration: "Service at the closest point of contact (in the community, not a distant hospital); service by the lowest level provider appropriate to the task."

In a growing number of contexts, national Christians without formal professional education or ongoing connection to Western missionaries will be trained as community health workers, surgical technicians, lay birth attendants, dental hygienists, and rehabilitation technicians. As these workers go out, they will have abundant opportunities to share their faith in culturally appropriate ways, often in favorable, behind-closed-doors settings. In many parts of the world, local churches, including those with limited resources, are developing health-related strategies that meaningfully serve their neighbors and create new disciples and churches. This has been the genius of Stan Rowland's flexible Community Health Evangelism (CHE), described in Dalrymple and Collinge's chapter.

As these authors remind us, innovation must engage all of us at the local level so that we can invite our brothers and sisters in our local congregations to participate in healthcare as a crucial aspect of shalom. Gorske and Myers point out the need for local churches to respond to the "slow-motion disaster" resulting from obesity and smoking; they call congregations to recover their mission of healing and restoring shalom by using simple, lay-friendly approaches such as Church-Based Health Screening and Education. Long and Dortzbach describe coordinated care efforts for those living with HIV and AIDS that relied on church members who visited and cared for patients in their homes. A larger, more diverse, and more effective movement of Christian health workers may very well decrease the need for large NGOs—or even for dedicated "missionaries."

While innovation is clearly necessary, Soderling reminds us that we must reconsider past interventions for their relevance and effectiveness, and he questions the phenomenon he dubs "the short-term missions tsunami." In many ways this phenomenon is deeply indebted to the unprecedented "widening, deepening and speeding up of worldwide interconnectedness in all aspects of contemporary social life" (Held 1999, 2). In short, it is symptomatic of globalization. We must research this rapidly growing and highly influential phenomenon, asking if short-term healthcare missions do indeed promote God's holistic shalom. One important response has been the thoughtful conversation on best practices for short-term healthcare teams that is being spearheaded by the Center for Health In Mission (see www.centerforhim.org).

In looking to our future, we must consider a key opportunity and challenge of technology, asking what constitutes innovative and appropriate use. After all, the short-term healthcare missions tsunami is possible because of innovative advances in such areas as transportation, medical technology, and the Internet. How can we adopt the lens of shalom as discussed here so that we can utilize the gifts of technology as God desires?

Building on the earlier call to imitate the incarnation, one guide that we might emphasize in regard to technological innovation is the importance of moving at a pace that the local participants set. Japanese theologian Kosuke Koyama insightfully noted that Jesus could have come with a host of angels to proclaim his message to all the corners of the earth. Instead, he came as a humble "three mile an hour God" who walked the dusty roads of Galilee and personally proclaimed the gospel of the kingdom (Koyama 1980). In an age that often values efficiency over relationship, let the followers of Christ follow the three-mile-an-hour Jesus who listened to his Father and built relationships that valued people.

A Final Word

While our influence has declined in the West due to factors such as the emergence of a trillion-dollar pharmaceutical and healthcare industry, Christians continue to influence healthcare. This book argues that we can and should reclaim our legacy. To do so, we will have to ruthlessly examine our assumptions and models.

As American Christians, we often assume that a career in a health-related field should be prestigious and financially rewarding. In addition, we assume that how and where we practice our professions is largely up to us. Lastly, despite grossly unjust health disparities, most of us find it acceptable to allot only token amounts of time and resources to caring for the underserved. In many cases, we are not even sure the poor deserve our assistance because of their own unwise choices.

In this context, the incarnation slaps us in the face. The Lord of the universe surely could have chosen wealth and prestige, but instead came to us, emptying himself and serving others. He fully entered into our human condition, experienced our physical infirmities, suffered all manner of trials and temptations; he endured rejection, hatred, torture, and death from those who should have worshiped him. Even on the cross, he pleaded for the possibility of restoration and reconciliation for those who killed him. While we were his enemies—undeserving of assistance and drowning in our own unwise choices—he offered us friendship and made us coheirs.

Healthcare missionaries seeking to imitate Jesus and embrace the truth of the gospel will continuously choose the path less traveled. They will search for places of need with reckless faith, spending themselves for the glory of God and Christ's kingdom of peace and justice. We must practice incarnation ourselves by forgoing our own cultural comforts and false securities. In doing so, we do not pursue the American Dream. Rather, we set our eyes on the narrow way that leads to life, which few find, but which yields joy to those who walk it with their servant-king.

Furthermore, as disciples of Jesus we have theological and philosophical resources to challenge the assumptions of modernity that dis-integrate human beings. In his earthly ministry, Jesus addressed the heart, mind, soul, and strength. He decisively confronted mental, physical, and spiritual abnormalities, demonstrating that "Your sins are forgiven" and "Take up your mat and walk" are interconnected. Christian healthcare workers have access to liberating weapons unavailable to those who discount the notion that we are created in the image of God, made to live and reign with him. Following Christ's model and that of the apostles, the church has always linked preaching and healing by the power of the Holy Spirit; indeed, as much as any sermon, the ministry of physical healing powerfully speaks the gospel, while other words and actions also tell of God's desire for our wholeness through Christ. As we work for the flourishing shalom of individuals, families, and communities, may we pray that Jesus' reign will be realized on earth as it is in heaven. While we cannot predict what the healthcare missions movement will look like in ten years—let alone forty or fifty—we hope and pray that it is marked by followers of Christ who are committed to kingdom healthcare that is identity-transforming, incarnational, integrative, and innovative.

References Cited

BBC. 2014. "US Ebola Patient Kent Brantly 'Thrilled to be Alive.'" BBC News: US and Canada. August 21. http://www.bbc.com/news/world-us-canada-28885753.

Held, David. 1999. *Global Transformations: Politics, Economics and Culture.* Stanford, CA: Stanford University Press.

Hiebert, Paul G. 2008. *Transforming Worldviews: An Anthropological Understanding of How People Change.* Grand Rapids, MI: Baker Academic.

Koyama, Kosuke. 1980. *Three Mile an Hour God: Biblical Reflections.* Maryknoll, NY: Orbis.

Middleton, J. Richard. 2005. *The Liberating Image: The Imago Dei in Genesis 1.* Grand Rapids, MI: Brazos Press.

Newbigin, Lesslie. 1995. *The Open Secret: An Introduction to the Theology of Mission.* Rev. ed. Grand Rapids, MI: Eerdmans.

Ramachandra, Vinoth. 1999. *Faiths in Conflict? Christian Integrity in a Multicultural World.* Downers Grove, IL: InterVarsity Press.

Sanneh, Lamin O. 2008. *Disciples of All Nations: Pillars of World Christianity.* Oxford Studies in World Christianity. Oxford: Oxford University Press.

van Weel, Chris, Jan De Maeseneer, and Richard Roberts. 2008. "Integration of Personal and Community Health Care." *Lancet* 372 (9642): 871–72. doi:10.1016/S0140-6736(08)61376-8.

Walls, Andrew F. 1996. *The Missionary Movement in Christian History: Studies in the Transmission of Faith.* Maryknoll, NY: Orbis.

Contributors

Jody Collinge, MD, FAAP, CTropMed, MSc, is a pediatrician working with the Global Community Health Evangelism Network. Community Health Evangelism, or CHE, is a wholistic ministry that integrates evangelism and discipleship with community-based development. Her areas of responsibility include developing training resources for the network and the development of Children's CHE ministries around the world—working with and through children to reach their families and communities.

Terry Dalrymple, MDiv, is founder and coordinator of the Global Community Health Evangelism Network and vice president of the Alliance for Transformational Ministry. His passion and work is equipping and mobilizing believers for holistic ministries that integrate evangelism and discipleship with disease prevention and community development in rural poor villages worldwide.

Rick Donlon, MD, is co-founder of Resurrection Health in Memphis, Tennessee, which provides health-related services among the underserved, while simultaneously proclaiming the gospel of Jesus Christ and advancing healthcare justice.

Debbie Dortzbach, MN, MPH, is the director of health and social development with World Relief. A public health nurse, she has served with both World Presbyterian Mission and Mission to the World since 1980 and also with World Relief since 1997. Dortzbach has coauthored two books, one, *The AIDS Crisis: What We Can Do,* with W. Meredith Long (2006) and the other, *Kidnapped* (1975), coauthored with her husband, Karl Dortzbach, chronicling her experience as a missionary captive in Ethiopia in 1974. Her current research interests include community and child health and HIV/AIDS.

Erin Dufault-Hunter, PhD, is assistant professor of Christian ethics in the School of Theology at Fuller Theological Seminary. She has written *The Transformative Power of Faith: A Narrative Approach to Conversion* (2012). Her research interests include bioethics, sociology of religion, diversity, and sexuality/gender.

Cynthia Eriksson, PhD, is associate professor of psychology in the School of Psychology at Fuller Theological Seminary. She is part of the Headington Program in International Trauma at Fuller. Her research interests include trauma and post-traumatic stress disorder; missionary mental health and self-care; and chronic stress and burnout in caregivers.

Daniel E. Fountain, MD, MPH, went home to be with the Lord on February 12, 2013, at the age of eighty-two. Dan served as a medical missionary in the Democratic Republic of the Congo with American Baptist International Ministries from 1961 to 1996 and will be remembered as an architect of a comprehensive, Christ-centered healthcare service. Dan also served as overseas faculty for the Christian Medical and Dental Associations; with Southwest Medical Group in Stevensville, Michigan, training lay ministers; at King College in Bristol, Tennessee, as director of the Global Health Training Program; and as facilitator for workshops in health, agriculture, culture, and community with ECHO's Global Health Training Program in Fort Myers, Florida. Fountain's publications include *Health, the Bible and the Church* (1988), *God, Medicine, and Miracles* (1999), and (posthumously) *Health for All: The Vanga Story* (2014).

Rebecca Gagne Henderson, APRN, ACHPN, PhD candidate, is the program manager of the Yale New Haven Hospital Palliative Program, faculty of the Yale Medical School End of Life Interdisciplinary Course, and affiliate faculty of the Yale Medical School Program for Bioethics. Her research interests include goals of care communication, validation of triggers for palliative care, and end of life communication in the emergency department.

Arnold Gorske, MD, FAAP, is the chief executive officer of Standards of Excellence in Healthcare Missions. He is also director of the Health Education Program for Developing Countries. His research interests include congregation-based holistic health programs, high-quality sustainable healthcare systems, evidence-based participatory health education, and transformational development.

Kathleen Henry, PA-C, is a physician assistant at Foothill Community Clinic in East San Jose, California. She has thirteen years of experience working as a physician assistant in conjunction with urban ministry in Los Angeles as a

Companion of InnerCHANGE, a Christian order among the poor. She is a long-time member of Christian Community Health Fellowship (CCHF).

W. Meredith Long, DrPH, is senior advisor for International Health and Integral Mission for World Concern. He is exploring the issues of fielding integral mission in places where churches are not viable partners because of restrictive political systems or because Christians are a small minority population. In *Health, Healing and God's Kingdom* (2000) he explores how worldviews underlying African, biomedical, and public health perspectives on health and healing can be brought into a distinctively biblical model of Christian ministry. He also coauthored *The AIDS Crisis: What We Can Do* (2006) with Debbie Dortzbach.

Bryant L. Myers, PhD, is professor of international development in the School of Intercultural Studies at Fuller Theological Seminary. He worked for over thirty years with World Vision International. Myers's books include *Walking with the Poor: Principles and Practices of Transformational Development* (2011) and *Working with the Poor: New Insights and Learnings from Development Practitioners* (2008). His research interests include poverty and development in Christian perspective and the integration of evangelism and development.

Carolyn "Care" Newhof developed and implemented the Parent Child Ministry at Cary Christian Center in Cary, Mississippi. This ministry included prenatal and parenting education with a home visiting component and has been recognized nationally for impacting and lowering the infant mortality rate.

David H. Scott, PhD, is assistant professor of intercultural studies and children at risk and directs the Children at Risk area of emphasis in the School of Intercultural Studies at Fuller Theological Seminary. His research interests include mission with children at risk, child participation, human rights for children, and theology of children.

Anntippia Short, RN, MSN, CNE, is currently on the nursing faculty at Santa Monica College in Santa Monica, California, and is a volunteer at the Los Angeles Christian Health Centers clinic in Watts, California.

Michael J. Soderling, MD, MBA, is the director for the Center for Health in Mission at William Carey International University in Pasadena, California, and an adjunct professor at Hope International University. His research interests include a biblical understanding of health, education for transformation, transformational development, and the use of Christian healthcare services as a platform to reach unreached people groups.

Grace Tazelaar, MS, RN, serves as the missions director for Nurses Christian Fellowship, a strategic ministry of InterVarsity Christian Fellowship. Her research interests include best practices in healthcare missions, service learning and short-term healthcare missions, and community health development.

Judith M. Tiersma Watson, PhD, is associate professor of urban mission in the School of Intercultural Studies at Fuller Theological Seminary and a member of InnerCHANGE, a Christian order among the poor connected with Church Resource Ministries. Her research interests are urban mission and contemplation, self-care and member care for urban workers, and spirituality and mission.

Isaac B. Voss, MPH, is assistant professor of anthropology at Vanguard University. After receiving his master's degree in public health (Boston University), he served for nine years as the health ministry director for World Impact–Los Angeles, a Christian nonprofit organization. Isaac is presently a PhD candidate in urban community development at Fuller Theological Seminary. His research interests include church-based health programs, participatory evaluation methods, and the role of agency in poverty and development.

Katy White, MD, MPH, serves as the chief medical officer and as a family physician at the Los Angeles Christian Health Centers. Her research interests include spiritual and whole-person care in a medical context and engaging the church in health care among the underserved.

Ashley Wilkins, MA, is a PhD in clinical psychology student at Fuller Theological Seminary. Her research interests include trauma, member care, and social support.

Ana Wong-McDonald, PhD, is currently serving in private practice in Los Angeles, California. As an alumna of Fuller Theological Seminary with a doctorate in clinical psychology and a master's in theology, she previously served as the clinical director at the Salvation Army Haven and as the director of psychosocial rehabilitation at the County of Los Angeles Department of Mental Health.

Index

and trauma, 114–15,
    119–20, 127–29
Community-Based
    Health Screening and
    Education, 84, 88–96
community health development
    (CHD), 235–39
Community Health Evangelism
    (CHE), 249–50, 251–
    53, 255, 257–63
community health workers
    (CHWs), 70, 233,
    235, 238–40, 246
compartmentalized view
    of human beings, 3–5,
    17, 32–33, 271. *See
    also* reductionism in
    medicine; Western vs.
    traditional worldview
compassion, 33, 60, 101, 149,
    154–55, 182, 190, 195,
    230, 245, 253, 256–57
    as a spiritual practice, 224–26
Conde-Frazier, Elizabeth,
    218, 221–22
Congo. *See* Democratic
    Republic of the Congo
Corbett, Steve, 167
Cornelius, 220
Corsaro, William, 72
creation narrative, 16,
    19, 22, 37, 76
crime/criminalization,
    116, 118, 152
culture, creation of, and
    imago Dei, 18–19

curses, 2, 6–7, 47, 143–44,
    148, 154, 237

D

Dauermann, Stuart, 207
Davis, Ellen, 190
Davis, Mary, 242–43
Day, Dorothy, 52
death and dying, 1–2, 5–7,
    10, 20–21, 26, 30, 58–59,
    83–84, 87, 95, 100,
    105, 107, 115, 117–18,
    120–21, 140, 142–43,
    148, 153–57, 161, 191–95,
    228, 234, 243, 263, 268
    children. *See* infant mortality
    end-of-life care, 171–85
    of Jesus, 23, 36, 124,
        154, 157, 277
dehydration, 173, 177,
    179–80, 182
Delta Infant Mortality
    Elimination, 243
Democratic Republic of
    the Congo, 1–5, 118,
    123, 127, 252, 270,
demons/evil spirits, 26, 43,
    46–47, 49, 54, 271
dependency, 165, 244–45,
    255–57, 259
depression, 4, 10, 27, 99, 108,
    114–16, 118–20, 127–28
discipleship, 17, 84, 96,
    103, 251, 253, 257